concepts in ECONOMICS

Twelth Edition

Debbie A. Meyer
Professor of Economics
Brookdale Community College

Boston Burr Ridge, IL Dubuque, IA New York San Francisco St. Louis
Bangkok Bogotá Caracas Lisbon London Madrid
Mexico City Milan New Delhi Seoul Singapore Sydney Taipei Toronto

The McGraw-Hill Companies

Concepts in Economics, Twelth Edition

1 2 3 4 5 6 7 8 9 0 TPS TPS 13 12 11

ISBN-13: 978-1-25-981377-1
ISBN-10: 1-25-981377-0

CONTENTS

MICROECONOMICS

UNIT I

UNIT II:

UNIT III:

To The Student

This workbook is your "portable tutor." It contains the following information and is recommended for you to bring to class, as well as use anytime, anywhere! Good luck!

Concepts in Economics is split between Macroeconomics and Microeconomics. Within each area, there are three units, which correspond to your course syllabus.

Each unit is composed of several concepts. Each chapter is broken down into:

- Chapter Orientation - to acquaint you with the purpose and focus of the chapter.
- Learning Objectives - are brief statements of expected learning which require you to define, compare, explain, contrast, list, and evaluate each chapter.
- Chapter Highlights - a detailed outline of the chapter's most essential points.
- Web-based Question/Problem - opportunity for your Instructor to give you an up-to-the-moment assignment.
- Key Terms - lists the important concepts which you should be able to define.
- Problems - a "hands on approach" to learning the material.
- Self-Test - provides additional opportunities to assess your mastery of the material. Be sure to check your answers with the "Answer Key" provided, located at the back of this workbook.

This student manual is designed to be used in conjunction with Economics, by Campbell R. McConnell, Stanley L. Brue, and Sean Flynn. However, this manual may be used to stand alone or accompany another introductory economics textbook. If you attend the class lectures, read the text carefully and complete the exercises in this concepts book, you should achieve mastery of the economic principles and their applications.

Below is the suggested format for studying:

1. Read the "Chapter Orientation", "Learning Objectives", "Chapter Highlights", and "Key Terms" sections in this workbook prior to reading the chapter in the text (this gives you an idea of what will be covered in the chapter).
2. Then read the chapter in the text, highlighting important points.
3. After reading the chapter, take notes on the chapter worksheet located at the back of this workbook (use the "Chapter Highlights" in this workbook as a guide).
4. Attend the classroom lecture of the chapter and take notes.
5. Reread the "Chapter Highlights", "Key Terms", and your lecture notes. If there is any concept that seems unclear to you, go to the text and reread the topic.
6. Tackle the problems in this workbook and any additional problems that have been assigned.
7. Answer the questions under the "Self-Test" section. Be sure to check your answers (located at the back of this workbook).
8. Finally, go back to the "Learning Objectives" and see if you can answer each item.
9. Upon completion of a unit, be sure to do the "Review Sheet" in your workbook and review your worksheets.

Acknowledgements

I would like to thank everyone who helped with the production of this workbook — my family, friends and colleagues. A special note of gratitude goes to Dawn Turner, who spent countless hours on production of this workbook. Dawn, I would like to say thanks for your patience, professionalism, expertise and encouragement.

Also, to my family and friends thanks for your patience and understanding — I know I wasn't much "fun" during this revision.

Lastly, I am grateful to the students at Brookdale Community College, for without their support and encouragement this Concepts Book would never have come into existence.

To my inner circle—my family

MACROECONOMICS

Unit I

"Limits, Alternatives and Choices"

Chapter Orientation

These introductory concepts set the stage for your study of economics. After studying these concepts, you will have a foundation with which to build. You will be acquainted with many reasons for studying economics; how economic policy is derived; a review of graphing techniques (in the appendix) and several important terms. Consumers' wants are unlimited, but their resources are limited – so choices must be made. The "Law of Scarcity" defines this for us and the Production Possibilities Curve graphically illustrates it. Your study of economics will be more meaningful/enjoyable if you grasp the general framework of the economic concepts outlined below.

Learning Objectives

After studying this chapter in the text and completing the following exercises in this concepts book, you should be able to:

1. Define economics and give several reasons for studying the economy.
2. List the steps, using positive economics, in deriving economic policy.
3. Cite several potential pitfalls in economic models.
4. Define the law of scarcity
5. List and define the four factors of production (resource categories).
6. Calculate the trade-offs (sacrifices) when producing on good over another.
7. Construct a production possibilities curve from a schedule.
8. Illustrate economic growth, under-employment, and the law of increasing costs using a production possibilities curve.
9. Understand the role of economic models, theory, and assumptions in the study of economics.
10. List the difficulties that economics students often face in studying economics.
11. Construct graphs from data presented, calculate slopes, and define their relationship.

Chapter Highlights

I. The Economic Perspective

A. Scarcity and choice (sacrifices or "opportunity cost")

B. Purposeful behavior (self-interest - based on "utility")

C. Marginal Analysis: benefits and costs (which is higher?)

II. Theories, Principles, and Models

A. The Scientific Method (positive economics)

1. Gathering of relevant facts (descriptive or empirical economics)
2. Deriving principles from facts (economic theory), also called "laws", "theories", and "models"
   a. Generalizations, assumptions, and abstractions
   b. Forms of economic models: verbal statements, numerical tables, graphs, and mathematical equations
3. Test (inductive vs. deductive methods)

III. Macroeconomics and Microeconomics

A. Definition of Economics – The social science concerned with how we make optimal choices under conditions of scarcity.

B. Macro vs. Micro Economics defined – Macro is concerned with the performance and behavior of the economy as a whole. Micro is concerned with individual units or markets.

C. Positive and Normative Economics – Positive economics is the analysis of facts or data to establish scientific generalizations about economic behavior. Normative economics involved value judgments about what the economy should be like (policy).

IV. Individuals' Economizing Problem

A. Limited Income

B. Unlimited Wants

C. A Budget Line (budget constraint)

1. Attainable or unattainable
2. Tradeoffs and opportunity costs

V. Society's Economizing Problem

A. Fundamental Facts

1. Society's material wants are unlimited and insatiable
2. Economic resources are limited or scarce

B. Definition of the Law of Scarcity and Utility: Consumers have unlimited wants but limited resources

C. Factors of production or resource categories and (money payments)

1. Land (rental income)
2. Labor (wages)
3. Capital (interest)
4. Entrepreneurial ability (profits)

VI. Production Possibilities Model

A. Assumptions (4):

1. Full employment - economy is operating at full employment and full production
2. Fixed resources - supplies are fixed in quantity and quality and may be shifted
3. Fixed technology - technology is constant at a point in time
4. Two products - only two goods are produced. For example, capital goods (robots) and consumer goods (pizza).

B. Production Possibilities table (list of possible combinations)

1. Law of Increasing Opportunity Costs (concave curve vs. straight line) as you tradeoff resources, the sacrifice becomes greater and greater. This concept is reflected in the shape of the PPC.
2. Allocative Efficiency revisited - requires the economy to produce at the optimal point

VII. Unemployment, Growth, and the Future

A. A Growing Economy

1. Increase in resource supplies
2. Advances in technology

B. Present Choices and Future Possibilities

C. A Qualification: International Trade

VIII. Last Word: Pitfalls to Sound Economic Reasoning

IX.Appendix: Graphs and their Meaning

A. Construction of a Graph

B. Tools

1. Determining direct or inverse relationships
2. Dependent and Independent Variables
3. Ceteris Paribus (other things equal)
4. Calculating the slope of a straight line and a nonlinear curve
5. Plotting points from a schedule of data
6. Vertical intercept

X. Web-based Question/Project (see your Instructor)

"Limits, Alternatives and Choices"

Key Terms

economics
scientific method
descriptive method
economic theory
generalization
abstraction
economic models
inductive/deductive
economic policy
graphing techniques
tradeoffs
marginal analysis
law of scarcity
economics
land, labor, capital, and entrepreneurial ability
production possibilities curve
consumer goods
direct/inverse relationship
slope of a line
positive/normative economics
economic goals
complementary goals
mutually exclusive goals
fallacy of division
post hoc fallacy
correlation
causation
macro/micro economics
ceteris paribus
economic contraction
optimum product mix
opportunity cost
efficiency
law of increasing opportunity costs
full-employment

WORKING WITH GRAPHS

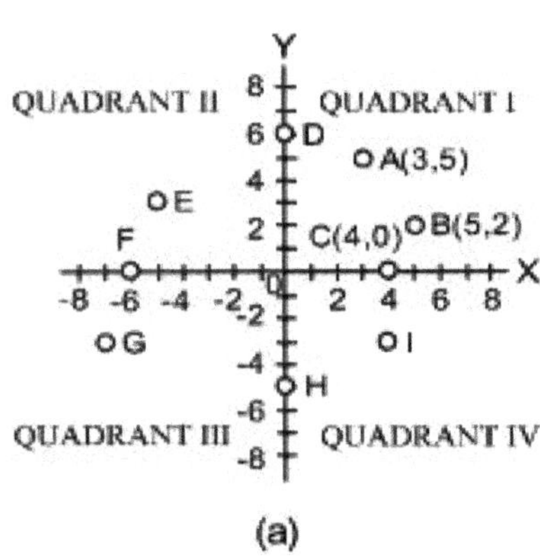

(a)

Chart (a). The two intersecting straight lines divide the chart into four quadrants numbered counterclockwise. Positive values are measured to the right along the X axis and upward along the Y axis. Any point on the chart can be located by its coordinates.

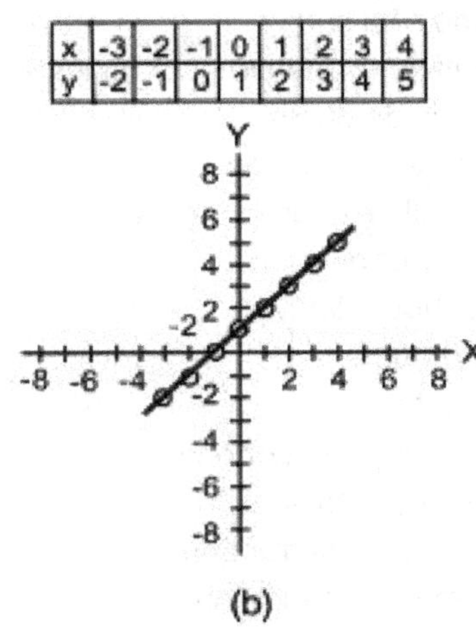

x	-3	-2	-1	0	1	2	3	4
y	-2	-1	0	1	2	3	4	5

(b)

Chart (b). A line that slopes upward from left to right exhibits a direct relation between the two variables. As one variable increases, so does the other; as one decreases, so does the other.

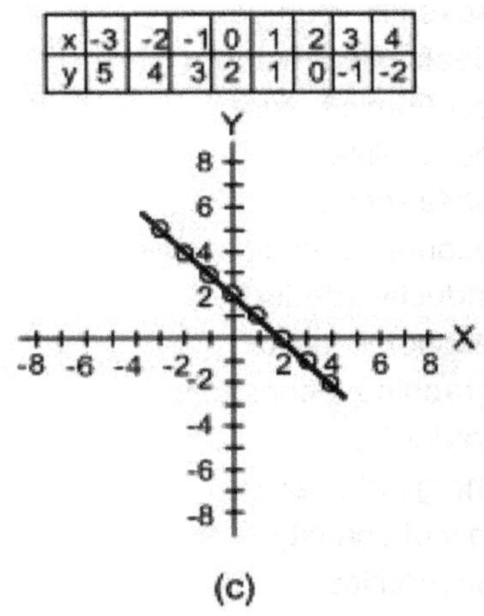

x	-3	-2	-1	0	1	2	3	4
y	5	4	3	2	1	0	-1	-2

(c)

Chart (c). A line that slopes downward from left to right exhibits an inverse relation between the two variables. As one variable increases, the other decreases; as one decreases, the other increases.

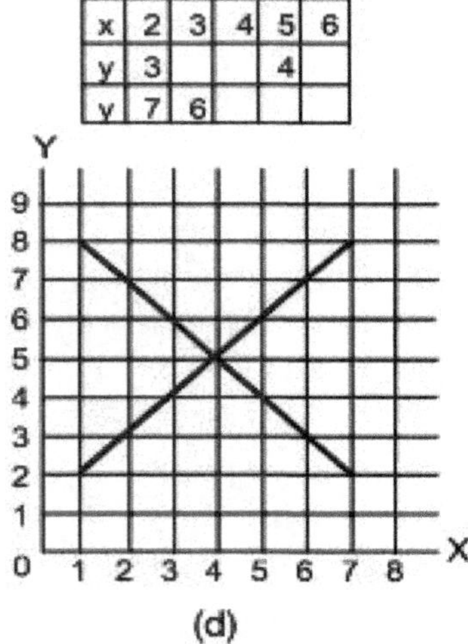

x	2	3	4	5	6
y	3			4	
y	7	6			

(d)

Chart (d). Two or more lines may be graphed on the same chart in order to study their interrelationships. Can you complete the table from the graph?

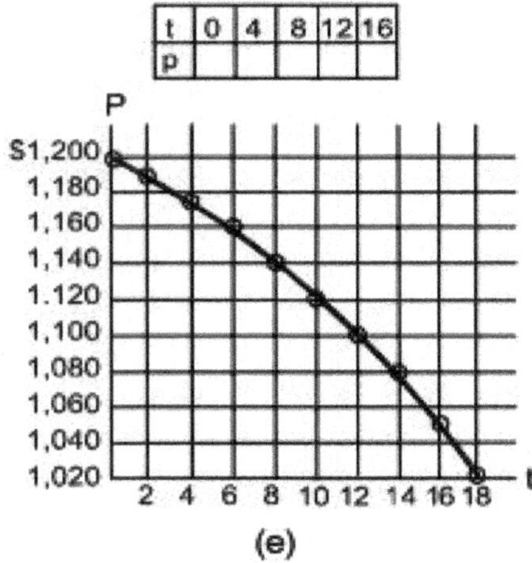

t	0	4	8	12	16
p					

(e)

Chart (e). Scales should be chosen and axes labeled in the manner that best suits a particular problem. Can you use the graph to estimate the missing numbers in the table?

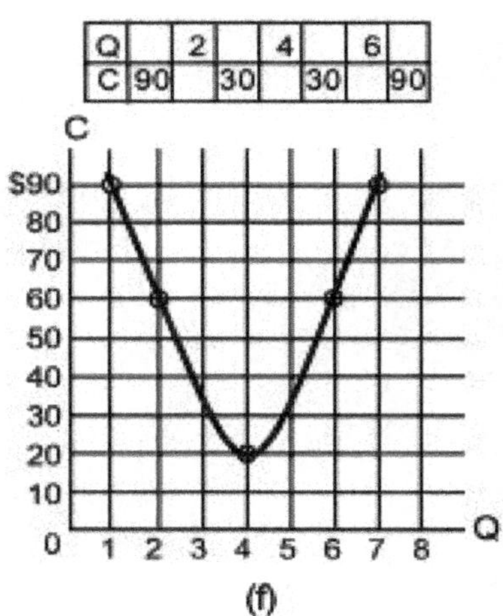

Q		2		4		6	
C	90		30		30		90

(f)

Chart (f). The points should be connected with care because the resulting curve may be quite pronounced. Can you fill in the table from the graph?

MACRO PROBLEMS

Please use graph paper.

For problems 1-6, sketch the graphs of the following relationships and calculate the slopes for problems 1-4 only.

1.

X	Y
1	1
2	2
3	3
4	4
5	5
6	6
7	7
8	8

2.

X	Y
1	7
2	6
3	5
4	4
5	3
6	2
7	1

3.

X	Y
-2	-8
0	-4
2	0
4	4

4. Sketch the following data on the same graph. Estimate the coordinates of the point of intersection of the two lines. Calculate the slope of each line.

X	Y
1	2
2	3
3	4
4	5

X	Y
1	5
2	4
3	3
4	2

5. Sketch the graph of prices as a function of time:

X time (t)	Y prices (P)
0	8
1	33
2	40
3	35
4	24
5	13
6	8
7	15
8	40

MACRO PROBLEMS (continued)

6. You are given the following relationship between A and B:

A	B
2	9
3	7
4	6
5	8
6	9

a. Graph the relationship, putting A on the X axis and B on the Y axis.

b. The relationship between A and B is inverse when A is between ______ and ________ and direct when A is between ________ and ______.

c. The coordinates of the point at which B is a minimum are ______, ______.

7.

TABLE I

X Income	Y Savings
5,000	- 0-
10,000	1,000
15,000	2,000

a. Graph Table I above.
b. Calculate the slope.
c. Do you have a direct or inverse relationship?

8.

TABLE II

X Billions of Dollars	Y Rate of Interest
$0	10%
5	8
10	6
15	4
20	2

a. Graph Table II above.
b. Calculate the slope.
c. Do you have a direct or inverse relationship?

MICRO PROBLEMS

Please use graph paper.
For exercises 1-3
(a) Sketch the graphs of the following relationships.
(b) Calculate the slopes.
(c) State whether there is a direct or inverse relationship.

1.

X Qty of ties	Y Price per tie
20	$10
30	9
40	8
50	7
60	6

2.

X Qty of wallets	Y Price per wallet
300	$100
250	80
200	60
150	40
100	20

3.

X	Y
- 6	- 2
- 4	0
- 2	2
0	4
2	6
4	8

4. (a) Sketch the following curves on the same graph.
(b) Calculate the slope for each.
(c) What are the coordinates of the point of intersection?

X	Y
4	$9.00
6	8.50
8	8.00
10	7.50
12	7.00
14	6.50

X	Y
16	$9.00
14	8.50
12	8.00
10	7.50
8	7.00
6	6.50

5. Plot the graph from the following data:

X Years	Y Profits (in billions)
1980	$50
1981	45
1982	43
1983	48
1984	55
1985	64
1986	62

PRODUCTION-POSSIBILITIES PROBLEMS

1. You are given the "production-possibilities schedule" below:

Alternative	X Consumer Goods	Y Capital Goods	Sacrifice of Capital Goods for Consumer Goods
A	0	15	________
B	1	14	________
C	2	11	________
D	3	6	________
E	4	0	________

a. Fill in the last column of the table.
b. Graph the production-possibilities curve from the data above.
c. Plot a point "U" which represents underutilization on your graph.
d. Show economic growth on the same graph.
e. What law is represented given the table above? Why?
f. Redraw the diagram from part b (above). Show what would happen if there was a technological break-through in capital goods only. Label this new curve "T".
g. Illustrate what would happen if a natural resource used in production of consumer goods only were restricted. Label this new curve "R".

The following graph applies to questions 2-5.

2. At point D, the economy's resources:
   a. are fully employed
   b. are efficiently utilized
   c. are underemployed
   d. unable to determine
3. The shifting of the curve from AB to EG represents:
   a. economic contraction
   b. inefficient utilization
   c. recession
   d. economic expansion
4. To reach point H the society must:
   a. improve technology
   b. show economic growth
   c. operate at technical efficiency
   d. all of the above
5. The production possibilities curve is:
   a. concave
   b. convex
   c. linear
   d. positive

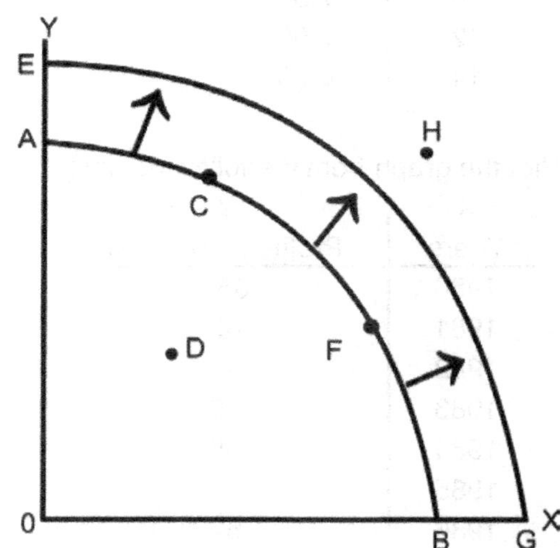

"Limits, Alternatives and Choices"

Self-Test

1. Assume that an economy is operating at an output level, which leaves some of its productive resources unemployed. Given that the curve below is the production-possibility curve of that economy, which of the following output combinations would the economy most likely be producing?
   a. (13, 16)
   b. (10, 13)
   c. (7, 9)
   d. (18, 2)

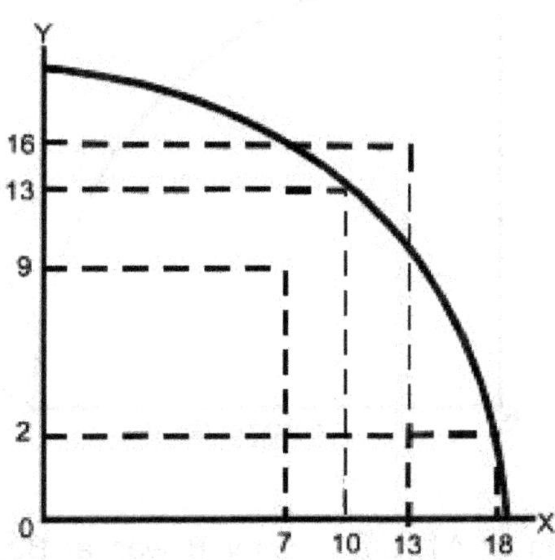

2. The United States and the United Kingdom are able to produce the same commodities, machine tools, and automobiles. The U.S., for its part, is producing more of both outputs, but the United Kingdom is relatively more efficient (higher productivity) in the production of machine tools than the United States. Select the diagram, which has production possibility curves most appropriate for this situation.

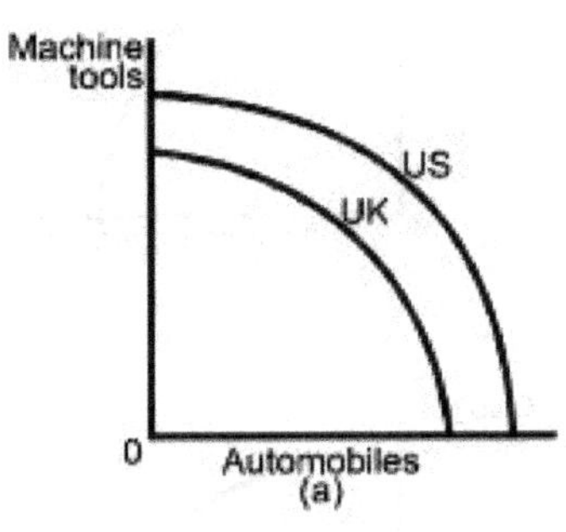

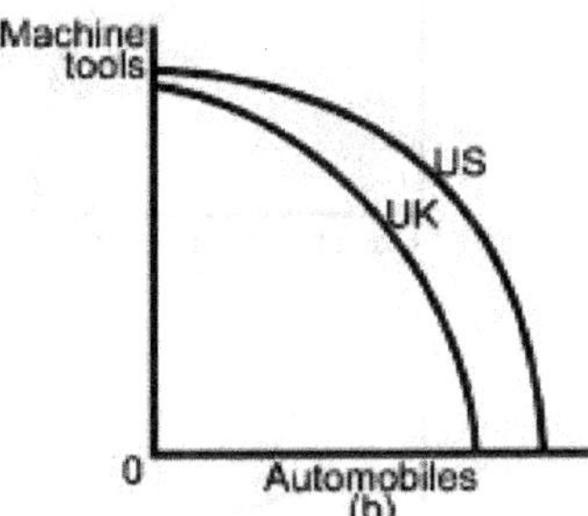

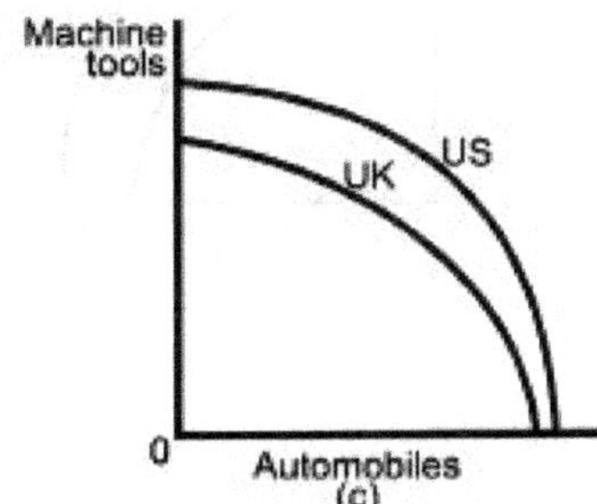

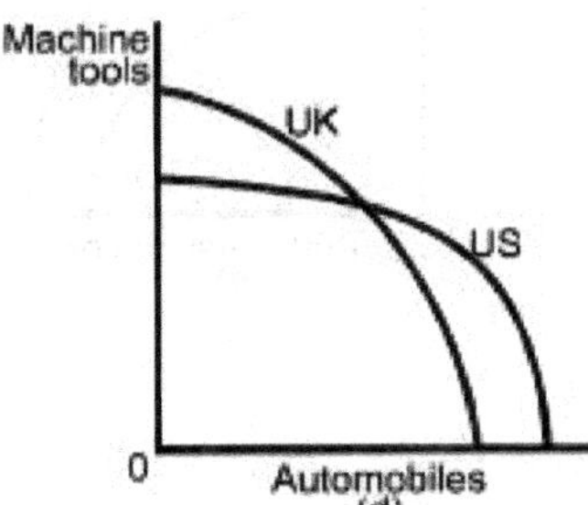

Self-Test (continued)

3. In the year 2015, country A and country B were both producing on the same production possibility curve for current consumption vs. new capital formation. Country A was at A1 and country B was at B1 on the curve; otherwise the countries were identical.

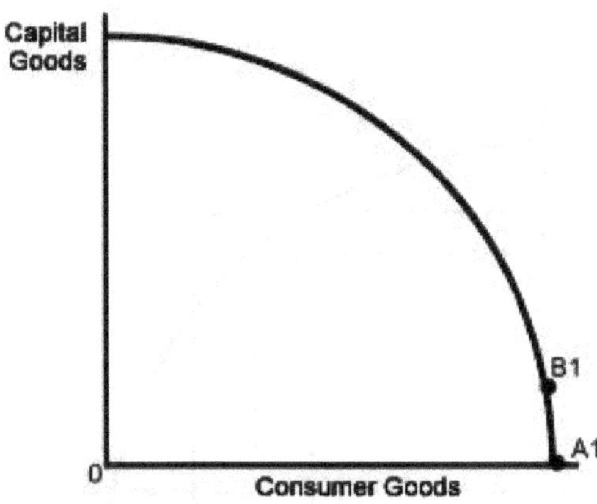

In 2020, country A was still producing at A1, but country B was at B2. Which figure most likely reflects the production possibility frontiers for each in 2020?

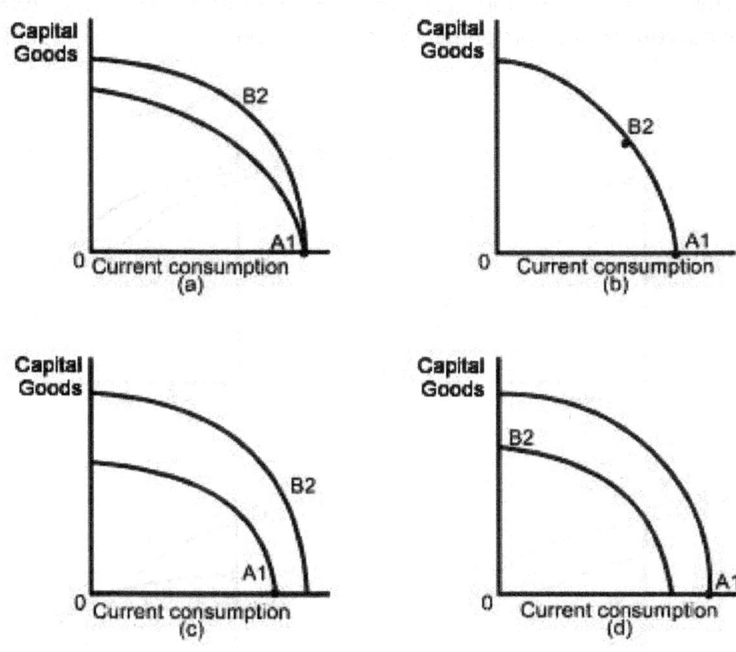

Self-Test (continued)

4. Assume that in 1817 the United States was producing at full employment of all resources. By 1825, the completion of the Erie Canal had speeded up transportation and lowered costs to the extent that the price of grain was reduced by two-thirds. This greatly lowered the real costs of producing both bread and whiskey. Select the diagram which best shows the change in this two-commodity production possibility curve, all other things unchanged.

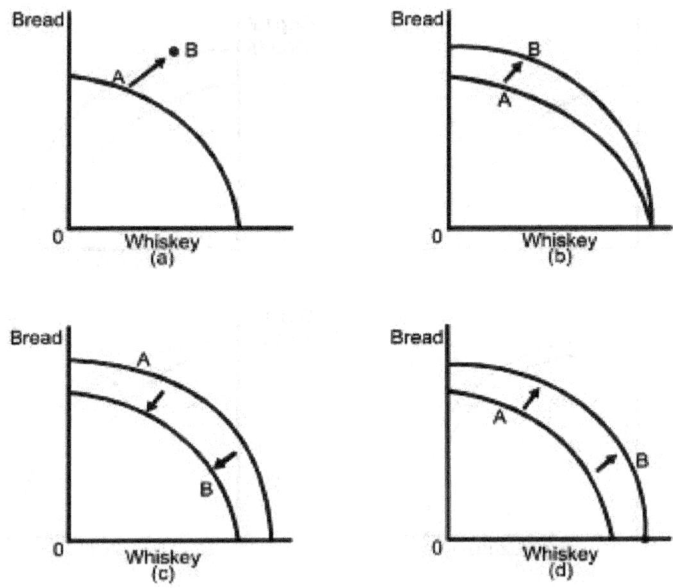

5. Consider a society, which is producing at full employment of all resources. Assume that this economy produces only 2 goods: apples and butter. Suppose a new fertilizer is invented which greatly increases the productivity of apple trees. From the figures below, choose the one which best shows the change in production possibilities caused by this increased productivity, all other things unchanged.

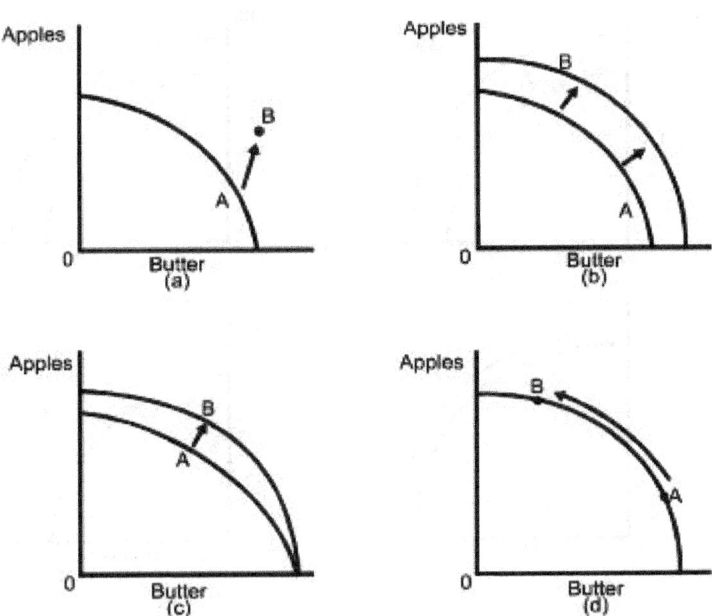

Self-Test (continued)

6. Consider a society, which is producing at full employment of all resources. Suppose that the percentage of the population in the labor force increases because of the baby boom twenty years earlier. Given the following figures, choose the one which best shows the change in production possibilities caused by the change in the labor force, all other things unchanged.

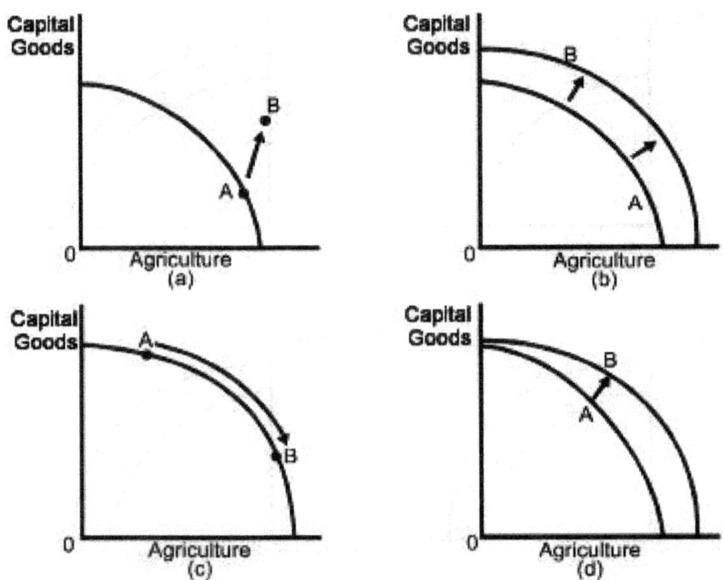

7. Consider a society, which is producing at full employment of all resources. Suppose that the discovery of new oil wells increases the country's supply of oil for lubricants and for paints. Given the following diagrams, choose the one which best shows the change in production possibilities caused by the increase in the supply of oil, all other things unchanged.

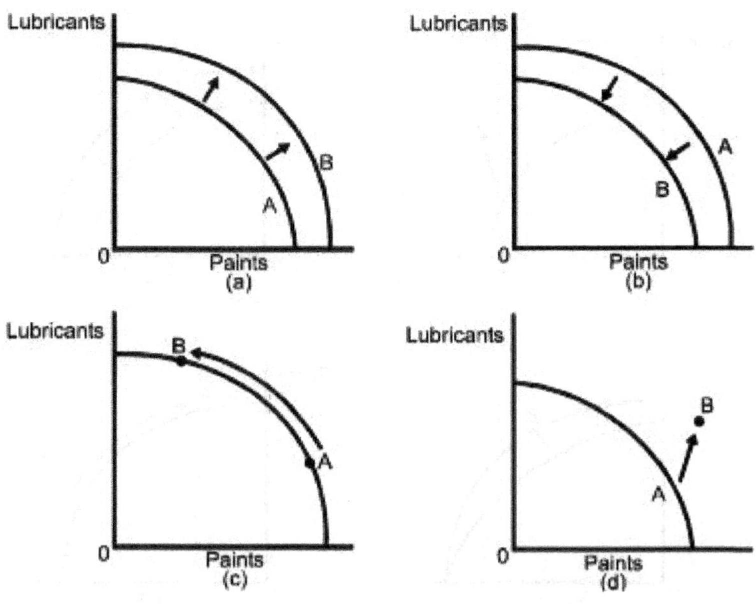

Self-Test (continued)

8. Consider a society which is producing at full employment of all resources. Suppose that an epidemic suddenly reduces its labor force greatly. From the following figures, choose the one which best shows the change in production possibilities caused by reduction of the labor force, all other things remaining unchanged.

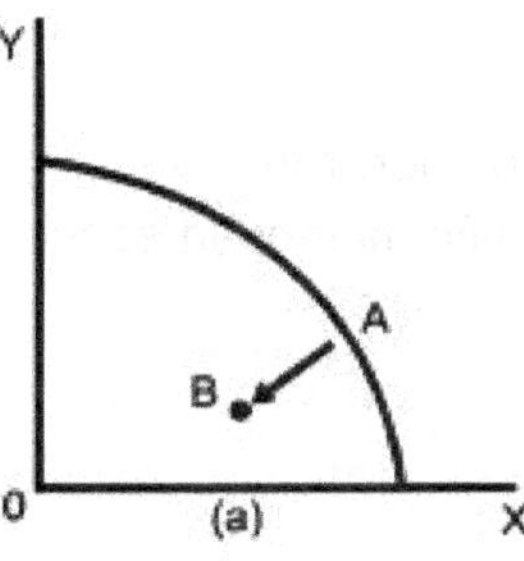

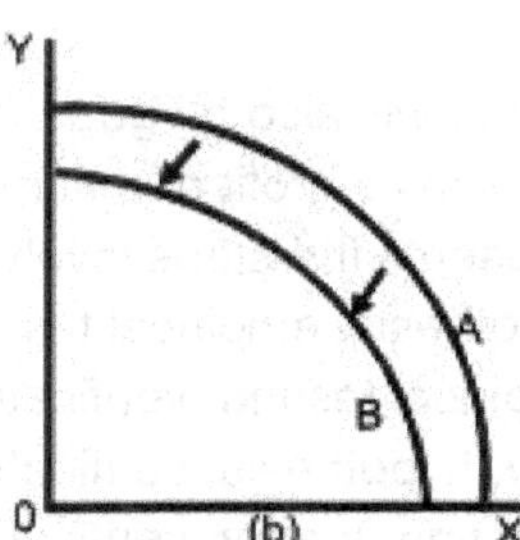

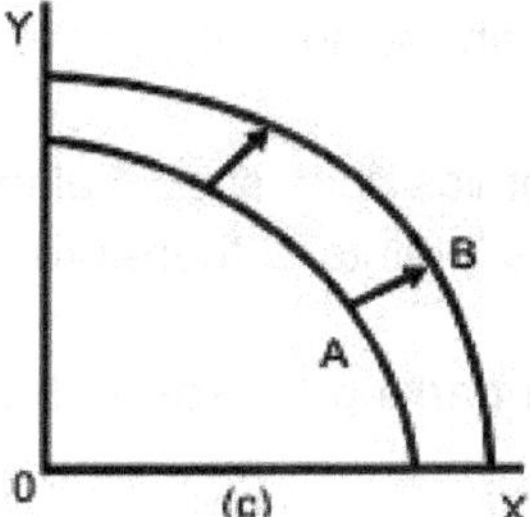

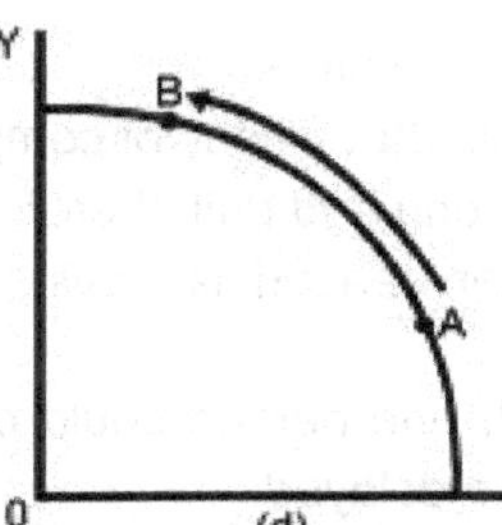

9. In 2015, a country was producing at point "P" on its production possibility curve for current consumption vs. new capital formation. At which of the following points is the country most likely to be producing by 2020, all other things unchanged?

   a. X
   b. Y
   c. Z
   d. P

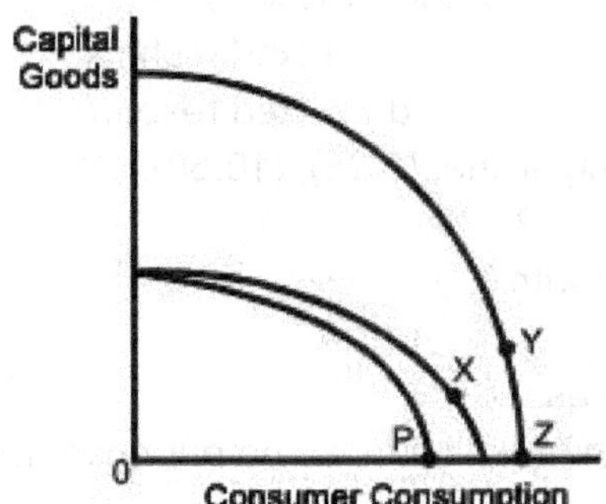

"Limits, Alternatives and Choices"

Self-Test : Terms

1. Macroeconomics is primarily concerned with:
   a. a company
   b. the total levels of income, employment, and output
   c. a union
   d. individual government sectors
2. Economics may be defined as:
   a. various amounts of a commodity that consumers are willing and able to purchase at alternative prices
   b. a social science dealing with the production of goods and services, with scarce resources, for production now and in the future
   c. what is good for the whole will also be good for the part
   d. the ability of firms to maximize profit or minimize loss in the short-run
3. Which of the following represents the steps involving the scientific method in economics?
   a. theory, verification, hypothesis, empirical testing
   b. theory, hypothesis, empirical testing, verification
   c. empirical testing, theory, hypothesis, verification
   d. hypothesis, empirical testing, theory, verification
4. Which of the following is not a reason for studying economics?
   a. inform citizens (voters)
   b. knowledge of the social environment
   c. information for business executives
   d. all of the above are valid reasons
5. Which of the following depicts the "fallacy of composition"?
   a. All economics texts are long and dull, therefore this economics book should also be long and dull.
   b. Tourism for the summer season is down; the ocean is polluted, therefore, tourism is down due to the pollution.
   c. At the end of a concert, one person could drive out of a parking lot easily, but if everyone tried to leave at once, everyone would be delayed.
   d. None of the above depict the "fallacy of composition".
6. If two variables are directly related, then:
   a. when one variable is increasing, the other is decreasing.
   b. when one variable is increasing, the other is increasing.
   c. when one variable is decreasing, the other is increasing.
   d. when one variable is decreasing, the other can either increase or decrease.
7. The term "ceteris paribus" is defined as:
   a. the value of the best alternative.
   b. other things being equal.
   c. unlimited wants with limited resources.
   d. taking facts of a generalization or principle.
8. Which of the following is not an assumption of the PPC Model?
   a. Two products are produced
   b. Fixed technology
   c. Money Payment
   d. Fixed resources
9. Calculate the slope of the following straight line: (5,25), (10,50), (15,75)
   a. 5 b. -5 c. .2 d. -.2
10. Microeconomics is primarily concerned with:
    a. establishing economic policy
    b. calculating national statistics, such as GDP
    c. studying the workings of specific units, which make up our economic system
    d. none of the above

"The Market System and The Circular Flow"

Chapter Orientation

This concept opens with the six foundations of pure capitalism - private property, freedom of enterprise and choice, the role of self-interest, competition, markets and prices, and a limited role for government. By examining the characteristics of a pure economic system, you can better understand our current economic systems. Three areas, common to all advanced economic systems are: (1) extensive use of capital goods, (2) specialization, and (3) the use of money. In addition, the key features help explain the five fundamental questions in economics: WHAT?, HOW?, FOR WHOM?, ACCOMMODATING CHANGE?, and PROMOTING PROGRESS.

Lastly, the concept explains the Circular Flow of Economic Activity.

Learning Objectives

After studying this chapter in the text, and completing the following exercises in this concepts book, you should be able to:

1. Identify and define the six foundations of pure capitalism.
2. List the three characteristics common to all economic systems.
3. Apply the PPC to comparative advantage.
4. List and explain the Five Fundamental Questions in economics.
5. Explain how a command economy and a free market economy answer the five questions in economics.
6. Draw the Simple Circular Flow Diagram and explain.

Chapter Highlights

I. Economic Systems (to make these decisions)

- A. Def. - A particular set of institutional arrangements and a coordinating mechanism. Economic systems differ as to (1) who owns the factors of production and (2) method used to direct economic activity.
- B. Types of Systems
  1. Pure or laissez-faire Capitalism (pure capitalism) - decentralizd decision making in the market. This system is hypothetical today – an extreme.
  2. Command system - Command economy (communism) - centralizd decision making at the top. Many countries are "opting out" of this system and moving toward a market system.
  3. Market system (socialism, capitalism) - real world economies lie in between pure capitalism and the command economy.

II. Characteristics of the Market System

- A. Foundations (See chart next page)
  1. Private property
  2. Freedom of enterprise and choice
  3. Self-interest
  4. Competition
  5. Markets and prices
- B. Technology and capital goods
  1. Extensive use of technology and capital goods
  2. Specialization and efficiency
     - a. Division of labor
     - b. Geographic specialization
  3. Use of money for trade and specialization
  4. Limited role for government

III. The Five Fundamental Questions

A. The Five Fundamental Questions are:
   1. What goods and services will be produced?
   2. How will the goods and services be produced?
   3. Who will get the goods and services?
   4. How will the system accommodate change?
   5. How will the system promote progress?

B. "What goods and services will be produced?"
   1. Calculation of profit
      a. Economic cost - tangible and intangible expenses
      b. Total revenue = price x quantity
      c. Normal profit - an expected rate of return
      d. Economic (pure) profit = total revenue - total cost [over and above a normal rate of return (excess or surplus profit)]
   2. Profits and losses are industry "signals"
      a. Expanding industry (profit)
      b. Declining industry (loss)
   3. Consumer sovereignty (dollar votes)
   4. Derived demand (market restraints on freedom)

C. "How will the goods and services be produced?"
   1. Profitability insures resources
   2. Economic efficiency
   3. Least-cost production

D. "Who will get the goods and services (output)?"
   1. Resource prices determine money income for households
   2. Prices for goods and services are set in the market
   3. Ability (income) to pay for these goods and services

E. "How will the system accommodate (adapt) change"
   1. Directing or guiding function of prices
   2. Competition and control

F. "How will the system promote progress?"
   1. Technical Advance
   2. Capital Accumulation

IV. The Invisible Hand

A. Merits of the Market System
   1. Efficiently
   2. Incentives
   3. Freedom

V. The Demise of the Command Systems

A. The Coordination Problem (under central planning)

B. The Incentive Problem (under central planning)

VI. The Circular Flow Model

A. Circular flow diagram (text page 43)
   1. Definition of the circular flow – a dynamic market economy (no government) creates continuous, repetitive flows of goods and services resources and money
   2. Sectors and markets:
      a. households and businesses
      b. product (output bought and sold) and resource (input bought and sold)
   3. Two flows:
      a. goods and services
      b. money

B. How the market deals with risk
   1. The Profit System – business risk is concentrated on a firm's owner(s).
   2. Shields employees and suppliers from risk, but in exchange, they are excluded from profit.
   3. Benefits to restricting risk to owners – it is an incentive to owner and less stress for employees.

VII. Last Word: "Shuffling the Deck"

VIII. Web-based Question/Project (see your Instructor)

<u>Key Terms</u>

private property
free enterprise
freedom of choice
self-interest
competition
specialization
Five Fundamental Questions
division of labor
"invisible hand"
consumer sovereignty
directing (guiding) function of prices
command economy (communism)
economic expansion
Circular Flow Model
market (or mixed) capitalism
money
capital goods
medium of exchange
economic costs
normal vs. economic profits
expanding industry vs. declining industry
barter
Adam Smith
risk
dollar votes
derived demand
pure (laissez-faire) capitalism
resource market
product market

PROBLEMS

TABLE 1 Production Costs for 100 Units of Product X

Inputs	Input Unit Price	Production Technique A	Production Technique B
Labor	$10	5	4
Capital	8	4	5

1 a. Calculate from Table 1 (above), the total cost of Technique A and Technique B.
  b. Which technique represents the least-cost combination?
  c. Why will virtually all firms opt for the least-cost technique?
  d. If Product X sells for $85 each unit, what will be the total profit or loss?

2. What are the advantages of specialization and what are the drawbacks?

3. Explain why the institution of private property forms a basis for pure capitalism. How does this relate to Adam Smith's "invisible hand"?

4. Define risk and discuss the impact to owners, employees and suppliers under the market system.

5. Discuss the pros and cons of a market (or mixed) system.

6. Draw the Simple Circular Flow diagram. Label and describe how the model works.

"The Market System and The Circular Flow"

Self-Test

1. Which of the following is not a characteristic of pure capitalism?
   a. private property
   b. self-interest
   c. government management of capital goods
   d. the price system
2. Which of the following is not common to all modern economic systems?
   a. specialization
   b. quality
   c. money
   d. capital goods
3. The price system
   a. helps to determine what will be produced.
   b. aids business executives in deciding what resources to use in production.
   c. influences which goods and services people receive.
   d. all of the above.
4. Bartering in the United States
   a. is illegal
   b. is inefficient due to transactions costs
   c. is efficient because there are no taxes involved
   d. no longer exists
5. Which of the following is not one of the Five Fundamental Questions?
   a. What goods and services should be produced?
   b. How is production organized?
   c. Which firms will produce?
   d. Who receives the output?
6. Which of the following statements represents Adam Smith's "invisible hand" concept?
   a. the government robs the private sector with its invisible hand
   b. the government and the private sector work together, guided by an invisible hand
   c. the government guides the economy with an invisible hand
   d. individuals acting in their own self-interest will guide the market through an invisible hand that will benefit both the buyer and the seller.
7. Which of the following represents a drawback to specialization?
   a. jobs tend to become routine and boring
   b. jobs tend to be more interdependent
   c. workers specialize in various production tasks
   d. both a and b are correct
8. Economic profits are:
   a. the same as "Gross Profit" in accounting.
   b. a normal rate of return according to economists.
   c. a cost because they are paid to the owner.
   d. not a cost because they are "surplus profits" and were an unexpected pleasure.
9. Which of the following counties best exhibits Pure or Laissez-faire capitalism?
   a. Cuba
   b. China
   c. United States
   d. North Korea
10. The term "mixed economy" refers to an economy:
    a. diversifying production of goods and services
    b. has elements of both command and pure market economics
    c. specializing in one product to enhance efficiency
    d. the construction and use of capital to produce consumer goods

"Demand and Supply and Market Equilibrium"

Chapter Orientation

This concept presents the most basic and important tools of economics -- supply and demand. A complete understanding of these concepts will provide insights into how price and output are determined. Supply and demand provide answers to many economic questions.

When studying demand, put yourself in the role of the consumer or "buyer" to figure out the relationship between price and quantity. How do people react to a sale? (Certainly at a lower price people will want a higher quantity of the product). How do people react to prices going up? (Many people will not be able to, or want to, afford the product, which causes a decrease in the quantity being purchased). As you can see, when there is a price change, people purchase higher or lower quantities, which is called a "change in quantity demanded" (movement along the original demand curve), due to a change in price. This represents an inverse relationship between price and quantity demanded. Other than price, what non-price factors would cause people to demand more or demand less of a product (income, taste, expectation, number of buyers, and related goods)? These factors would cause a change in demand -- an all new demand curve shifting to the right (an increase) or to the left (a decrease). Note: the word "quantity" is omitted.

When studying supply, put yourself in the role of the seller or "producer" to determine the relationship between price and quantity. What happens when there is a price war? (Think of the airlines, many companies cannot afford to compete and drop out of the market, which causes a decrease in the quantity of seats available). When price increases, more sellers are interested in making the product available for sale (higher quantity). This is called a "change in quantity supplied" (movement along the original supply curve) due to a change in price. This represents a direct relationship between price and quantity supplied. Other than price, what non-price factors would lure businesses into the market or steer them away (resource prices, technology, prices of related goods, number of sellers, expectations, and taxes and subsidies)?

Market forces act to maintain an equilibrium market (quantity demanded equals quantity supplied). A surplus results when the selling price is above the equilibrium; a shortage results when the selling price is below the equilibrium.

The government may legally set prices above the equilibrium price (price floor or price supports) or may set prices below the equilibrium price (price ceilings or price caps) to reduce fluctuations in the economy. The artificially setting of price is currently under debate. (Example: increasing the minimum wage).

Learning Objectives

After studying this chapter in the text, and completing the following exercises in this concepts book, you should be able to:

1. Define a market and give two examples.
2. Define demand and supply.
3. Graph the supply and demand curves and explain the relationship between price and quantity (demanded or supplied) for each curve.
4. Distinguish between a "change in quantity demanded" and a "change in demand".
5. Distinguish between a "change in quantity supplied" and a "change in supply".
6. List the reasons behind a "change in demand" and a "change in supply".
7. Give two examples of complementary and substitute goods.

8. Distinguish between normal and inferior goods.
9. Label the equilibrium price and quantity on a supply and demand graph.
10. Explain how equilibrium is achieved in a competitive market.
11. Explain the effects of changes in supply and demand on equilibrium price and equilibrium quantity.
12. Present the rationale for the government's legally setting prices.

Chapter Highlights

I. Markets

A. Definition of a market - when you have a buyer and a seller willing and able to come together to buy and sell goods and services.

B. Examples: mall, roadside stand, Internet site, etc.

II. Demand (Consumers)

A. Definition of Demand - various amounts of a commodity that consumers are willing to purchase, at alternative prices during a certain time period, ceteris paribus.

B. Law of Demand
   1. Inverse relationship between price and quantity demanded
   2. Diminishing marginal utility
   3. Income and substitution effects (income effect indicates a lower price will increase purchasing power; substitution effect indications the buyer will replace a more expensive item with the sale item)

C. Demand Schedule (table)

D. Demand Curve (individual and market)

E. "Change in Demand" (new curve) -- non-price determinants:
   1. Tastes
   2. Number of buyers
   3. Income (superior/normal have a direct relationship with income or inferior have an inverse relationship with income)
   4. Prices of related goods (complements, substitutes, and unrelated goods)
   5. Consumer Expectations

F. "Change in quantity demanded"
   1. Price change (movement along the curve) due to changes in price

III. Supply (Sellers)

A. Definition of Supply - various amounts of a commodity that sellers are willing and able to offer for sale at alternative prices during a certain time period, ceteris paribus.

B. Law of Supply
   1. Direct relationship between price and quantity supplied

C. Supply schedule (table)

D. Supply curve (individual and market)

E. "Change in Supply" (new curve) -- non-price determinants:
   1. Resource prices
   2. Technology
   3. Taxes and subsidies
   4. Prices of other goods
   5. Producer Expectations (price)
   6. Number of sellers

F. "Change in quantity supplied"
   1. Price change (movement along the curve) due to changes in price.

"Demand and Supply and Market Equilibrium"

IV. Market Equilibrium

A. Equilibrium price and quantity (where Demand = Supply)
   1. Rationing function of prices (eliminates surpluses and shortages)
   2. Effects of changes in demand and supply (impacts the equilibrium price and quantity)

B. Application: Government - Set Prices
   1. Price ceiling or price cap (shortages) - Protects Buyer – keeps prices artificially low. An example is rent control.
   2. Price floor or support price - Protects Seller – keeps prices artificially high. An example is the price of wheat.

C. Chapter 3 Appendix
   1. Additional examples of supply and demand

V. Last Word: A Legal Market for Human Organs?

VI.Web-based Question/Project (see your Instructor)

Key Terms

market
demand
law of demand
inverse relationship
diminishing marginal utility
quantity demanded
individual demand
market demand
non-price determinants of demand
increase (or decrease) in demand
normal and inferior goods
complementary and substitute goods
depreciation
appreciation
supply
law of supply
direct relationship
quantity supplied
individual supply
market supply
non-price determinants of supply
increase (or decrease) in supply
equilibrium price and quantity
rationing function of prices
price floor (support)
price ceiling (cap)
foreign exchange market

MACRO PROBLEMS

# of Bushels Demanded	Price per Bushel	# of Bushels Supplied	Amount of Surplus or Shortage
2,000	$5	12,000	________
4,000	4	10,000	________
7,000	3	7,000	________
11,000	2	4,000	________
16,000	1	1,000	________

1. Fill in the "Amount of Surplus or Shortage" column above and answer the following questions.
   a. What will be the equilibrium price and quantity?
   b. Where does a surplus occur? A shortage?
   c. "Surpluses drive prices up; shortages drive them down." Do you agree?
   d. Graph the demand and supply curves, using the schedules above. Label.
   e. Using the graph from part d, what would happen to the demand for a normal good if the buyers' incomes increased. Label the new curve D1. Also, show what would happen to the supply of a good if more competitors entered the market. Label the new curve S1. Label new equilibrium point (E'). List two reasons that might have been behind these changes.
   f. Now suppose the government establishes a ceiling price — show graphically. What might prompt the government to establish a ceiling price? (two reasons)
   g. Now assume the government establishes a floor (supported) price — show graphically. What rationale might prompt the government into this action? (two reasons)

2. The demand schedules for three people (Erin, Kristen, and Erica), for ice cream cones, are shown in Table 1 below.
   a. Assuming they are the only buyers of ice cream cones, calculate the total (market) demand for ice cream cones.
   b. Graph the market demand curve from table 1 below.

TABLE 1
Quantity demanded for ice cream cones

Price	Erin	Kristen	Erica	Total
$1.50	1	1	0	_____
1.25	2	2	1	_____
1.00	4	3	2	_____
.75	6	4	3	_____
.50	10	6	4	_____

   c. What happens to the demand for ice cream cones when we have a long and hot summer? Show the change on your graph from part (b).

"Demand and Supply and Market Equilibrium"

MACRO PROBLEMS (continued)

3a. Label the supply and demand curves below (D, D1, S, S1). The broken line represents a new curve.

b. Label the axes for each graph.

c. For each graph, state what has happened to demand and what has happened to supply (increase, decrease, or change in quantity).

d. Label the old (E) and the new (E1) equilibrium points on each graph.

e. Label the new equilibrium price (Pe) and equilibrium quantity (Qe) for each graph.

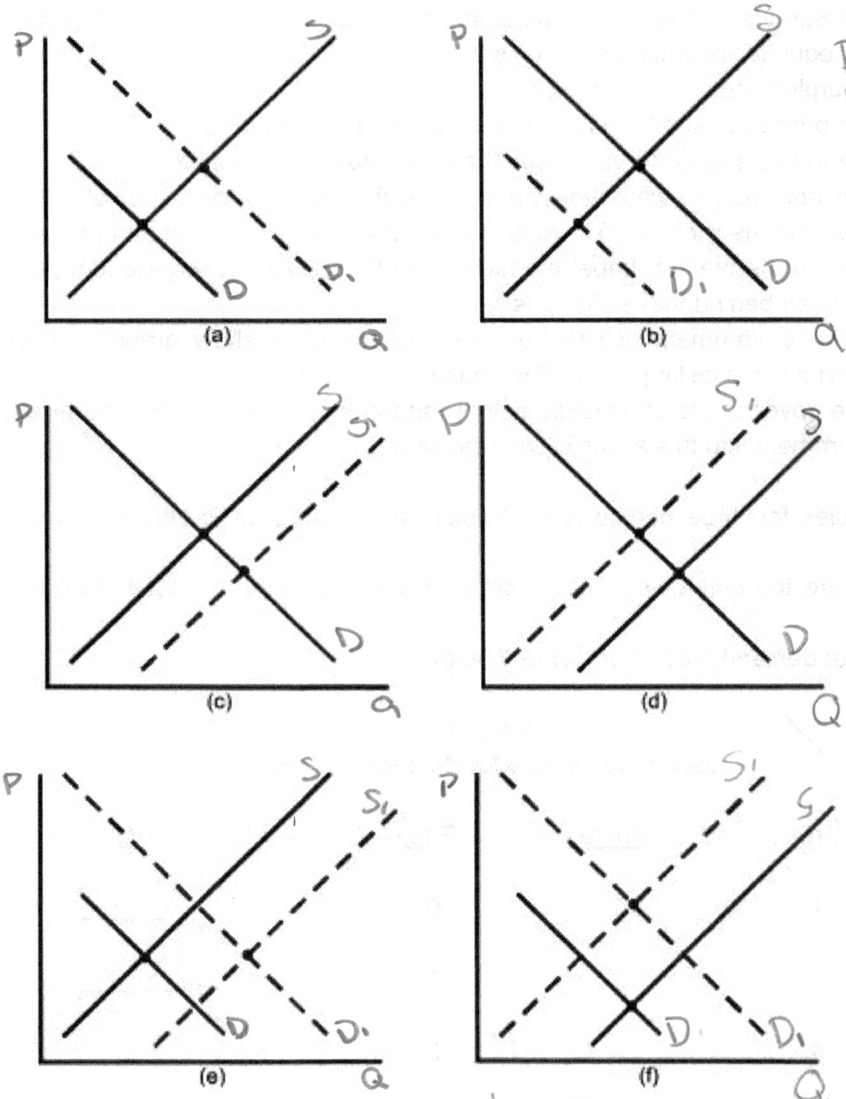

f. In each graph, state what has happened to the new equilibrium price and quantity.

(a) (b)

(c) (d)

(e) (f)

10pt prob on test

"Demand and Supply and Market Equilibrium"

MICRO PROBLEMS

D # of DVDs Demanded	P Price per DVD	S # of DVDs Supplied	Amount of Surplus (+) or Shortage (-)
200	$15	100	- 100
175	18	125	- 50
140	21	140	0
130	24	155	+ 25
100	27	175	+ 75
75	30	200	+ 125

1. Fill in the "Amount of Surplus or Shortage" column above and answer the following questions:
   a. What is the equilibrium price and quantity?
   b. Where does a surplus occur? Where does a shortage occur?
   c. "Surpluses drive prices up: shortages drive them down." Do you agree?
   d. Graph the demand and supply curves, using the table above—be sure to label the curves. Label the equilibrium point (E).
   e. Using the graph from part d, show an <u>increase</u> in demand and an <u>increase</u> in supply. Label the new equilibrium point (E'). List two <u>reasons</u> that might have been behind these changes.
   f. Now suppose the government establishes a ceiling price—show this graphically in relation to the equilibrium points. List two reasons why the government might establish a ceiling price.
   g. Now assume the government establishes a floor (supported) price—show this geographically in relation to the equilibrium points. List two reasons why the government might take this action.
   h. At a price floor (support) of $27, what happens in the market?
   i. If the quantity supplied increased by 50 DVDs at every price, what would be the new equilibrium price and quantity?

2. Below are the individual demand schedules for three people (Pat, Victoria, and Joey) for plants. Assuming they are the only buyers in the market,
   (a) Calculate the total market demand at each price.
   (b) Draw the demand curve below.
   (c) What is the relationship between price and quantity?

	Quantity Demanded of Plants			
Price	Pat	Victoria	Olivia	Total Market
$25	0	1	1	______
20	1	2	2	______
15	2	4	5	______
10	4	6	7	______
5	5	8	10	______

   (d) Suppose that Pat learns that she is allergic to plants, and therefore, purchases 0, regardless of the price.
      1. Recalculate the total market demand
      2. Graph the new curve on the graph above.
      3. What has happened to demand?

"Demand and Supply and Market Equilibrium"

Self-Test (Macro)

1. A decrease in the price of pretzels occurs. What happens to the demand for mustard, its complement?
   a. demand increases
   b. demand decreases
   c. a change in quantity demanded
   d. unable to determine

2. In question number one (above) what happens to the demand for pretzels?
   a. increase in demand
   b. decrease in demand
   c. increase in quantity demanded
   d. decrease in quantity demanded

3. New information is disclosed that kale helps to keep consumers healthy and therefore, demand increases. What happens to the supply of kale?
   a. increase in quantity supplied
   b. decrease in quantity supplied
   c. increase in supply
   d. decrease in supply

4. What happens to the demand for single-family houses when the mortgage rates increase?
   a. increase in demand
   b. decrease in demand
   c. a change in the quantity demanded
   d. unable to determine

5. The H.O.T. company sells extensions for women's hair. Last month the company sold 1,000 extensions @ $30 each. This month the company sold 1,000 extensions @ $40 each. Obviously, the company has experienced:
   a. a change in quantity demanded
   b. an increase in demand
   c. a decrease in demand
   d. unable to determine

6. What would cause the quantity demanded for orange juice to rise or fall?
   a. a freeze in Florida
   b. a change in price
   c. a bumper crop of oranges
   d. unable to determine

"Demand and Supply and Market Equilibrium"

<u>Self-Test</u> (Macro - continued)

Fill in questions 7-13 based upon Graph 1 below:

GRAPH 1

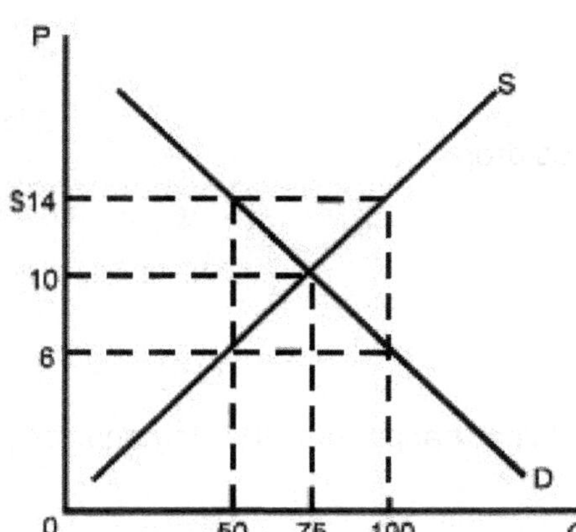

GRAPH 2

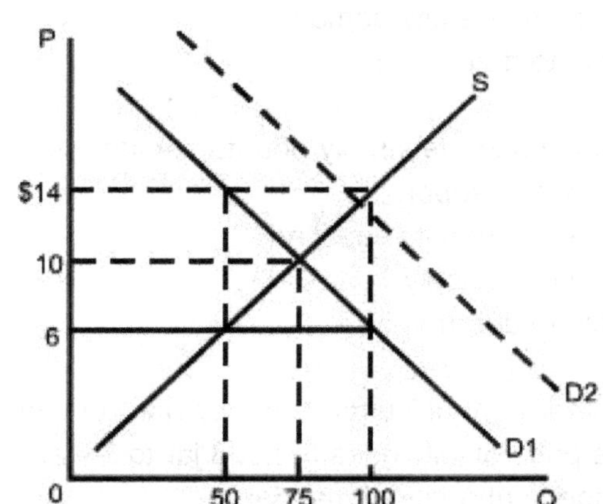

7. The equilibrium price is _________ and quantity is __________.
8. At $14, there is a _____________ of _______________, in the market.
9. At $6, there is a _____________ of _______________, in the market.
10. $______________ is the highest price the buyer will pay for 100 items.
11. $______________ is the lowest price the producer will offer 50 items for sale.

12. Which of the following prices represents a price ceiling?
    a. $14
    b. $10
    c. $6
    d. Unable to determine

13. Which of the following represents a price floor?
    a. $14
    b. $10
    c. $6
    d. Unable to determine

14. Rent control is an example of a price ________________.

15. In Graph 2, (above), which of the following would cause a shift from D1 to D2?
    a. Price of a complement increases
    b. Price of a substitute decreases
    c. Price of a complement decreases
    d. Unable to determine

"Demand and Supply and Market Equilibrium"

Self-Test (Micro)

1. If the price of wine goes from $10/bottle to $7/bottle, what will happen to the demand for cheese—its complement?
   a. increase in demand
   b. decrease in demand
   c. change in quantity demanded
   d. unable to determine

2. What happens to the supply of automobiles when the interest rates drop?
   a. decrease in supply
   b. change in quantity supplied
   c. increase in supply
   d. unable to determine

3. Assume that peanut butter and jelly are complementary goods. What happens to the demand for peanut butter when the price of jelly goes from $3/jar to $4/jar.
   a. change in quantity demanded
   b. increase in demand
   c. decrease in demand
   d. unable to determine

4. Price ceilings:
   a. benefit the consumer
   b. keep prices artificially low
   c. are utilized for wage and price controls
   d. all of the above

5. When the price of product "B" increases, the demand for "C" decreases. Obviously, "B" and "C" are:
   a. complementary goods
   b. substitute goods
   c. inferior goods
   d. independent goods

6. When the demand for a product increases as consumer income increases, that product is said to be:
   a. complementary
   b. competitive
   c. normal/superior
   d. inferior

"Demand and Supply and Market Equilibrium"

Self-Test (Micro - continued)

Fill in questions 7-14 based upon Graph 3 below:

GRAPH 3

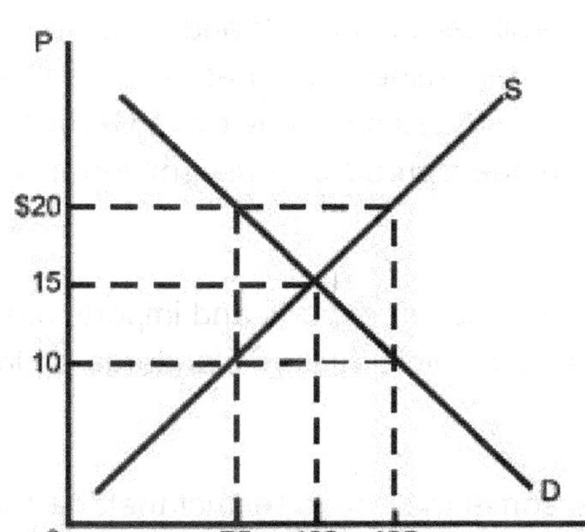

GRAPH 4

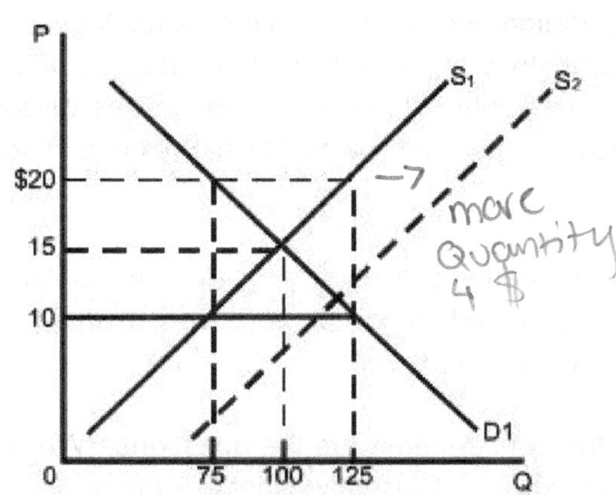

7. The equilibrium price is $15 __________ and quantity is 100 __________.
8. At $10, there is a 75 __________ of quantity __________, in the market.
9. At $20, there is a 75 __________ of quantity __________, in the market.
10. $ 20 __________ is the highest price the buyer will pay for 75 items.
11. $ 20 __________ is the highest price the producer will offer 125 items for sale.
12. Which of the following represents a price ceiling?
    a. $20
    b. $15
    c. $10
    d. Unable to determine

13. Which of the following represents a price floor?
    a. $20
    b. $15
    c. $10
    d. Unable to determine

14. Minimum wage is an example of a price floor __________.

15. In graph 4 (above) which of the following would cause a shift from S_1 to S_2?
    a. Increase in resource pricing
    b. Decrease in consumer demand
    c. Decrease in resource pricing
    d. Unable to determine

"International Trade"

Chapter Orientation

This chapter explores the global economy and its influences on the United States. Although the U.S. accounts for a diminishing percentage of world trade, the absolute volumes of American imports and exports exceed those of any other nation.

Transportation and communication technology coupled with an overall decline in tariff and peaceful relations have all contributed to our expanding global market. It is often difficult to determine just what is, or isn't an American product. For example, a Finnish company owns Wilson Sporting Goods; a Swiss company owns Gerber Baby Food, a South African corporation owns Miller Brewing. Also, parts may be made abroad and assembled in U.S. and vice versa.

Supply and demand analysis reveals how equilibrium prices and quantities of exports and imports are determined. Specialization according to comparative advantage permits nations to achieve higher standards of living through exchange with other countries.

Lastly, the concept answers the questions, "Why do governments sometimes try to restrict the free flow of imports or subsidize exports? Currently, what are the regional free-trade zones around the globe? Can American businesses compete in a global economy? Is "offshoring of jobs" good economic policy?

Learning Objectives

After studying this chapter in the text, and completing the following exercises in this concepts book, you should be able to:

1. Explain the importance of international trade to the American economy in terms of volume, dependence, trade patterns, and financial linkages.
2. Discuss several factors that have facilitated the rapid growth of international trade since World War II.
3. Identify the key participating nations in international trade.
4. Add the international trade dimension to the circular flow model.
5. Explain the basic principle of comparative advantage based on an individual example.
6. Compute the comparative costs of production from production possibilities data from a table.
7. Determine which of the units have a comparative advantage or absolute advantage in the example.
8. Indicate the range in which the terms of trade will be found in the example.
9. Show the gains from specialization and trade in the example.
10. Describe the three considerations as a basis for world trade.
11. Demonstrate how supply and demand analysis applies to the equilibrium price and quantity of exports and imports.
12. Identify four types of trade impediments and subsidies.
13. Discuss two reasons why governments intervene in international trade.
14. Estimate the cost to consumers from trade restrictions.
15. List the major features of the General Agreements on Tariffs and Trade (GATT) of 1947.
16. Describe the purpose and function of the World Trade Organization (WTO).
17. Describe the history, goals, and results from the European Union.
18. Explain the features and significance of the North American Free Trade Agreement (NAFTA).
19. Discuss the "offshoring of jobs", include both pros and cons.
20. Define the Trade Adjustment Assistance Act of 2002. Why do critics feel it is unfair?

"International Trade"

Chapter Highlights

I. Some Key Trade Facts

A. The following are several important facts relating to international trade:
1. U.S. exports and imports have more than doubled as a percentage of GDP since 1980.
2. A trade deficit occurs when imports exceed exports. A trade surplus is the opposite. The U.S. has a trade deficit in goods and a surplus in services.
3. Principal U.S. exports include chemicals, agricultural products, consumer durables, semiconductors and aircraft; principal imports include petroleum, automobiles, metals, household appliances and computers. Some categories are both imported and exported. Example: automobiles
4. Canada is the United States' most important trading partner quantitatively. In 2012, about 20% of U.S. exports were sold to Canadians, who in turn provided 15% of imported U.S. goods.
5. The U.S. has a sizable trade deficit with China ($315 billion in 2012)
6. In 2012, the U.S. imported $181 billion of goods from OPEC members, while exporting only $82 billion of goods to those countries.
7. The U.S. leads the world in the combined volume of exports and imports. In 2012, the top five exporters by dollar were China, U.S., Germany, Japan and Netherlands.
8. The U.S. provides about 8.1 percent of the world's exports (in 1950 it supplied 33%)
9. Exports of goods and services make up about 14 percent of total U.S. output (lower than many other nations)
10. China has become a major international trader, with an estimated $2.05 trillion of exports in 2012.
11. International trade links world economies and is often the center of debates over economic policy (here and abroad).

II. The Economic Basis for Trade

A. World trade is based on three considerations:
1. The uneven distribution of economic resources among nations
2. The fact that efficient production of various goods requires particular techniques or combinations of resources (labor-intensive; land-intensive or capital-intensive goods)
3. Differentiated products produced among nations

B. Comparative Advantage
1. Specialization and international trade increases the productivity of U.S. resources and allows the U.S. to obtain greater total output, by exploiting absolute advantages and comparative advantages.
2. "Absolute advantage" is when a country can produce more of a particular product from a specific quantity of resources than some other country. A nation has a "comparative advantage" in some product when it can produce that product at a lower domestic opportunity cost than can a potential trading partner.
3. In 1776, Adam Smith published, The Wealth of Nations and argued that with free trade, each nation could specialize in the production of those commodities in which it had an "absolute advantage" and import where it had an "absolute disadvantage."
4. David Ricardo, writing some 40 years later, further explained Smith's theory, with the Law of Comparative Advantage—even if a nation were better in all economic activities, it still would be mutually advantageous for this country to specialize and trade with other countries.
5. A numeric table is presented in your textbook starting on page 842.

C. Terms of Trade
1. The terms of trade must be such that both nations can get MORE of a particular output via trade than they can get at home.
2. A numerical example is presented in your textbook starting on page 844.

D. Gains for Specialization and Trade

1. Specialization, according to comparative advantage, improves global resource allocation. The same total inputs have now resulted in greater global output.

III. Supply and Demand Analysis of Exports and Imports

1. Supply and demand analysis reveals how equilibrium prices and quantities of exports and imports are determined.
2. The amount of a good or a service that is exported or imported depends of the difference between the world price and the domestic (home) price.
3. A numeric graph is presented in your textbook starting on page. 848.

IV. Trade Barriers and Export Subsidies

1. While a nation as a whole gains from trade, certain industries may be harmed. Those industries might seek to preserve their economic positons by persuading their respective governments to protect them from imports (though tariffs, import quotas, etc.)
2. Economists conclude that the outcome of these "political deals" may be a robust network of trade barriers which include:
   a. Tariff—excise taxes or duties placed on imported goods. They are designed to shield domestic producers from foreign competition (foreign good become more expensive to purchase).
   b. Import quota—maximum limits on the quantity or total value of specific imported items, regardless of the demand.
   c. Nontariff barrier (NTB)—includes licensing requirements, unreasonable standards pertaining to product quality, or "red tape" in customs procedures.
   d. Voluntary export restriction (VER)—foreign firms "voluntarily" limit the amount of their exports to a particular country.
   e. Export subsidy—consists of government payments to domestic producers to reduce their production costs thus domestic producers can charge lower prices and sell more exports in world markets.
3. Direct effects include: Decline in consumption; increased domestic production; decline in imports; tariff revenue
4. Indirect effects include: promotion of inefficient industries that do not have a comparative advantage and also indirectly cause the contraction of efficient industries that do have comparative advantage.

V. The Case for Protection: A Critical Review

1. Military self-sufficiency argument (protect industries that supply our military)
2. Diversification-for-stability argument—not dependent on one or two commodities
3. Infant industry argument –need time to develop efficiencies
4. Protection against dumping argument—protect against foreign producers from "dumping" (selling goods below cost or a home price—creating a monopoly).
5. Increased domestic employment argument—to "save U.S. jobs" from abroad
   a. The Smoot-Hawley Tariff Act of 1930 was meant to reduce imports and stimulate U.S. production, it raised tariffs on foreign goods and those countries retaliated with tariffs equally high. International trade fell, lowering the output and income of all nations. Many agree that act was a contributing cause of the Great Depression.
6. Cheap foreign labor argument—domestic firms and workers need to be shielded from competition from countries where wages are very low. This will cause cheap imports to flood the U.S. market and U.S. goods and wages will be pulled down, as will our living standards. This argument can be rebutted in two ways:
   a. If U.S. does not trade, it will have to pull resources away from an efficient industry to make room for another.
   b. When measuring a unit of output against the cost of a worker, it often works out to be identical (i.e., the more expensive worker is producing more).

VI. Multilateral Trade Agreements and Free-Trade Zones

A. General Agreement on Tariffs and Trade (GATT)

1. In 1947, GATT was formed to:
    a. Encourage nondiscriminatory treatment for all trading nations.
    b. Reduce tariffs by multilateral negotiation
    c. Eliminate import quotas

B. World Trade Organization (WTO)

1. The Uruguay Round agreement established the WTO as GATT's successor
2. As of 2013, 159 nations belong to the WTO.
3. The WTO oversees trade agreements reached by the member nations and rules on trade disputes among them.
4. It also provides forums for further rounds of trade negotiations (latest "Doha Development Agenda"). The negotiations are aimed at reducing tariffs and import quotas, as well as agricultural subsidies that distort trade.
5. The WTO is controversial
6. Their website is www.wto.org

C. The European Union (EU)

1. Began in 1958 as the "Common Market, the European Union (EU) had 15 European nations. In 2013, the EU had 28 nations.
2. The EU has abolished tariffs and import quotas on nearly all products traded among members. In addition, is established a common system of tariffs applicable to all goods received from nations outside the EU.
3. It has liberalized movement of capital and labor within the EU and created common policies in other economic matters of joint concern.
4. EU integration has achieved for Europe what the U.S. has achieved with their states. The economies of scale have enabled industries to achieve lower costs than if they were single-nation markets.
5. A significant achievement was the establishment of the "Eurozone" in the early 2000s. As of 2013, 17 members of the EU use the "euro" as a common currency.
6. Economists expect the adoption of the euro to raise the standard of living over time by enhancing the free flow of goods, services and resources among members.

D. North American Free Trade Agreement (NAFTA)

1. In 1993, Canada, Mexico and the U.S. formed a trade bloc called NAFTA, having about the same combined output as EU, but a much larger geographical area.
2. Previously, the U.S. and Canada signed a free trade agreement in 1989. That agreement was far less controversial than Mexico.
3. NAFTA has eliminated tariffs and other trade barriers between Canada, Mexico and the U.S.
4. Although concern had been expressed about job losses in the U.S. or the potential for abuse by other nations, employment in the U.S. has increased more than 20 million. This increased trade has enhanced the standard of living in all three countries.

E. Recognizing Those Hurt by Free Trade

1. Some industries can be hurt by free trade (examples include steel and textiles)

F. Trade Adjustment Assistance

1. The Trade Adjustment Assistance Act of 2002 provides cash assistance (beyond unemployment insurance) for up to 78 weeks for workers displaced by imports or plant relocations abroad. Critics feel it is unfair to help only those workers who lost their jobs from imports, sending some work abroad....many workers lose their jobs due to other reasons (technology) and do not get "special treatment".

G. Offshoring of Jobs
1. Some U.S. jobs are lost due to "globalization" of resources, which has put increased pressure on American businesses.
2. Most firms have met this challenge by lowering production costs, improving products or using new technology.
3. One way for business to lower production costs is to shift work, previously done by American workers to workers located in other countries ("offshoring")
4. Recent advances in computer and communications technology have enabled U.S. firms to offshore service jobs to countries such as India.
5. Some firms are having difficulty remaining competitive and continue to lose market share and will eventually go out of business and those workers will lose their jobs.
6. However, the U.S. has a sizable trade surplus with other nations in service by specializing in high-valued services and we trade off lower services abroad.
7. In addition, by lowering cost, U.S. companies will be more competitive and profitable. This is turn might create more jobs in the higher-level positions, as the company grows.
8. Overall, increased trade has produced substantial benefits for American consumers (lower prices and more products) and enabled the nation to make more efficient use of its scarce resources.

VII. Last Word: Petitions of the Candlemakers, 1845
VIII. Web-based Question/Problem (see your Instructor)

<u>Key Terms</u>

opportunity – cost ratio
comparative advantage
import quotas
export subsidies
Reciprocal Trade Agreements Act of 1934
General Agreement on Tariffs and Trade (GATT)
World Trade Organization ("WTO")
Uruguay Round
DOHA Development Agenda
labor-intensive goods
land-intensive goods
capital-intensive goods
gains from trade
voluntary export restriction (VER)
trading possibilities line
terms of trade
protective tariffs
nontariffs barriers (NTB)
Smoot-Hawley Tariff Act of 1930
European Union (EU)
North American Free Trade Agreement (NAFTA)
Trade Adjustment Assistance Act oof 2002
offshoring
dumping
world price
domestic prince
export supply curve
import demand curve
equilibrium world price
revenue tariff
Eurozone

PROBLEMS

1. Table 1 shows bushels of corn and the watches that the U.S. and Switzerland can produce with one hour of labor under four different cases.

TABLE 1

	Case A		Case B		Case C		Case D	
	U.S.	Swiss	U.S.	Swiss	U.S.	Swiss	U.S.	Swiss
Corn	4	1	4	1	4	1	4	2
Watches	1	2	3	2	2	2	2	1

a. In each case identify the commodity in which the U.S. and Switzerland have absolute advantage or disadvantage.

b. In each case identify the commodity in which the U.S. and Switzerland have comparative advantage or disadvantage.

c. For each case, indicate whether or not trade is possible and the basis for trade.

d. Suppose in case B, the U.S. exchanges 4 corn for 4 watches with Switzerland.
(1) How much does the U.S. gain?

(2) How much does Switzerland gain?

(3) What about if they exchanged 4 corn for 6 watches.

"International Trade"

DISCUSSION QUESTIONS

1. Why does the United States account for a diminished percentage of world trade? Who is our most important trading partner (quantitatively)? What is our trade deficit with China?

2. Who are the world's top five counties (in terms of exports)?

3. Name the three considerations for world trade.

4. How does specialization and international trade increase productivity?

5. Why do nations put up trade barriers? Name five barriers.

6. What is "offshore outsourcing"? List pros and cons.

"International Trade"

Self-Test

1. The concept of comparative advantage illustrated that:
   a. specialization enhances efficiency even if a nation can produce both goods at lower cost.
   b. specialization can be inefficient if a country has absolute advantage
   c. countries should be self-sufficient
   d. none of the above.
2. Which tends to be a drawback to specialization?
   a. jobs tend to become routine and boring
   b. jobs tend to be more interdependent
   c. workers specialize in various production tasks
   d. both a and b are correct.
3. Which of the following has not been a facilitating factor in world trade?
   a. general declines in tariffs
   b. implementation of strict import quotas
   c. dramatic improvements in communications technologies
   d. improvements in transportation technology
4. The objectives of the European Union (EU) include:
   a. the establishing of a common system of tariffs for nonmember nations
   b. the eventual free movement of labor and capital among member nations
   c. the abolition of tariffs and import quotas among members
   d. all of the above

Answer the next 2 questions based on the information below:

5. If with one hour of labor time Nation A can produce either 3X or 3Y while Nation B can produce either 1X or 3Y (and labor is the only input)
   a. Nation A has a comparative disadvantage in Commodity X
   b. Nation B has a comparative disadvantage in Commodity Y
   c. Nation A has a comparative advantage in Commodity X
   d. Nation A has a comparative advantage in neither Commodity
6. With reference to question 5:
   a. Px/Py = 1 in Nation A
   b. Px/Py = 3 in Nation B
   c. Py/Px = 1/3 Nation B
   d. all of the above
7. According to Adam Smith, international trade is based on:
   a. absolute advantage
   b. comparative advantage
   c. both absolute and comparative advantage
   d. neither absolute nor comparative advantage

"International Trade"

Self-Test

8. Which is our most important trading partner in terms of the quantity of trade volume?
   a. Japan
   b. Canada
   c. Germany
   d. United Kingdom

9. How is most of the trade deficit financed by a nation such as the U.S.?
   a. by selling securities or assets from other nations
   b. by selling securities or assets to other nations
   c. by borrowing from the Federal government
   d. by lending to the Federal government

10. Why do governments often intervene in international trade?
    a. to expand a nation's production possibilities
    b. to improve the position of multinational corporations
    c. to protect domestic industries from foreign competition
    d. to increase revenue from tariff duties and excise taxes

"Economic Growth"

Chapter Orientation

Are consumers in the United States ever satisfied? As we learned from the "Law of Scarcity", people have unlimited wants but limited resources—we want better quality, faster, more convenient, etc. Therefore, our economy needs to grow to try to accommodate these wants, as well as absorb new workers into the labor force.

This concept will look at how the United States has done over the last century to grow its economy, as well as other industrialized countries. Also, it will take a look at how our economy has fared since 1950, the contributing factors and what the outlook for the future holds. Economic growth has been perhaps the most revolutionary and powerful force in history and therefore, merits our understanding.

Learning Objectives

1. Define the two ways to measure economic growth.
2. Calculate the economic growth for a society.
3. List the four supply ingredients for growth, as well as the other two ingredients.
4. Explain how economic growth is illustrated on the PPC and on the AD-AS Model.
5. State the Real GDP and Per Capita GDP rates and discuss areas that are not taken into account.
6. List the forces behind economic growth in the United States.
7. Discuss developments that detract from economic growth.
8. Discuss the significance of the U.S. productivity slowdown and the impact on our economy.
9. List some possible causes of the U.S. productivity slowdown.
10. Discuss if the U.S. experiencing a resurgence of productivity growth? Is it long-term?
11. Discuss "Demand-side" and "Supply-side" Public Policies to stimulate economic growth.

Chapter Highlights

I. **Economic Growth**
   A. Definition
      1. An increase in real GDP occurring over some time period
      2. An increase in real GDP per capita occurring over some time period
   B. Growth as a Goal
      1. Growth lessens the burden of scarcity
      2. Growth affords a higher standard of living and rising real wages
   C. Arithmetic of Growth
      1. Rule of 70 – a formula, which tells us the number of years it will take for some measure to double
   D. Growth in the United States
      1. "Real GDP" has grown at an annual rate of about 3.2 percent between 1950 and 2012. "Per Capita GDP" has increased nearly 2.0 percent annually since then. However, these numbers do not include:
         a. Improved products and services
         b. Added leisure
         c. Environmental effects
         d. Introduction of new inventions
         e. Position on business cycle
         f. International comparisons

"Economic Growth"

II. Modern Economic Growth

A. Era of wireless high-speed Internet, genetic engineering, space exploration, etc., has increased growth
B. Affect on cultural, social, and political arrangements
C. Uneven distribution among countries
D. Catching up is possible for follower countries

III. Institutional Structures that Promote Growth

A. Strong property rights
B. Patents and copyrights
C. Efficient financial institutions
D. Literacy and widespread education
E. Free trade
F. A competitive market system

IV. Determinants of Growth

A. Supply factors:
   1. Natural resources (need increases)
   2. Quantity and quality of human resources (need increases)
   3. Supply (or stock) of Capital Goods (need increases)
   4. Technology (need improvements)
B. Demand factor
   1. A growing economy needs an increasing level of aggregate demand by households, business, and the government.
C. Efficiency factor
   1. A growing economy must use its resources in the most efficient way
      a. Produce in the least costly way
      b. Produce for the society's well-being

V. Production Possibilities Analysis

A. Growth and the Productions Possibilities Curve (PPC)
   1. Recall from the PPC, that Economic growth is shown by a rightward shift of the PPC. This can be accomplished by increasing the inputs of resources and labor.
   2. Labor and productivity - growth can be accomplished by raising its inputs of resources and by raising their productivity.
B. Growth in the AD-AS Model
   1. Increase in Short- and Long-run Aggregate Supply
      a. Shift the curves to the right
   2. Increase in Aggregate Demand
      a. Shift the curve to the right
   3. Economic Outcomes
      a. The increases in AS and AD result in increases in real output and the price level, which results in economic growth, accompanied by mild inflation.

VI. Accounting for Growth (in the U.S.) - as assessed by The President's Council of Economic Advisors

A. Labor Inputs versus Productivity
   1. Productivity growth has been the most important force underlying growth
   2. Our population and labor force have grown—of most significance has been the tremendous surge of women in the labor force
B. Technological Advance
   1. Technological advance is extremely important, it is linked with the discovery of new knowledge which permits firms to combine resources in new ways to achieve a greater output.

C. Quantity of Capital
   1. A worker will be more productive if he/she is equipped with more capital goods. A nation acquires more capital through saving and investment in plant and equipment.

D. Education and Training
   1. One important measure of labor quality is education and training. By 2012, 88 percent (41 percent in 1960) of U.S. population had a high school education and 31 percent (8 percent in 1960) had a college education or more. Unfortunately, scores on standardized college admissions tests have declined relative to scores of a few decades ago. Also, U.S. students in science and mathematics do not do as well as students in many other industrialized nations. The U.S. has been producing fewer engineers and scientists.

E. Economies of Scale and Resource Allocation
   1. Economies of Scale - Markets have increased in size over time and firms have increased output levels, permitting more efficient production methods to be used in production.
   2. Improved resource allocation, such as movement of labor into high technology, the decline of discrimination and barriers to international trade (such as tariffs, quotas, etc.) have helped expand output.

VII. Productivity Acceleration: The Rise in the Average Rate of Productivity Growth

A. Reasons for the Productivity Acceleration
   1. The microchip and information technology has created a wide array of new products and services and new ways of doing business.
   2. New firms and increasing returns - many new start-up firms in technology have experienced increasing rates of return.
      a. More specialized inputs
      b. Spreading of development costs
      c. Simultaneous consumption
      d. Network effects
      e. Learning by doing
   3. Global competition
      a. NAFTA, EU, WTO

B. Implications for Economic Growth
   1. Higher productivity growth allows the economy to achieve higher economic growth.
   2. Foster noninflationary growth
   3. Low natural rate of unemployment
   4. Growing tax revenues

C. Skepticism about Permanence
   1. Many economists caution that we should "wait and see" if these effects produce a long-term trend.

VIII. Is Growth Desirable and Sustainable?

A. The Antigrowth View
   1. Critics of growth cite pollution, global warning, ozone depletion and other environmental problems.
   2. Also, there is little compelling evidence that growth solves poverty, homelessness, and discrimination.
   3. Growth does not ensure the "good life".
   4. Critics argue that our planet has finite amounts of resources and therefore growth is not sustainable in long-run.

B. In Defense of Economic Growth
   1. Majority of population desire higher living standards and natural wealth.
   2. Those who support growth state that growth enables society to improve the nation's infrastructure,

enhance care of the sick and elderly, provide greater access for the disabled, and provide more police and fire protection.

3. New machinery is less taxing and less dangerous than the older models.
4. Growth has increased our leisure time.
5. Many argue that increases in economic growth need not mean increase in pollution.
6. Economic growth is the expansion of <u>human</u> knowledge and information (which is only limited by human imagination).

IX. Web-Based Question/Problem (see your Instructor)

X. Last Word: Can Economic Growth Survive Population Decline?

<u>Key Terms</u>

Economic growth
Supply factors
Demand factors
labor-force participation
economies of scale
efficiency factor
labor productivity
infrastructure
increasing returns
human capital
information technology
start-up firms
learning by doing
network effect
read GDP

PROBLEMS

1. On graph paper, draw the PPC and illustrate economic growth. Also, explain how this change is made possible.

2. On graph paper, draw economic growth in the extended AD-AS Model, illustrating both the short-run and the long-run.

3. Capitalist countries have experienced impressive economic growth during this century. Discuss how the United States has fared as compared to other advanced industrial countries.

4. Why is economic growth important? What are the major causes of economic growth?

5. List two ways that economic growth is measurable.

6. What are the four supply factors of economic growth? What is the demand factor?

7. What public policies should be implemented to sustain economic growth?

8. Where does the U.S. rank on test scores (2012 – 2013) in Mathematics and Science for eighth-graders?

9. Compare the rates of productivity in the U.S. in 2012 with 1973 - 1995.

10. Explain the pros and cons of "Economic Growth".

"Economic Growth"

Self-Test Questions

1. Which of the following is NOT a supply factor for growth?
   a. natural resources
   b. efficiency
   c. human resources
   d. technology

2. When there is an increase in short- and long-run AS and an increase in AD, the result of this dynamic is:
   a. economic growth with deflation
   b. economic contraction with hyper-inflation
   c. economic growth with mild inflation
   d. economic contraction with deflation

3. Which of the following areas has the U.S. experienced tremendous economic growth?
   a. service sector
   b. computer industry
   c. agricultural sector
   d. None of the above

4. Detriments to growth include:
   a. discrimination
   b. worker safety
   c. environmental concerns
   d. all of the above

5. Which of the following is/are reason(s) for increasing returns and economies of scale?
   a. more specialized inputs
   b. spreading of development costs
   c. network effects
   d. all of the above are reasons

6. Which of the following is <u>not</u> a Macro implication for growth?
   a. business loans
   b. growing tax revenues
   c. low rate of natural unemployment
   d. faster noninflationary growth

7. Real GDP in the United States has grown at what approximate rate, since 1950?
   a. 2%
   b. 5.4%
   c. 3.2%
   d. 0%

8. Real "Per Capita" GDP in the United States has grown at what approximate rate, since 1950?
   a. 2%
   b. 5.4%
   c. 3.1%
   d. 0%

9. Which of the following statements expresses the "antigrowth" viewpoint?
   a. Growth has increased leisure time.
   b. Economic growth is the expansion of human knowledge and information.
   c. Majority of the population desires higher standard of living.
   d. Growth causes more pollution, global warming, and ozone depletion.

10. Which of the following has been "the most important force" underlying the growth of U.S. real output and income?
    a. labor
    b. productivity
    c. technological advance
    d. economies of scale

ECON 105 – UNIT I REVIEW

Be sure to bring a #2 pencil, graph paper and calculator!

PART I: 40 Multiple Choice questions (2 points each or a total of 80 points)

1. Know a definition of "Economics".
2. Know the difference between Macro and Micro Economics
3. Know how to determine direct and inverse relationships (table and graph).
4. Be able to calculate the slope of a straight line.
5. Know what is meant by "ceteris paribus".
6. Know the Five Fundamental Questions in Economics and how they are answered under different economic systems.
7. Know the definitions of "laissez faire" and "the Law of Scarcity".
8. Know about the Law of Increasing Costs.
9. Know what is meant by and examples of opportunity costs.
10. Know about the Production Possibilities Curve (PPC): what it illustrates, about a point inside of the curve, a point outside of the curve, what would cause a movement along the curve, what would cause a shifting of the curve and why it can be linear (straight line) or concave ("bowed") shaped.
11. Know about the Theory of Comparative Advantage and specialization.
12. Know what the Simple Circular Flow Model illustrates.
13. Know the three fallacies: Composition, Division, and False Cause.
14. Know what the Law of Demand and the Law of Supply state.
15. Know the difference between and what would cause a movement along the demand and supply curves and a shifting of the demand and supply curves. (Be sure to know how normal, superior, inferior, substitute and complementary goods effect the demand curve).
16. Know what is meant by equilibrium and how to graphically determine the old and new equilibrium price (Pe) and quantity (Q_e).
17. Know about price ceilings and price floors and how to graphically determine the amount of a surplus or a shortage.
18. Know the annual percentage of real GDP in the U.S. (last 50 years).
19. Know the characteristics of "Pure Market", "Command" and "Mixed Economies".
20. Know from Adam Smith's book, The Wealth of Nations, the concepts of the "invisible hand" and "self-interest".
21. Know the four "factors of production" and their money payments.
22. Know the factors that have helped facilitate world trade.
23. Define "excise taxes" and "import quotas"; "free-trade zone".
24. Define the objectives for the following trade agreements: NAFTA, EU, GATT, and WTO.
25. Know the forces underlying growth and the detriments to growth in the U.S.
26. Identify our most important trading partner in terms of trade volume.
27. Define the Trade Adjustment Assistance Act of 2002 and why critics say it is unfair.
28. Define the "Euro Zone" and discuss its importance.
29. Why is the WTO controversial?
30. Define "offshoring". Discuss the pros and cons.

Answer only TWO of the THREE problems, listed on the exam.
Problem #1: Supply and Demand (Example: Workbook page 25, #1)
Problem #2: Production Possibilities Curve (Example: Workbook page 10, #1)
Problem #3: Diagram and explain the "Simple Circular Flow Model".
Problem #4: Comparative Advantage Problem (Example: Macro Worksheet Unit 1)

REVIEW TEXTBOOK, CLASS NOTES (ON WORKSHEET), WORKBOOK, CANVAS (QUIZZES AND PP SLIDES)

Any questions please contact your Instructor or visit our new "Learning Commons" located in the Bankier Library.

GOOD LUCK!!

UNIT I FORMULAS

$$\text{Slope} = \frac{\blacktriangle Y}{\blacktriangle X} = \frac{\text{rise}}{\text{run}} = \frac{Y_2 - Y_1}{X_2 - X_1}$$

Notes:

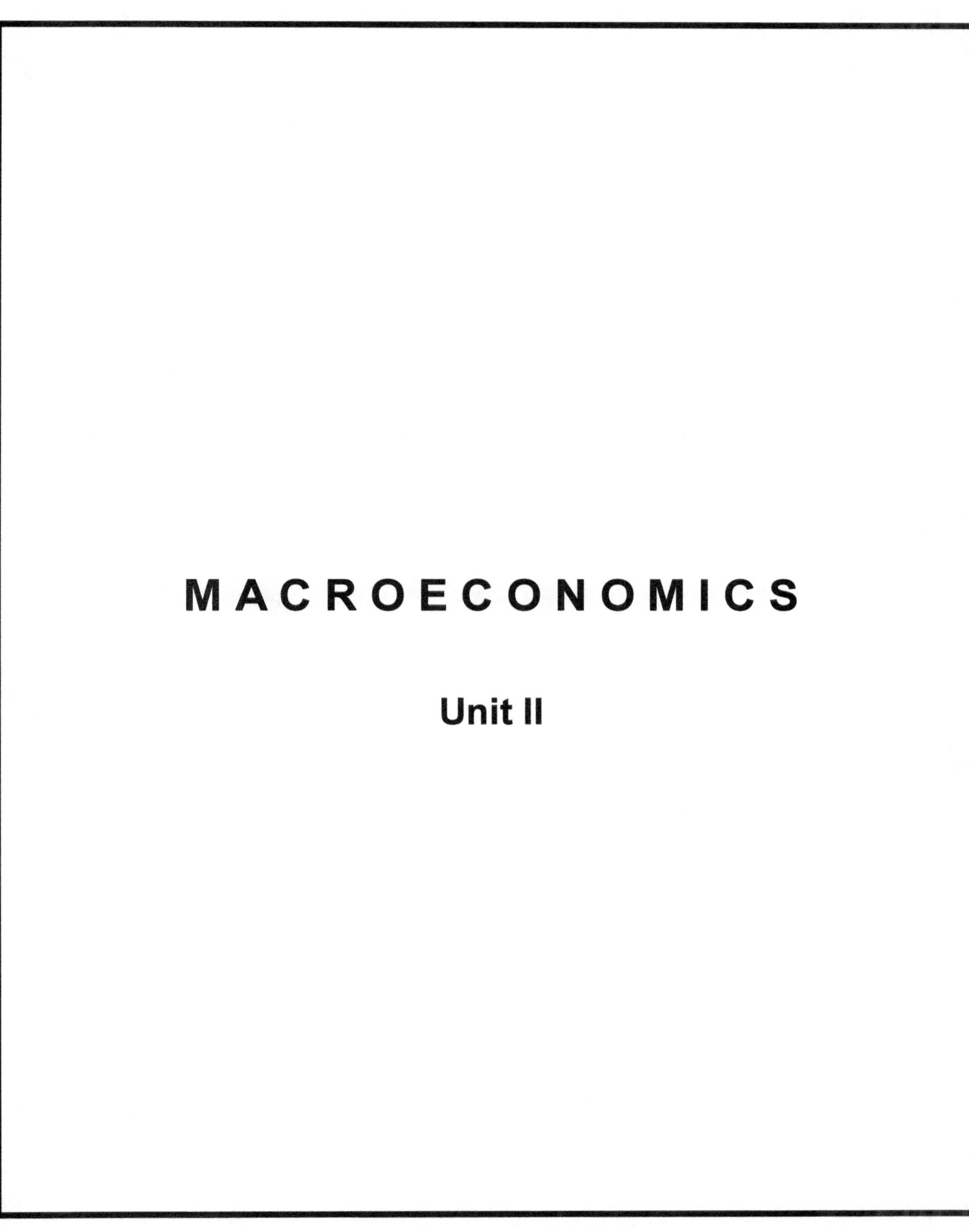

MACROECONOMICS

Unit II

"Measuring Domestic Output and National Income"

Chapter Orientation

National income accounting gives us a method to measure our nation's (as well as other nation's) overall economic health. Calculation of the "bottom line" figures (GDP, NDP, NI, PI, and DI) allows us to see how well off we are (standard of living) as compared to other years. In addition, by looking at several years, we can plot the trend and predict the future cycle of the economy. In 1992, the United States switched from using Gross National Product (GNP) to Gross Domestic Product (GDP), as the broadest measure of our economic health. In 2015, GDP for the U.S. was estimated at approximately $17 trillion and is estimated to become approximately $22 trillion by 2020.

To simplify the process of calculating national income accounting, "NIA sheets" are provided in this concepts book (they will also be given to you at the time of the test). The more practice, the better you will get, so six countries' data is given to you. More important than just memorizing the accounts to tally, is the knowledge of what the account means, as well as the interpreting figures.

National income accounting can be analyzed in two ways: the expenditures approach (monies spent) and the incomes approach (monies received). An elaborate circular flow diagram in your text shows both approaches. Economists avoid multiple accounting by including only the final (final use) goods, using a value added approach. In addition, only productive activities are included; nonproductive are excluded. To accurately compare years, GDP must be adjusted for inflation (using a GDP deflator or chain-weighted price index) called "Real GDP" since money is not a stable measuring rod.

Lastly, since GDP measures the total overall production, is it a good measure of social welfare (for individuals)? Why is studying "national income accounting" relevant? The answers to these questions will be discussed in the chapter.

Learning Objectives

After studying this chapter in the text and completing the following exercises in this concepts book, you should be able to:

1. Define GDP and state its significance.
2. Distinguish between the expenditures approach and the income approach to measuring GDP.
3. Calculate GDP, NDP, NI, PI, and DI (using the NIA sheets provided) given the necessary data.
4. Define NDP, NI, PI and DI and their components.
5. Compute Real GDP by adjusting money GDP using the GDP deflator.
6. Calculate the price index in a given year.
7. Discuss GDP as a measure of social welfare.

Chapter Highlights

I. Assessing the Economy's Performance

A. This accounting enables economists and policymakers to:
   1. Measures the nation's economic health ("keep a finger on the economic pulse")
   2. Mode of comparison (year to year or with other countries)
   3. Explain its size and the reason for changes
   4. Aids in the creation of economic policies

"Measuring Domestic Output and National Income"

II. Gross Domestic Product

A. Definition of Gross Domestic Product (GDP) — the total market value of all <u>final</u> goods and services produced within the boundaries of the U.S., whether by American or foreign-supplied resources, within a year (monetary measure).

B. Avoiding Multiple Counting
   1. Final goods vs. intermediate goods - final goods are purchases (not resold) by ultimate consumer.
   2. Value added approach - (market value of output less the value of inputs purchased from others)

C. Define "per capita GDP" (output per person) $= \dfrac{\text{Real GDP}}{\text{Population}}$

D. GDP excludes nonproduction transactions
   1. Transfer payments: Public and Private
   2. Securities transactions
   3. Used (second hand) goods sales
   4. Gross national disproduct
   5. Leisure
   6. Quality changes

E. Calculation (use the NIA sheets provided)
   1. The <u>Expenditures Approach</u> (or "output approach") is a method that adds all expenditures made for final goods and services to measure GDP. Expenditures Approach = C + I + G + Xn = GDP
   2. The <u>Income Approach</u> (or "earnings approach") is a method that adds all the income generated by the production of final goods and services to measure GDP. Incomes Approach = Compensation for Employees (Wages) + Rents + Interest + Proprietors' Income + Corporate Profits + Indirect Business Taxes + Depreciation + Net Foreign Factor Income
   3. Include productive activities:
      a. Rent of owner occupied homes
      b. Farm consumption of homegrown food
   4. In theory, both approaches should yield the same GDP. However, in practice, there is always a difference, so NIPA accountants add "statistical discrepancy" to natural income (due to various factors).

III. Other National Income Accounts

A. Define NDP, NI, PI, and DI

B. Calculation of NDP, NI, PI, and DI (using the NIA sheets provided)

C. Relationship between the major social accounts
   1. The circular flow diagram (revisited) - national output and the flows of expenditures of income. (Text page 558)

IV. Nominal GDP versus Real GDP

A. Money is not a stable measuring rod (because of inflation or deflation)

B. Definition of Real GDP vs. Nominal GDP (Real GDP is adjusted for price-level changes)
   1. The adjustment process
      a. Inflating and deflating using a chain-weighted price index

C. Calculation of Real GDP using a GDP deflator or a chain-weighted price index

$$\text{Real GDP} = \frac{\text{nominal GDP}}{\text{GDP deflator or chain-weighted price index*}} \times 100$$

*GDP deflator is given by government

D. Real-world considerations and data

1. As of December 1995, the Commerce Department's Bureau of Economic Analysis (BEA) began using a chain-type price index for computing Real GDP. Therefore, when more than one good or service is produced, government accountants must assign weights to various categories, based on their relative proportions of total output. This is a chain-type annual weights price index, which is always changing.

E. You will not have to calculate the "chain-weightedprice index", as it is reported by the U.S. Department of Commerce.

V. Shortcomings of GDP

A. GDP is <u>not</u> an index of social welfare because it fails to include:
   1. Nonmarket transactions
   2. Leisure
   3. Improved product quality
   4. The underground economy
   5. GDP and the environment (disproduct)
   6. Composition and distribution of output
   7. Noneconomic sources of well-being

VI. Last Word: Magical Mystery Tour

VII. Web-based Question/Problem (see your Instructor)

<u>Key Terms</u>

National Income Accounting (NIA)
Gross Domestic Product (GDP)
Net Domestic Product (NDP)
National Income (NI)
Personal Income (PI)
Disposable Income (DI)
nominal GDP
real GDP
GDP deflator or
  chain-weighted price index
base year
multiple counting
value added
nonproductive
incomes approach
expenditures approach
final and intermediate goods
nominal dollars
net exports (Xn)
gross private investment (I)
government expenditures for goods
  and services (G)
personal consumption expenditures (C)
capital consumption allowance (depreciation)
indirect business taxes
corporation profit before taxes
dividends
undistributed corporate profits
disproduct
nonmarket transactions
proprietor's income
rental income
net interest
social contributions
transfer payments
personal income taxes
personal savings
underground economy
wages and salaries

"Measuring Domestic Output and National Income"

PROBLEMS

1. Below are the National Product and Income Data (in billions of dollars) for six countries for a given year. A dash (-) opposite any account means that the number is not given to you - do not assume zero. Calculate GDP, NDP, NI, PI, and DI for each country using the NIA sheets provided.

Account	Countries 1	2	3	4	5	6
1. Personal consumption expenditures	100	180	- --	- --	400	267
2. Corporation profits (before taxes)	---	- --	50	- --	- --	70
3. Corporate taxes	15	15	10	- --	36	28
4. Depreciation	10	25	10	52	43	14
5. Government expenditures for goods and services	50	---	60	84	128	69
6. Transfer payments	10	30	15	- --	10	16
7. Gross private investment	---	- --	50	46	88	- --
8. Proprietors income	- --	- --	20	- --	52	25
9. Indirect business taxes	20	30	40	22	50	15
10. Net interest	---	- --	10	- --	15	12
11. Net private investment	50	- --	- --	---	- --	47
12. Personal income taxes	15	24	20	38	15	38
13. Personal savings	---	40	30	10	- --	- --
14. Rental income	- --	- --	20	- --	12	18
15. Social contributions	0	12	5	23	5	8
16. Undistributed corporate profits	10	9	10	---	22	19
17. Wages and salary earnings	- --	- --	250	- --	369	240
18. Net exports	0	0	0	---	- --	- --
19. Exports	- --	- --	- --	9	10	14
20. Dividends	---	- --	- --	13	24	23
21. Imports	- --	- --	- --	12	3	17

GDP: ______________________________

NDP: ______________________________

NI: ______________________________

PI: ______________________________

DI: ________________ 190________________

PROBLEMS (continued)

2 a. Complete the table below, which shows actual data for the U.S. economy billions of chained 2009 dollars.*

*Go to the Bureau of Economic Analysis website (www.bea.gov) and in the middle section under "National" click on "GDP". Then under GDP, click on "current dollar and "real" GDP (excel). Fill in figures below from the data given.

Year	Current GDP in Billions of Dollars	GDP in Billions of Chained 2009 Dollars
1980	$2,862.5	________________
1990	5,979.6	________________
2000	10,284.8	________________
2005	13,093.7	________________
2010	14,964.4	________________
2014	17,418.9	________________

3 a. Complete the table below using year 2 as the base year (hypothetical data).
b. Calculate the table below using year 3 as the base year.
c. This economy has been characterized by ________________________.

a.

Year	Qty.	Price	Price Index	Nominal/or Current $	Real/or Constant $
1	3	$2	_____	________	__________
2	5	4	_____	________	__________
3	6	5	_____	________	__________
4	8	6	_____	________	__________
5	9	8	_____	________	__________

b.

Year	Qty.	Price	Price Index	Nominal/or Current $	Real/or Constant $
1	3	$2	_____	________	__________
2	5	4	_____	________	__________
3	6	5	_____	________	__________
4	8	6	_____	________	__________
5	9	8	_____	________	__________

"Measuring Domestic Output and National Income"

FORMULAS:

$$\text{Real GDP} = \frac{\text{Nominal GDP}}{\text{GDP deflator or chain weighted price index}} \times 100$$

Current \$ = Price x Qty.

$$\text{Constant \$ or Real \$} = \frac{\text{Current \$}}{\text{Price Index}}$$

$$\text{Price Index} = \frac{\text{Each year's price}}{\text{Base year's price}}$$

"Measuring Domestic Output and National Income"

Self-Test

Below are the National Product and Income Data in billions of dollars. Use the NIA sheets provided to compute the following accounts to answer questions 1 - 6.

Corporate Taxes	30
Depreciation	25
Government Expenditures for goods and services	95
Indirect Business Taxes	47
Net Private Investment	60
Personal Income Taxes	57
Undistributed Corporate Profits	26
Exports	75
Imports	60
National Income	343
Disposable Income	277

1. GDP is:
   a. $415
   b. $400
   c. $435
   d. unable to determine

2. NDP is:
   a. $375
   b. $400
   c. $390
   d. unable to determine

3. PI is:
   a. $56
   b. $334
   c. $278
   d. unable to determine

4. Personal consumption expenditures are:
   a. $57
   b. $205
   c. $220
   d. unable to determine

5. Personal savings is:
   a. $57
   b. $334
   c. $220
   d. unable to determine

6. Gross private investment is:
   a. $35
   b. $85
   c. $60
   d. unable to determine

7. GDP is not a good measure of social welfare; which of the following is not a reason why?
   a. fails to include nonmarket transactions
   b. fails to include changes in quality
   c. fails to include productive activities such as home grown food
   d. fails to include the underground economy

Self-Test (Continued)

TABLE I

Year (1)	Nominal GDP (2)	Chain weighted price index GDP Deflator (3)	Real GDP (4)
1	$550	140	________
2	560	135	________
3	576	120	________
4	586	117	________
5	604	108	________

8. In Table I, "Real GDP" in year 1 is________.
9. In Table I, "Real GDP" in year 3 is________.
10. In Table I, "Real GDP" in year 5 is________.
11. In Table I, this economy is experiencing inflation or deflation?__________

12. Which of the following is not considered a nonproductive activity?
    a. government purchases
    b. consumption
    c. net export
    d. gross private investment

13. The largest component of GDP is:
    a. the monetary value of all goods and services produced by Americans in U.S. or abroad.
    b. the monetary value of all final goods and services produced by Americans in U.S. or abroad.
    c. the monetary value of all intermediate gods and services produced by Americans in U.S. or abroad.
    d. the monetary value of all economic resources produced by Americans in U.S. or abroad.

14. Net exports is a negative figure when:
    a. exports exceed imports
    b. the country's imports exceed exports
    c. the country's equity is declining
    d. net private investment exceeds gross private investment

15. Real GDP and nominal GDP differ because real GDP:
    a. excludes depreciation or capital consumption allowance
    b. has been adjusted for changes in the price level
    c. does not include nonproductive activities
    d. includes the international sector

16. The GDP may be defined as:
    a. the monetary value of all goods and services produced within the U.S.
    b. the national income minus all nonincome charges against output.
    c. the monetary value of all economic resources used in the production of a year's output.
    d. the monetary value of all goods and services, final and intermediate, produced in a given year, within the U.S.

"Business Cycles, Unemployment and Inflation"

Chapter Orientation

Nothing ever seems to stay the same . . . whether we look at business or economic activity, we see fluctuations in income, output, employment, and prices. When we look back at the history of these business fluctuations, we see irregular cycles that are recurrent.

On a micro level, predicting or forecasting the business cycle would enable you to plan your investment strategy accordingly (buy/sell securities, take out loans, etc.) in the hope of higher profits.

On a macro level, the ability to predict the start of a recession or an expansion in the economy, affords policymakers the lead time needed to make adjustments in the economy to avoid severe fluctuations.

Two of the most important aspects of the business cycle are changes in unemployment (unemployment rate) and changes in prices (inflation rate) which will be covered in detail in this concept.

What are the types of unemployment? How is unemployment measured? How can the unemployment rate be overstated, as well as understated? What are the costs of unemployment?

Lastly, will look at inflation. How is inflation defined? How is it measured? What causes inflation? How does the U.S. compare to other advanced nations? What are the redistributive effects of inflation? These questions will be explored in detail.

Learning Objectives

After reading this chapter in the text, and completing the following exercises in this concepts book, you should be able to:

1. Define the business cycle and explain the four phases of an idealized business cycle.
2. Identify the two noncyclical fluctuations.
3. List the two facts, which explain industry vulnerability to the business cycle.
4. Explain the types of unemployment: frictional (transitional), cyclical, structural, and seasonal.
5. Describe how the Bureau of Labor Statistics measures the unemployment rate.
6. Explain how the unemployment statistic is overstated and understated.
7. Define full-employment and the full-employment unemployment rate (natural rate).
8. Describe the economic and social costs of unemployment.
9. Define inflation (and deflation) and the "rule of 70".
10. Explain the three indexes used to measure inflation: (a) Consumer Price Index -- CPI, (b) Producer Price Index -- PPI, and (c) the GDP deflator (covered in Chapter 25).
11. Contrast the types of demand-side inflation: demand-pull with supply-side inflation: cost-push, structural, and expectational.
12. Explain the effect of increasing output on the price and employment levels in ranges 1, 2, and 3.
13. Discuss the costs and benefits of inflation -- who it hurts and who it helps.
14. Explain three output effects of inflation.
15. Understand that other countries have experienced severe inflation (Ex. Zimbabwe's inflation soared 14.9 billion percent in 2008).

"Business Cycles, Unemployment and Inflation"

Chapter Highlights

I. The Business Cycle

A. The historical record - our long term economic growth has not been steady.

B. Definition -- fluctuations (ups and downs) in general economic activity. The fluctuations are recurrent but nonperiodic (irregular).

C. Phases -- there are four phases of an idealized business cycle:

1. Peak -- full-employment with near-capacity production
2. Recession -- decline in output and employment with "sticky" prices
3. Trough -- a "bottoming out" of output and employment
4. Expansion -- output and employment rise toward full-employment

D. Causation: A First Glance

1. Irregular innovations
2. Productivity changes
3. Monetary impact
4. Political and random events
5. Financial instability

E. Cyclical impact: Durables and Nondurables

1. Durable goods (hard goods) do not have to be replaced at a particular time (postponability) -- they can be repaired to last longer
2. In a recession or depression, "hard goods" industries experience wide declines in output and employment, but small changes in price. The reverse holds true for nondurable, or "soft goods" industries.
3. During recovery and prosperity, "hard goods" industries or experience wide increases in output and employment but, small changes in price. The reverse holds true for "soft goods" industries.
4. The degree of competition in an industry is often influenced by the number of sellers, which in turn impacts on production and price. (Monopoly Power)
   a. Durable-goods industries tend to be characterized by a few sellers (a highly concentrated industry), who maintain price stability to avoid touching off a price war. As a result, during hard economic times, they try to maintain profit margins by cutting costs (cutting production and employment).
   b. Nondurable industries have many sellers (very competitive) competing in the same market. Consequently, when aggregate demand declines, these firms drop their prices while holding output and employment relatively constant.

II. Unemployment

A. Measurement of unemployment -

1. Definition of unemployment — the percentage of people in the labor force who are not working.
   a. The labor force is defined as all people 16 years of age or older who are employed, plus those unemployed who are <u>actively</u> seeking work.
   b. The total labor force includes those in the armed services, as well as those in the civilian labor force.
2. The Bureau of Labor Statistics (BLS) conducts a random survey of 60,000 households each month to determine who is employed and who is not employed.
3. The unemployment rate (%) = $\frac{\text{\# of unemployed}}{\text{labor force}} \times 100$
4. In 2015, the unemployment rate was 5.4%
5. Reliability of the unemployment rate
   a. The statistic can be <u>overstated</u> because those workers in the underground economy (false information) are not counted and because of false information.

   b. The statistic can be understated because "discouraged workers" (given up looking for a job) are not counted in the labor force and part-time workers, who want more hours (full-time) are counted as fully-employed.

B. Types of unemployment – there are three types of unemployment:
   1. Frictional (transitional) -- is the loss of work that occurs when workers change jobs or locations. It is usually temporary. It consists of search unemployment and wait unemployment.
   2. Structural -- usually results from a major industrial change in a region, causing many people to lose their jobs, or when people's skills become outdated or obsolete.
   3. Cyclical -- is the relationship between unemployment and the business cycle: the more prosperous the economy, the lower the unemployment rate. This type of unemployment is severe because it reflects the entire nation. It is also called "deficient-demand unemployment."

C. Definition of "full employment"
   1. The "full-employment unemployment rate" or the "natural rate of unemployment" (NRU) is equal to the total of frictional and structural unemployment. Today it is 5 to 6 percent.

D. Economic costs of unemployment
   1. Economic costs -- lost production of potential goods and services (GDP gap).
      a. Okun's Law -- for every 1% increase in the unemployment rate over the natural rate, a 2% GDP gap is generated.
      b. Unequal burdens -- unemployment is not equally divided among all demographic groups (occupation, age, race, gender, education, and duration).
   2. Noneconomic (social costs) -- unemployment causes people to experience social trauma -- depression, suicide, etc.
      a. Our responsibility to try to "head-off" severe unemployment in our society (Employment Act of 1946).
   3. International Comparisons
      a. Unemployment varies from country-to-country because of differing natural rates of unemployment as well as on different phases of the business cycle.
      b. Between 2002 and 2008, the U.S. unemployment rate was below Italy, Germany, and France, then during the "Great Recession", the U.S. unemployment rate spiked to the highest level of all.

III. Inflation

A. Meaning of Inflation
   1. Definition -- inflation is a rising general level of prices, resulting in a loss of the purchasing power of money (inverse relationship). In 2015, inflation is expected to be 2% because of lower oil prices.

B. Measurement of Inflation
   1. Rate of Inflation CPI $= \frac{P2 - P1}{P1} \times 100$ P1: Old price (market basket in 1982-1984) P2: Old price (market basket in current year)

   2. Rule of 70 -- number of years required for a doubling of the price level.
      Approximate # of years required to double $= \frac{70}{\text{\% annual rate of increase}}$
   3. Consumer Price Index (CPI) -- measures the change in prices of a fixed market basket of goods and services (300 items in 100 areas). Payments made to half of our population are tied to CPI.
   4. GDP deflator (covered in the last chapter) -- adjusts for GDP for inflation -- "Real GDP".

C. The Facts of Inflation
   1. In 2009, the U.S. inflation rate had been in the middle range of rates for other advanced nations, and far below the rates experienced by some nations (Democratic Republic of Congo 46%, Afghanistan (31%, Venezuela 27%, Zimbabwe 14.9 billion percent in 2008).

D. Types of Inflation
   1. Demand-Pull inflation
      a. Definition -- consumers "bid-up" prices as the economy nears full-employment
      b. Three Ranges of Graph
         (1) Range I - (constant prices) output and employment expand, while prices remain constant.
         (2) Range II - (premature or creeping inflation) relatively low rates of inflation, which occurs before the economy reaches full-employment.
         (3) Range III - (hyperinflation) output and employment are constant at the full-employment level, however, prices are rising.

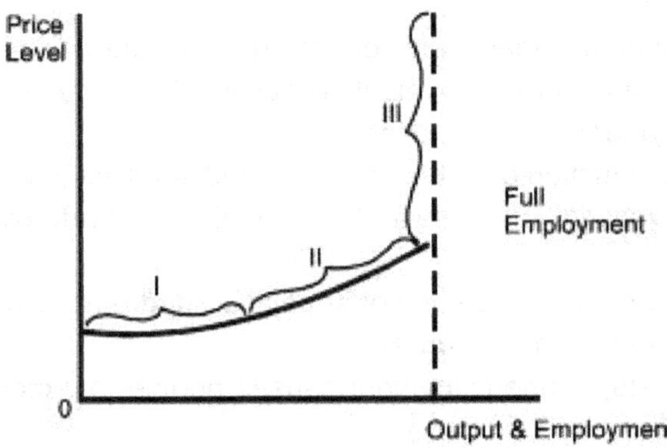

   2. Cost Push or Supply-side inflation
      a. Cost-push or "sellers' inflation" occurs when prices increase because businesses' <u>costs have risen</u> (Example: wage increase without productivity increases).
      b. Supply-Shocks — Production costs increase due to the costs of new materials such as oil (1973-1974; 1979-1980).
   3. Complexities - It is hard to distinguish demand-pull and cost push inflation, also they differ in their sustainability. Food and energy experience rapid changes in supply and demand and are price volatile.

IV. Redistributive Effects of Inflation

A. Nominal and Real-Income costs -- Nominal Income measures how many dollars we have received, Real Income measures how much we can buy (changes in our standard of living).
B. Anticipated inflation -- cost-of-living adjustments (COLA) automatically adjust workers' incomes to inflation. The Nominal interest rate = real interest rate + inflation premium.
C. Fixed-nominal income receivers -- people on fixed incomes without indexing for inflation, lose purchasing power.
D. Savers -- people who do not consumer their entire income may lose purchasing power if the rate of return on their investment does not at least keep up with inflation.
E. Debtors (borrowers) and creditors (lenders) are affected by inflation. The debtors benefit in that they are paying back their loan with cheaper dollars.
F. Other redistribution issues
   1. Deflation - would enhance real income
   2. Mixed effects - inflation may lessen fixed value assets, but may increase property value.
   3. Arbitrariness - the redistributive effects of inflation occur regardless of society's goals and values.

G. Does Inflation Affect Output?
   1. Cost-push inflation may cause output and employment to contract. (Example: price of oil)
   2. Mild demand-pull inflation usually increases output, employment and spending. However, proponents of "zero inflation" cite studies to bolster their case.
   3. Hyperinflation (extraordinary rapid inflation) may lead to the demise of the economy (economic collapse), as it may undermine the monetary system and cause severe declines in real output. Examples include Germany after the First World War and Japan after the Second World War. Zimbabwe's 14.9 billion percent inflation in 2008 is the latest example.

V. Last Word: Unemployment after the Great Recession

VI. Web-based Question/Problem (see your Instructor)

Key Terms

business cycle
contraction/recession
expansion/recovery
trough/depression
peak/prosperity
nonperiodic
seasonal variations
secular trends
durable goods
nondurable goods
NBER indicators
labor force
unemployment
unemployment rate
full-employment
discouraged workers
natural rate of unemployment (NRU)
frictional unemployment
structural unemployment
cyclical unemployment
seasonal unemployment
GDP gap
Okun's Law
inflation
deflation
Rule of 70
consumer price index (CPI)
GDP deflator
demand-side inflation
demand-pull inflation
core inflation
hyperinflation
supply-side inflation
cost-push inflation
wage-push variant
supply-shock variant
real income
nominal income
anticipated inflation
unanticipated inflation
cost-of-living adjustments (COLA)
real interest rate

"Business Cycles, Unemployment and Inflation"

The Ups and Downs of Business

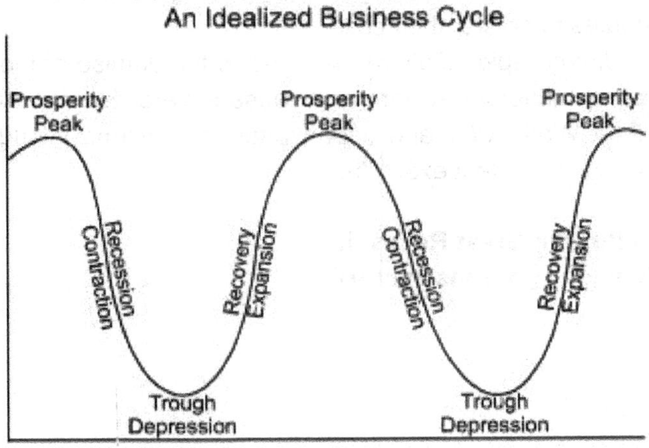

An Idealized Business Cycle

Recovery: the recession has run its course

- Businesses have cut costs
- Interest rates are at a low point
- New factory orders arrive

Faster Growth:

- Consumers and firms begin to spend and borrow again
- Businesses scramble to meet demand

Bursting the Bubble: as the economy expands, imbalances appear

- Shortages of skilled labor and raw materials
- Consumers become over-extended

Recession: the strains become too great

- Consumers retrench and save more income
- Businesses cut expenses

"**Business Cycles, Unemployment and Inflation**"

PROBLEMS

1. Is the U.S. at full employment or at the "natural rate"? What implications do you see for growth, inflation, labor-costs, etc. now and in the future?

2. How do we "read" the economy (what are the indicators to watch)?

3. What are two occupations expected to increase in New Jersey to 2020? In the United States? Why?

4. What are two occupations expected to decline in New Jersey to 2020? In the United States? Why?

5. List and explain the four phases of the business cycle. Why do we have these imbalances? Name at least three theories to explain business fluctuations.

6. If you were to compare the automobile industry with the agricultural industry, over the course of the business cycle, what changes would you encounter in comparing output, employment, and prices?

7. How is unemployment measured? Explain why the employment rate may be overstated or understated?

8. What are the economic and social costs of unemployment?

9. How is the Consumer Price Index (CPI) used to measure inflation? The BLS revamps the market basket with the aim of having it reflect consumers' spending patterns --how has it changed?

10. List and explain the costs and benefits of inflation.

"Business Cycles, Unemployment and Inflation"

Self-Test

1. Business cycles are defined as:
   a. fluctuations which are recurrent and periodic.
   b. ups and downs in certain industries.
   c. fluctuations which are nonperiodic and recurrent
   d. fluctuations that include seasonal and secular trends.

2. The GDP gap measures:
   a. how much nominal GDP exceeds real GDP.
   b. the difference between and GDP.
   c. the amount potential GDP exceeds actual GDP.
   d. the amount actual GDP exceeds potential GDP.

3. The United States is considered to be at full-employment when:
   a. frictional and structural employment equal zero.
   b. cyclical unemployment is zero.
   c. when 100% of the labor force is employed.
   d. when every American, over age 16, is working.

4. Which of the following is not a type of unemployment?
   a. frictional
   b. expectational
   c. structural
   d. cyclical

5. If the rate of inflation is 10%, the price level will double in about:
   a. 12 years
   b. 10 years
   c. 7 years
   d. 4 years

6. Which of the following is not a type of inflation?
   a. demand-pull
   b. cost-push
   c. hyperinflation
   d. cyclical inflation

7. According to Okun's Law, for every 1% that the actual unemployment rate exceeds the natural rate, what GDP gap is generated?
   a. 3.0%
   b. 2%
   c. .01%
   d. equilibrium

8. Which of the following does not measure inflation?
   a. Rule of 70
   b. consumer price index
   c. producer price index
   d. GDP index

9. During a recession, you should expect:
   a. durable goods' industries to cut output and employment, without changing the price level
   b. durable goods industries to increase output and inventories and cut price
   c. nondurable goods industries to raise the price since their goods are essential
   d. nondurable goods industries to lower price, output, and employment

10. Which of the following will be hit the hardest by unanticipated inflation?
    a. a homeowner
    b. a small business owner
    c. developer
    d. a retired person living on a fixed pension

"The Phillips Curve"

Chapter Orientation

For many years, the major economic problems facing our country were inflation and unemployment. This concept focuses on the tradeoffs between inflation and unemployment.

It was believed that we could expand output, employment, and income, up to full-employment, without raising the price level. However, pioneering work in the late 1950's and 1960's showed an inverse relationship between inflation and unemployment, which was named after British economist A.W. Phillips -- the "Phillips Curve". As demand for any commodity increases, its price rises, and unemployment falls. Hence, if unemployment is low, any increased demand for labor will result in rising wage rates. If unemployment is high, wages will rise less rapidly and may even fall.

One group of economists said the Phillips curve represented a long-run tradeoff between inflation and unemployment. Another group said that the Phillips curve was stable only in the short-run. Those economists stated that in the long-run, the "Phillips curve" is vertical at the natural or full-employment, level of output. People will adjust their expectations accordingly -- wages will "catch up" with inflation in the long-run.

Events of the 1970's and early 1980's were clearly at odds with the Phillips curve. Stagflation (slow growth, high unemployment, and rising prices) seemed to discredit the Phillips curve. What happened?

A series of cost-push or supply shocks occurred in the oil and agriculture industries, (1973-75 and 1978-80) as well as a devalued dollar in 1971-73 which shifted the supply curve (which had been ignored in the demand-side models).

Learning Objectives

After reading this chapter in the text, and completing the following exercises in this concepts book, you should be able to:

1. Explain and contrast the typical Phillips Curve using the AD - AS model.
2. Discuss the rationale behind the Phillips Curve.
3. Define "stagflation" and discuss how "stagflation" may have discredited the Phillips Curve.
4. List the six aggregate supply-side shocks experienced by (the U.S. economy).
5. Explain how these "supply shocks" led to stagflation during the 1970's and early 1980's, using the AD - AS model.
6. Explain why demand-management policies cannot reduce or eliminate stagflation.
7. Illustrate the differences between the short-run and long-run Phillips Curve.
8. State the accelerationist hypotheses or the long-run Phillips Curve; and explain how economists use these tools to explain a vertical Phillips Curve.

"The Phillips Curve"

Chapter Highlights

I. The Inflation - Unemployment Relationship

A. Analytical and Historical Background

1. Because both low inflation and low unemployment rates are major economic goals of the Fed, economists are extremely interested in their relationship.

B. The Phillips Curve

1. A.W. Phillips (from Great Britain) studied inflation and unemployment data from the 1960s.
2. He found the existence of an inverse relationship between inflation and unemployment.
3. This means that high rates of inflation should be accompanied by low rates of unemployment and vice versa (inverse relationship).
4. The intersection of AS and AD determines real national output (and employment) and the price level.
5. Therefore, the greater the growth of AD, the greater will be the resulting inflation and the greater growth of real national output (and lower unemployment). See below.

Figure 1:
Phillips Curve – Short Run

Figure 2:
Curve Shifts Due to Supply Shocks

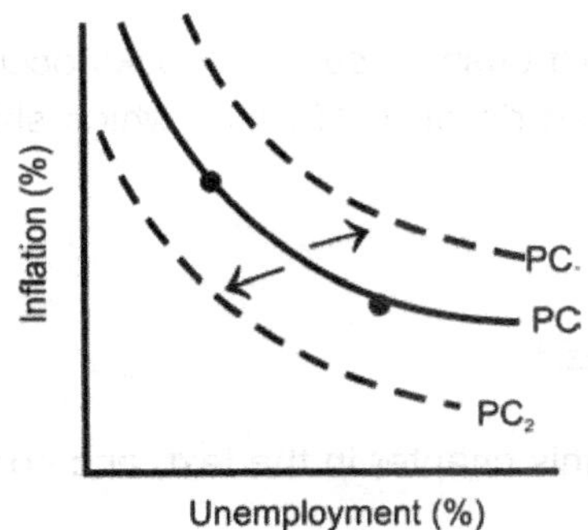

C. Logic of the Phillips Curve

1. Two reasons why inflation occurs before reaching full-employment:
   a. Labor market imbalances -- shortages start to appear before full-employment is reached.
      (1) Those unemployed workers may look for jobs elsewhere but bottlenecks occur -- time to train, relocate, obtain a license, etc.
   b. Market Power -labor unions and business firms have market power rearing full-employment and a prosperous economy, hence, wages production costs, and prices increase.

D. Tradeoffs

1. Although monetary and fiscal policies can be employed, to effect employment and inflation, they merely move the economy from one point on the Phillips Curve to another point along the same curve. Therefore, it is impossible to "full-employment without inflation".
2. In summation, movement along the Phillips Curve is caused by a change in fiscal or monetary policy. Shifts in the Phillips Curve (causing a new curve) would be caused by supply shocks (or changes in the natural rate of unemployment or the expected rate of inflation). Economists overall reject the idea of a stable, predictable Phillips Curve but agree on a short-term tradeoff between inflation and unemployment.

E. Stagflation: A Shifting Phillips Curve?
   1. Definition -- slow growth, high unemployment, and rising prices; occurred during the 1970's and early 1980's in the United States. This contradicted the Phillips Curve.

F. Adverse Aggregate Supply Shocks
   1. Aggregate Supply shocks shifted AS to the left (decrease) to increase prices and unemployment. These experiences confirmed that the Phillips Curve is not a model for economic policy. The six aggregate supply shocks are:
      a. OPEC and energy prices -- oil prices quadrupled which caused the cost of producing and distributing virtually every good and service to rise.
      b. Agricultural shortfalls
      c. Depreciated dollar
      d. Demise of wage-price controls
      e. Slower rates of productivity growth

G. Stagflation's Demise: 1982-1989
   1. Significant factors
      a. Deep recession of 1981-82 (unemployment at 9.5%)
      b. Foreign competition 1982-89 (held down wages)
      c. Deregulation of industries (airlines and trucking)
      d. Decline in OPEC's monopoly power
   2. Unemployment and inflation moved in the same direction
   3. Misery Index – combining rates of inflation and unemployment for comparison.

II. The Long-Run Phillips Curve

A. Definition - contends that the economy is stable in the long-run (vertical) at the natural rate of unemployment.

B. Short-run Phillips Curve
   1. When the actual rate of inflation is higher than expected, the unemployment rate will fall.

C. Long-run vertical Phillips Curve (see Figure 3 below)
   1. In the long-run, the traditional Phillips Curve does not exist: expansionary demand-management will shift the short-run Phillips Curve upward, resulting in increasing inflation with no permanent decline in unemployment.
   2. Expansion of AD, through Keynesian policies, may temporarily increase profits, which increase output and employment. However, when wages "catch up", this lowers profits and therefore lowers output and employment (cancels out the stimulus).

D. Disinflation
   1. Definition - reduction in the rate of inflation
   2. Restrictive Keynesian stabilization policies can reduce inflation without creating permanent increases in unemployment.

Figure 3
Long-Run Vertical Phillips Curve

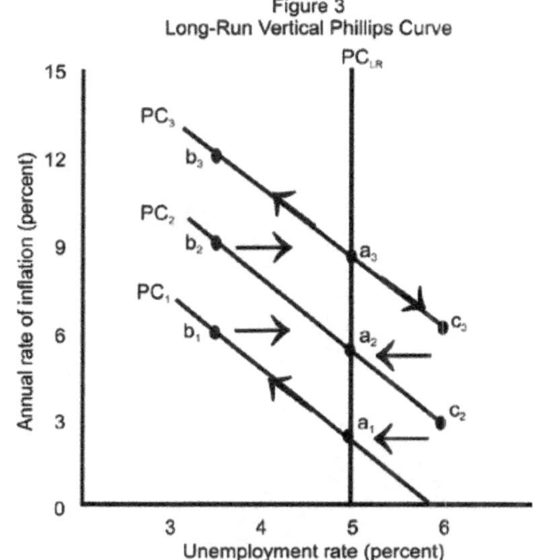

III. Last Word: Do Tax Increases Reduce Real GDP?

VII. Web-based Question/Problem (see your Instructor)

"The Phillips Curve"

Key Terms

stagflation
Phillips Curve
bottlenecks
sticky prices
supply shocks
stabilization policy dilemma
inflationary expectations
demand management policies
misery index
long-run vertical Phillips Curve
short-run
long-run

"The Phillips Curve"

PROBLEMS

1. Draw the Phillips Curve, what tradeoff is illustrated? What are two reasons why prices increase <u>before</u> reaching full-employment?

2. Overall, are economists in agreement (today) that the Phillips Curve works in the short-run? ____________

   Long-run? ___________

3. Draw and explain the long-run vertical Phillips Curve

4. What is "stagflation"? What are the causes of "stagflation"? When has it occurred in the United States?

5. List the six aggregate supply shocks and explain the impact of each on the U.S. economy.

"The Phillips Curve"

Self-Test

1. A Phillips Curve shows the relationship between:
   a. consumption and savings
   b. inflation and prices
   c. inflation and unemployment
   d. consumption and inflation
2. Short-run changes along a given Phillips Curve are accomplished through:
   a. fiscal policies only
   b. monetary policies only
   c. competitive policies
   d. both fiscal and monetary policies
3. In the mid-70's "Supply Shocks" caused the Phiips Curve to:
   a. shift to right
   b. shift to left
   c. stay the same
   d. unable to determine
4. The immediate effect of an adverse supply shock, caused by an increase in the price of imported oil would include:
   a. the AS curve would remain constant
   b. a downward shift of the AD curve
   c. an upward shift of the AD curve
   d. a leftward shift of the AS curve
5. The long-run Phillips Curve is:
   a. Horizontal
   b. Vertical
   c. Not equal to the natural rate of unemployment
   d. Unable to determine

"Basic Macroeconomic Relationships – Including All Multipliers"

Chapter Orientation

The next two concepts will focus on determining how our economy operates as a whole (aggregate). We will explore how aggregate demand (all planned expenditures for the entire economy added together) and aggregate supply (all planned production for the entire economy added together) determine the equilibrium real national output and the equilibrium price level of the economy. This concept begins with just the private sector of AD, which is consumption and investment. Remember, these are two components of the equation AD = C + I + G + Xn = AE = GDP.

The Keynesian viewpoint of what determines the demand for the real national output (real NDP), as well as the equilibrium level of output, will be covered in detail.

Learning Objectives

After studying this chapter in the text, and completing the exercises in this concepts book, you should be able to:

1. List the assumptions of our model to determine the equilibrium national output level (NDP).
2. Explain how consumption (C) and savings (S) are related to disposable income (DI).
3. Calculate APC, APS, MPC, and MPS when given the necessary data.
4. List and explain five nonincome determinants of consumption and savings.
5. Distinguish between a change in consumption (savings) and a change in quantity consumed (saved).
6. Define the "Paradox of Thrift."
7. List the two basic determinants of investment and explain why a firm will or will not invest their money.
8. Calculate the economy's investment-demand schedule and explain the inverse relationship between investment spending and the real interest rate.
9. List and explain five noninterest determinants of investment expenditures.
10. Distinguish between a change in investment-demand and a change in quantity of investment-demand.
11. Explain the variables found in the investment schedule and their relationship.
12. List what factors contribute to the instability of investment spending.
13. Locate the equilibrium output, employment, and income levels from a table.
14. Locate the equilibrium output, employment, and income levels using the Keynesian Cross and Leakage Injection Approach.
15. Distinguish between "planned" versus "actual" investment.
16. Be able to calculate all multipliers and their economic impact on our economy (word problems).

Chapter Highlights

I. The Income – Consumption and Income – Savings Relationships

A. Consumption and Saving

1. Consumption is the largest component of aggregate demand (aggregate expenditures).
2. It is assumed that any disposable income not spent will be saved. Hence, DI = C + S.
3. The consumption schedule shows the amount of consumption at various levels of disposable income, during a certain time period. The relationship between consumption and disposable income is called the "consumption function". There is a direct relationship between C and DI. "Break-even income" is when households spend their entire disposable income.
4. The savings schedule shows the amount of savings at various levels of disposable income, during a certain time period the relationship between savings and disposable income is called the "savings function". There is a direct relationship between S and DI.

5. The Average Propensity to Consume (APC) is the ratio of consumption to disposable income:

$$APC = \frac{C}{DI}$$

6. The Average Propensity to Save (APS) is the ratio of savings to disposable income:

$$APS = \frac{S}{DI}$$

7. The Marginal Propensity to Consume (MPC) measures the change in consumption resulting from a change in income. The MPC is the slope of the consumption function.

$$MPC = \frac{\blacktriangle C}{\blacktriangle DI}$$

8. The Marginal Propensity to Save (MPS) measures the change in savings resulting from a change in income. The MPS is the slope of the savings function.

$$MPS = \frac{\blacktriangle S}{\blacktriangle DI}$$

9. Since disposable income is either consumed or saved:
   APC + APS = 1.0
   MPC + MPS = 1.0
10. We can derive the average and marginal propensities from the consumption and savings schedules.

II. Nonincome Determinants of Consumption and Saving

A. In addition to income, there are four determinants of consumption and savings which cause a change (shift) in consumption (new curve):
   1. Wealth (assets minus liabilities) and "wealth effect" (tendency for people to increase or decrease consumption based on wealth
   2. Borrowing ("no free lunch")
   3. Expectations (about future)
   4. Real interest rates (affect consumption and saving)

B. Other Important Considerations
   1. Switching to Real GDP – (GDP adjusted for inflation)
   2. Changes along schedules - movement along the consumption (or savings) curve from one point to another, is called a change in quantity (amount) consumed (saved) due to a change in disposable income.
   3. Simultaneous Shifts - changes in wealth, expectation, interest rates, and household debt, shift the consumption and savings curves in opposite directions.
   4. Taxation -- a change in taxes shifts consumption and savings schedules the same direction.
   5. Stability – consumption and savings schedules are generally stable.

C. The Paradox of Thrift (text pg. 621 – "Box")
   1. Definition - the apparent contradiction that as households try to save more, they may find that they are only savings the same amount out of a smaller total income (autonomous investment) or even saving less than they were originally (induced investment).
   2. The "fallacy of composition" is illustrated by the "Paradox of Thrift". If I save, I am better off in the future, therefore, If everyone saves, everyone is better off in the future. (But are they?) Obviously, if everyone is busy saving, they are not, spending, hence AD falls. When AD falls below AS, the tendency in the market is to start slowing down production, laying off workers, etc. As a result, the tendency is to decrease O, E, and $ and the new GDP equilibrium level is lower.
   3. Explanation - a decrease in consumption causes income to fall by the amount of the decrease in consumption times the multiplier. A new GDP equilibrium level will be reached when income has fallen to a level where savings is equal to investment.

II. The Interest Rate – Investment Relationship

A. Definition - expenditures on new plants, capital equipment, machinery, etc. The investment decision is a marginal benefit-marginal cost decision. Businesses will invest when the expected rate of return exceeds the interest rate.

B. Determinants of net investment spending

1. Expected rate of return = $\frac{\text{Net Revenue}}{\text{Outlay cost}}$
2. Real rate of interest is the price paid for the use of money adjusted for inflation
3. Comparison of the expected rate of net profit and the real rate of interest must be made to determine if the firm will go ahead with the investment.
4. Therefore, the lower the real rate of interest, the higher will be the level of Investment spending and vice versa.

C. The Investment-Demand Curve

1. Definition - shows the inverse relationship between the real rate of interest and the level of spending (investing) for capital goods. See Exhibit 1 below:

Exhibit 1
Investment – Demand Curve

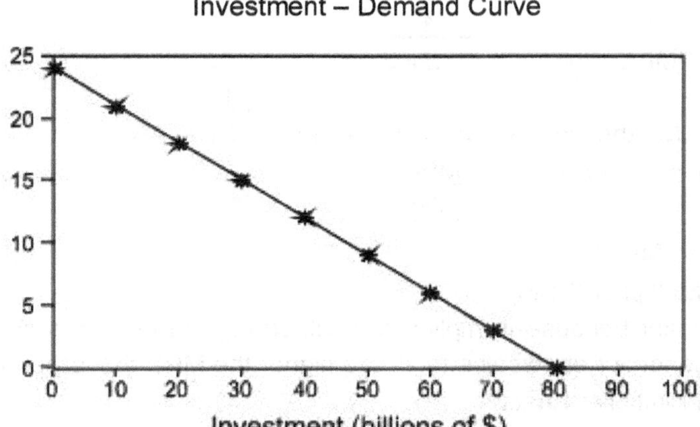

2. Movement along the Investment-Demand curve, from one point to another, is called a change in quantity (amount) of investment-demanded, due to a change in the interest rate.
3. In addition to the interest rate, there are six noninterest determinants of investment-demand which cause a change **(shift)** in the investment-demand (new curve):
   a. Acquisition, maintenance, and operating costs
   b. Business taxes
   c. Technological change
   d. Stock of capital goods on hand
   e. Planned inventory changes
   f. Expectations
4. Because these six noninterest determinants of investment-demand may change suddenly, investment spending tends to be unstable.

D. Investment Schedule
   1. We will assume that business investment is projected for long-term hence, it is independent of income (autonomous). However, in reality, business investment may be caused (induced) by changes in household and company incomes.

E. Instability of Investment
   1. The investment schedule is unstable as compared to the consumption schedule. The factors which explain the variability are:
      a. Variability of expectations
      b. Durability of capital
      c. Irregularity of innovation
      d. Variability of profits

III. The Multiplier Effect (see "Review of the Multipliers" next page)

A. Definition of the Multiplier - a change in Aggregate Demand (= AE) will cause a magnified change (in either direction) in the economy which in turn effects the equilibrium GDP. Today, the complex multiplier, which takes all leakages into account, is estimated at approximately 2, although it can range from zero to 2.5.

B. Techniques to calculate the Simple Multiplier (M):
   1. Numerical table
   2. Graph
   3. Formula: $M = \frac{1}{MPS} = \frac{1}{1 - MPC}$

   Example: when MPS = .25, the simple multiplier = 4 $M = \frac{1}{.25} = 4$

C. The Tax Multiplier (M_t) = M-1 or $\frac{MPC}{MPS}$

   1. Example: when M = 4, M_t = 3

D. The Balanced Budget Multiplier (BBM) = 1

E. The multiplier is significant because it implies a small change in leakages or injections will trigger a much larger change in the economy ("snowball effect", the higher the MPC the larger the multiplier).

F. How large is the actual Multiplier Effect?
   1. Effect -- the larger the multiplier, the greater the impact on the economy.
   2. Size -- is effected by changes in the price level.
      a. Price level increases weaken the multiplier because part of the effect is lost to inflation and only part is left to increase real income.

REVIEW OF THE MULTIPLIERS

Type	Formula	When to Use
Simple Multiplier (M)	$= \frac{1}{MPS} = \frac{1}{1 - MPC}$	▲G, ▲I, ▲X, ▲M
Tax Multiplier (M_t)	$= M-1 = \frac{MPC}{MPS}$	▲T only
Balanced Budget Multiplier (BBM) "short-cut"	= 1	Use when ▲G and ▲T by the same amount and in the same direction

IV. Last Word: Squaring the Economic Circle

V. Web-based Question/Problem (see your Instructor)

"Basic Macroeconomic Relationships – Including All Multipliers"

Key Terms

consumption schedule
consumption function
savings schedule
savings function
slope
break-even income level
dissavings
planned versus actual investment
public sector
GDP gap
induced investment
net exports
lump sum tax
change in quantity (amount) consumed or saved
expected rate of net profits
investment-demand schedule
induced investment
wealth effect
Average Propensity to Consume (APC)
Average Propensity to Save (APS)
Marginal Propensity to Consume (MPC)
Marginal Propensity to Save (MPS)
Paradox of thrift
Aggregate Demand (AD)
Aggregate Supply (AS)
crowding out
change in quantity (amount) of investment-demand
change in investment-demand
45^0 line
multiplier effect
autonomous investment
simple multiplier (M)
balanced budget multiplier (BBM)
tax multiplier (M_t)
nonincome determinants of "C" and "S"
change in consumption (savings)
real rate of interest
autonomous investment
noninterest determinants of investment

"Basic Macroeconomic Relationships – Including All Multipliers"

PROBLEMS

1. Complete the following table.

Disposable Income	C Consumption	S Savings	APC	APS	MPC	MPS
(1)	(2)	(3)	(4)	(5)	(6)	(7)
\$3,000	\$3,400	-400	____	____		
4,000	4,200	____	____	____	____	____
5,000	5,000	____	____	____	____	____
6,000	5,800	____	____	____	____	____
7,000	6,600	____	____	____	____	____
8,000	7,400	____	____	____	____	____

Formulas:

$$DI = C + S$$

$$APC = \frac{C}{DI} \qquad MPC = \frac{\Delta C}{\Delta DI}$$

$$APS = \frac{S}{DI} \qquad MPS = \frac{\Delta S}{\Delta DI}$$

a. Graph the consumption and savings curves (separately) from the table above.

b. Label the break-even points on the graphs.

c. Draw a 45-degree reference line on the consumption graph.

d. Label and shade the area of dissavings on both graphs.

e. Label and shade the area of savings on both graphs.

f. What is the break-even level of income? ____________________

g. What is the slope of the consumption function? ____________________

h. What is the slope of the savings function? ____________________

PROBLEMS (continued)

2. Answer the following questions based upon the consumption and savings curves below:

A Family's Consumption and Savings Curves

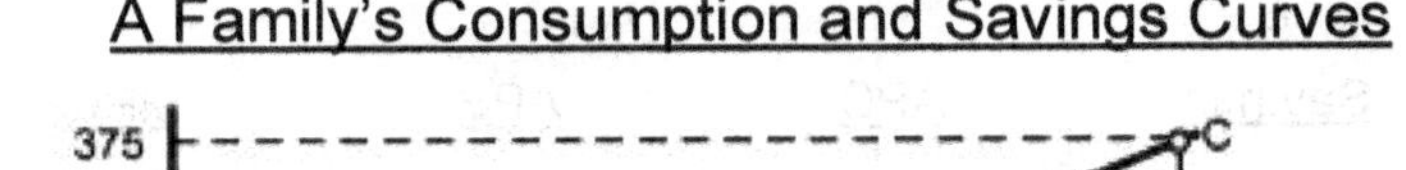

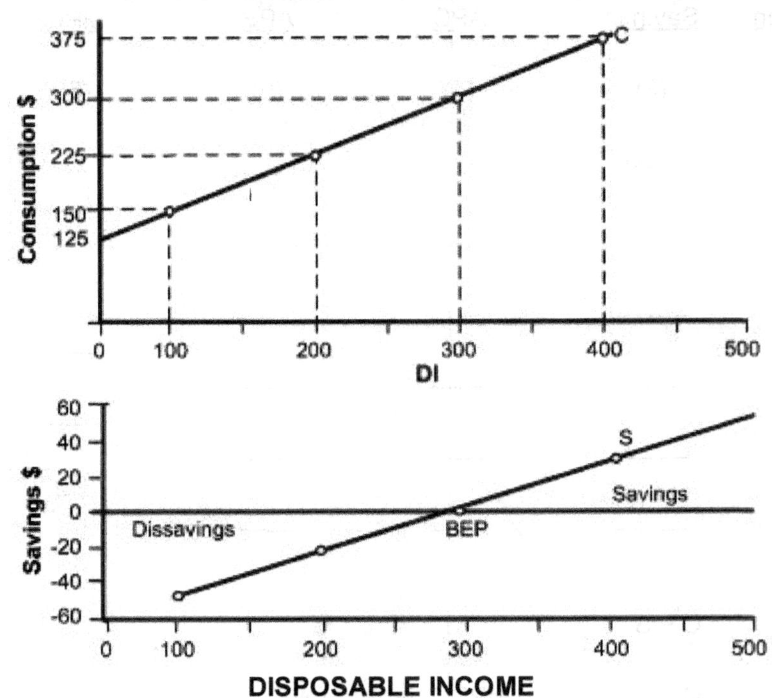

a. Draw and label the 45-degree reference line on the consumption graph.

b. Where is the break-even income level?__________________

c. At what levels of disposable income does savings take place?____________

d. At what levels of disposable income does dissavings take place?__________

e. What is the amount of autonomous (independent) consumption?______________

f. Where does induced (caused) consumption begin? _____________

g. At $400 of Disposable Income, what is APC? _________ APS? __________

h. What is the MPC when disposal income goes from $100 to $200? _____________

i. What is the MPS when disposal income goes from $200 to $300? _____________

j. What is the slope of the consumption curve when disposal income goes from $300 to $400?_________

k. Shade and label the areas of savings and dissavings.

l. Label the break-even points.

PROBLEMS

3. Fill in the tables given below, find the Simple Multiplier, the Tax Multiplier and the Balanced Budget Multiplier, from the data.

MPC	M	M_t	BBM
.9	___	___	___
.8	___	___	___
.75	___	___	___
.5	___	___	___
.6	___	___	___
.95	___	___	___

MPS	M	M_t	BBM
.2	___	___	___
.5	___	___	___
.4	___	___	___
.1	___	___	___
.05	___	___	___

Formulas:

$$M = \frac{1}{MPS} = \frac{1}{1 - MPC}$$

$$M_t = \frac{MPC}{MPS} = M - 1$$

Self-Test

Exhibit 2
Consumption and Savings Curves

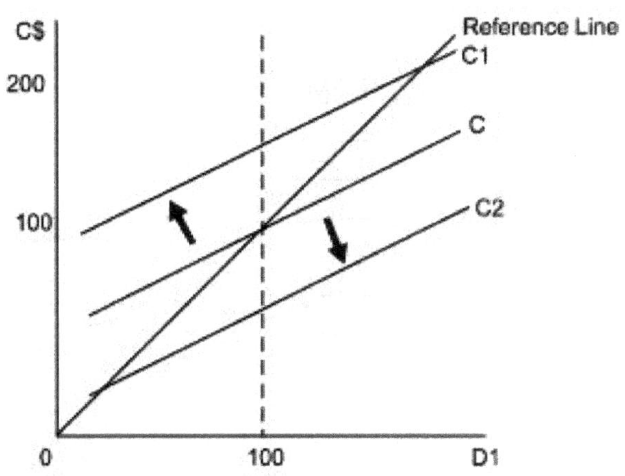

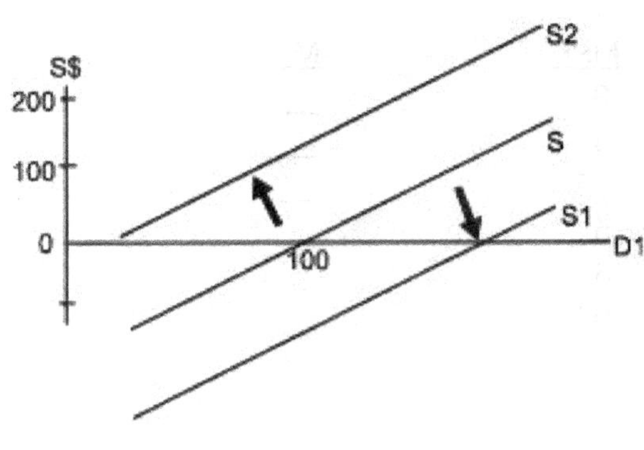

1. In Exhibit 2, when consumption shifts from C to C1, you would expect savings to:
   a. shift from S to S2
   b. shift from S to S1
   c. savings would remain at S
   d. movement along the S curve

2. In Exhibit 2, when savings shifts from S to S1, you would expect consumption to:
   a. shift from C to C2
   b. shift from C to C1
   c. consumption would remain at C
   d. movement along the consumption curve

3. In Exhibit 2, a change in the disposable income would cause consumption to:
   a. shift from C to C1
   b. shift from C to C2
   c. move along the consumption curve
   d. unable to determine

4. Which of the following would <u>not</u> cause a shifting of the consumption or savings curves?
   a. wealth
   b. price level
   c. expectation
   d. income

5. What are the two determinants of net investment spending?
   a. consumption and investment
   b. the real interest rate and the level of investment spending
   c. the real interest rate and the level of savings
   d. spending by households and national income

Self-Test (continued)

6. What is the relationship between the real rate of interest and the level of investment spending?
   a. direct
   b. inverse
   c. proportional
   d. exponential

7. Which of the following will not cause a change in investment-demand?
   a. interest rate
   b. technological change
   c. expectations
   d. taxes

Answer the next three questions based upon the following consumption schedule:

DI	C	S	APC	APS	MPC	MPS
$100	$140					
					______	______
200	210					
					______	______
300	300					
					______	______
400	340					
					______	______
500	400					

8. The marginal propensity to consumer when DI goes from $200 to $300 is?
   a. .7
   b. .9
   c. .4
   d. .1

9. At a disposable income level of $500,
   a. savings equals $100
   b. APC is .8
   c. APS is .2
   d. all of the above

Self-Test (continued)

10. The break-even income level is:
    a. $400
    b. $500
    c. $300
    d. unable to determine

11. Dissavings occurs when:
    a. income exceeds consumption
    b. savings exceeds consumption
    c. savings exceeds income
    d. consumption exceeds income

12. The wealth effect of an increase in the value of a portfolio would cause the consumption curve to:
    a. shift down
    b. not shift at all
    c. shift right
    d. shift up

13. If the marginal propensity to save is .25, the value of the simple multiplier (M) is:
    a. 1.3
    b. 1
    c. 4
    d. 3

14. If the marginal propensity to consume is .9, the value of the tax multiplier (M_t) is:
    a. 10
    b. 9
    c. 8
    d. 7

15. If the marginal propensity to consume is .6, the value of the balanced-budget multiplier (BBM) is:
    a. 1.67
    b. 2.5
    c. 1.5
    d. 1.0

16. If an economy saves 50% of any increase in income, then an increase in investment of $10 billion can produce an increase in income of as much as:
    a. $5 billion
    b. $10 billion
    c. $15 billion
    d. $20 billion
    e. infinity

Self-Test (continued)

Exhibit I

DI	S
$100	25
200	50
300	75
400	100
500	125

17. In Exhibit I, the value of MPS is:
    a. .25
    b. .75
    c. 1.00
    d. unable to determine

18. In Exhibit I, the simple multiplier (M) is:
    a. 1.0
    b. 3.0
    c. 4.0
    d. 1.3

19. In Exhibit I, the marginal propensity to consume (MPC) is:
    a. .25
    b. .75
    c. 1.00
    d. unable to determine

20. If the marginal propensity to consume is 0.9, a $100 increase in planned investment expenditure, other things being equal, will cause an increase in equilibrium GDP level of:
    a. $90
    b. $100
    c. $900
    d. $1000

21. If the marginal propensity to save is 0.4, the value of the simple multiplier (M) will be:
    a. 1.66
    b. 2.5
    c. 4
    d. 6

22. According to the balanced-budget multiplier model, if MPS is .2, a $500 increase in government spending combined with a $300 decrease in taxes, would result in what effect on GDP?
    a. $3,700 increase
    b. $3,700 decrease
    c. $1,300 increase
    d. $200 increase

23. If the equilibrium level of GDP is $10,000, the target level is $5,000, and the MPS is .4, what change in government purchases would be necessary to reach the target?
    a. $2,000 increase
    b. $2,000 decrease
    c. $2,994 approximately, increase
    d. $2,944 approximately, decrease

24. If the equilibrium level of GDP is $1,000 and the target level is $1,400, MPS is .5, what changes in lump sum taxes would be necessary to reach the target?
    a. $400 increase
    b. $400 decrease
    c. $200 increase
    d. $200 decrease

Self-Test (continued)

25. Suppose that in a two-sector economy consisting of households and businesses, (1) the MPC is .8, (2) consumption equals income at $240 billion, and (3) the level of investment is $50 billion. The new equilibrium level of GDP is:
    a. $250 billion
    b. $240 billion
    c. $290 billion
    d. $490 billion

26. Suppose you have recessionary gap of $600 million, MPC is .75, what change in exports would be necessary to reach the target?
    a. $150 increase
    b. $150 decrease
    c. $450 increase
    d. $600 increase

27. If the MPS is equal to 1/3, a $750 decrease in taxes combined with $750 decrease in government purchases will have what effect on GDP?
    a. $3,795 decrease
    b. $3,795 increase
    c. $750 increase
    d. $750 decrease

"The Aggregate Expenditures Model"

Chapter Orientation

This concept builds on what you have learned in the previous concept. Using the Consumption (C), Savings (S), and Investment (I) schedules, we build a model to determine the equilibrium levels of income, employment, and output for an economy. Two techniques were used to calculate the equilibrium level: The Keynesian Cross ("Aggregate Expenditures - Domestic Output") and the Leakages-Injections Approach ("Bathtub Theorem").

Then the foreign sector is brought into the model to show how exports and imports affect the equilibrium level of output, income, and employment. Finally, the public sector (government) is added to complete the model. Changes in government spending (G) and taxation (T) is calculated, magnified by the appropriate multiplier and graphed. This equilibrium level will tell us where we currently are; the next chapter will focus on where we want to be (target level) and what vehicles are available to reach our target level.

If you save money are you better off in the future? If everyone saves, will everyone be better off in the future? These questions, and their economic impact, will be addressed by the "Paradox of Thrift".

Lastly, the difference between the "potential GDP" and the "actual GDP" is called the "GDP gap". There are two types of gaps: recessionary (too little spending) and inflationary (too much spending). Under Keynesian Economics, the government will want to "fine tune" the economy to try to close these gaps. Historical examples are given to illustrate the GDP gaps.

Learning Objectives

After studying this chapter in the text and completing the following exercises in this concepts book, you should be able to:

1. Understand how the foreign sector affects the equilibrium.
2. Understand how the public sector affects the equilibrium.
3. Locate the equilibrium output (GDP) level using two techniques, when given the necessary data.
4. Explain the tendency of employment, output, and incomes toward equilibrium.
5. Explain what is meant by the GDP gaps?
6. Define an "inflationary gap" and a "recessionary gap".
7. Locate the inflationary and recessionary gaps on a graph.
8. Discuss the Recession of 2007-2009 to illustrate GDP gaps.
9. Discuss the four limitations of the Aggregate Expenditures Theory.

"The Aggregate Expenditures Model"

Chapter Highlights

I. Introduction

A. Assumptions and Simplification

1. Initially look at a private or closed economy
2. Real GDP = DI

II. Consumption and Investment Schedules

A. Revisit Consumption "C" and Planned Investment (I)

B. Equilibrium GDP occurs when GDP = C + I

C. Disequilibrium - no level of GDP other than the equilibrium level of GDP can be sustained.

III. Other Features of Equilibrium GDP

A. Savings equals Planned Investment

B. No unplanned changes in Inventories

C. Through the Multiplier Effect, a change in Investment can cause a magnified change in output and income.

IV. Changes in Equilibrium GDP and the Multiplier

A. The Multiplier Effect accompanies both increases and decreases in Aggregate Expenditure and also applies to changes in net exports (Xn) and government purchases (G).

V. Adding International Trade

A. Net Exports and Aggregate Expenditures

1. Net Exports (Xn) = X - M

B. The Net Export Schedule

1. When exports are greater than imports, the economy experiences a trade surplus (or a positive net exports figure).
2. When Imports are greater than exports, the economy experiences a trade deficit, (or a negative net exports figure).

C. Net Exports and Equilibrium GDP

1. Positive Net Exports, elevate the aggregate expenditure schedule and increase domestic GDP ("expansionary effect").
2. Negative Net Exports, decrease the aggregate expenditures schedule and reduce domestic GDP ("contractionary effect").

D. International Economic Linkages

1. Policies abroad affect our domestic GDP.
   a. Prosperity of our trading partners influences their ability to buy more imports.
   b. High tariffs on American goods reduces our exports.
   c. Value of the dollar relative to other currencies affects trade. (Exchange rates).

VI. Adding the Public Sectors

A. Government Purchases and Equilibrium GDP

1. Aggregate Demand in the private sector only is equal to consumption (C) by households at investment (I) by business. As a result, in equilibrium, planned savings equals planned investment.
   AD = C + I
2. Aggregate Demand (Expenditure) is both the private and public sectors is equal to:

	(C)	consumption by households
+	(I)	investment by business
+	(G)	government spending
+	(Xn)	net exports (Exports - Imports)
AD =		C + I + G + (Xn) = AE

3. Aggregate Supply is a 45-degree reference line, where every dollar of output generates a dollar of income.

Keynesian Cross
(Aggregate Expenditures/Demand – Aggregate Supply)

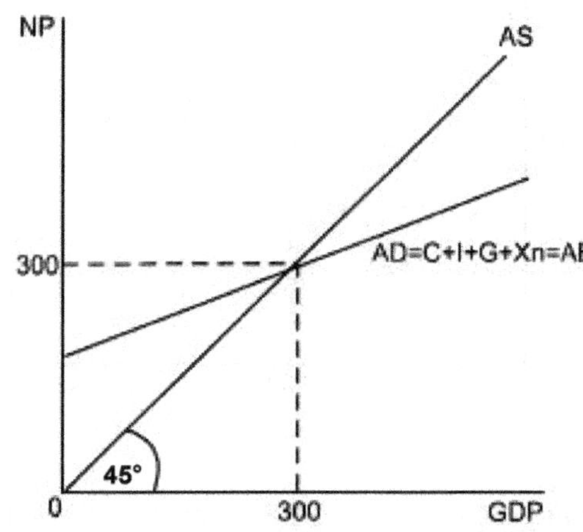

4. The intersection of AD and AS will determine the equilibrium level of output, employment, and income.

5. When AD is greater than, or less than AS, there will be a tendency for output, employment, and income to increase or decrease (business reaction to an increase (or decrease) in spending.

AD > AS ↑ 0, E, $
AD < AS 0, E, $

B. The Leakages-Injections Approach (The Bathtub Theorem) where total leakages equal planned injections.
   1. Total leakages in the economy are savings (S), taxes (T), and imports (M), which represent withdrawals from the economy.
   2. Planned injections in the economy are investment (I), government spending (G), and exports (X), which represent a supplement to the economy.
   3. S + T + M = I + G + X
   4. The intersection of total leakages and planned injections will determine the equilibrium level of output, employment, and income.
   5. Planned savings always equals actual investment because actual investment includes both planned and unplanned investment.

Leakages-Injections Approach
"The Bathtub Theorem"

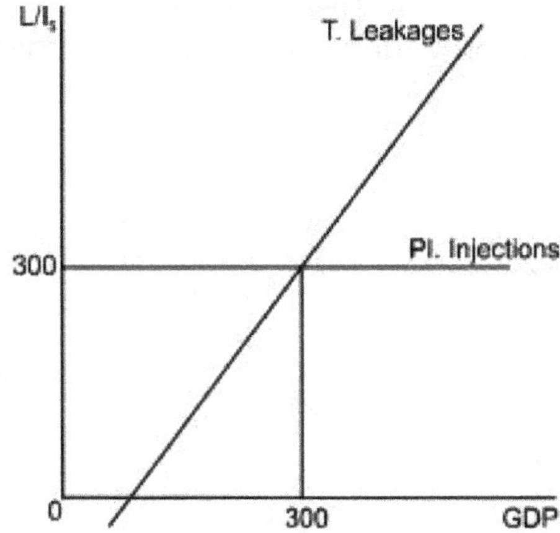

VII. Equilibrium versus Full-Employment GDP — The GDP Gaps:A. Definition - the difference between "potential GDP" and "Actual GDP" at a full employment GDP.

B. Types:
   1. Recessionary Expenditure gap - falls short (too little spending)
   2. Inflationary Expenditure gap - exceeds (too much spending)

C. Graphs (see next page).

D. Application: The U.S. Recession of 2007-2009
   1. In December of 2007, the U.S. economy entered the longest and deepest recession since the Great Depression of 1930s (called "The Great Recession").
   2. The Federal Government undertook various Keynesian Policies in 2008 and 2009 to try to eliminate the recessionary gap facing the economy.
      a. In 2008, $100b of tax rebate checks to taxpayers
      b. In 2009, $787b stimulus package was passed to increase aggregate expenditures (called the "American Recovery and Reinvestment Act of 2009")

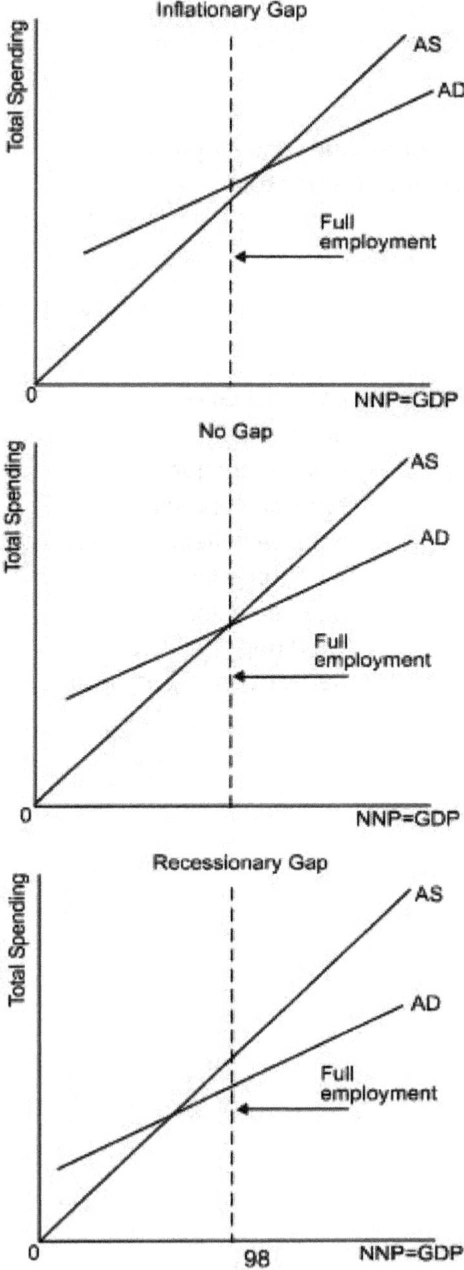
Inflationary and Recessionary
Expenditure Gaps
Inflationary Gap
Total Spending
AS
AD
Full
employment
0
NNP=GDP
No Gap
Total Spending
AS
AD
Full
employment
0
NNP=GDP
Recessionary Gap
Total Spending
AS
AD
Full
employment
0
98
NNP=GDP

VIII. Limitations of the Model

A. Five limitations:
   1. Price Level changes
   2. Premature Demand - Pull Inflation
   3. Real GDP Beyond the Full-Employment Level of Output
   4. Cost Push Inflation
   5. Self-correction

IX. Last Word: Say's Law, the Great Depression, and Keynes

X. Web-based Question/Problem (see your Instructor)

<u>Key Terms</u>

Keynesian Cross
aggregate expenditure
aggregate output
"Bathtub Theorem"
leakages
injections
actual investment
equilibrium GDP
public sector
induced investment
lump sum tax
potential GDP
actual GDP
inflationary gap
recessionary gap
snowball effect
45-degree line
private sector
GDP gap
net exports

"The Aggregate Expenditures Model"

PROBLEMS

1. Technique #1: Keynesian Cross
a. Fill in the table below.
b. Graph AS and AD and label equilibrium NI (on graph paper - top half).

(1) GDP (AS) = NI	(2) C	(3) I	(4) G	(5) (Xn)	(6) AD (= AE)
100	140	20	10	10	______
200	220	↓	↓	↓	______
300	300	↓	↓	↓	______
400	380	↓	↓	↓	______
500	460	↓	↓	↓	______
600	540	↓	↓	↓	______
700	620	↓	↓	↓	______
800	700	↓	↓	↓	______
900	780				______

AD = C + I + G + (Xn)

2. Technique #2: Leakages - Injections Approach
a. Fill in the table below.
b. Graph total leakages and planned injections (bottom half).
c. Label the equilibrium NI level.
d. Compare the equilibrium NI with technique #1.

(1) NI	(2) DI	(3) C	(4) S	(5) T	(6) (M)	(7) Total Leakages	(8) I	(9) G	(10) X	(11) Planned Injections
100	____	140	____	0	5	______	20	10	15	______
200	____	220	____	↓	↓	______	↓	↓	↓	______
300	____	300	____	↓	↓	______	↓	↓	↓	______
400	____	380	____	↓	↓	______	↓	↓	↓	______
500	____	460	____	↓	↓	______	↓	↓	↓	______
600	____	540	____	↓	↓	______	↓	↓	↓	______
700	____	620	____	↓	↓	______	↓	↓	↓	______
800	____	700	____	↓	↓	______	↓	↓	↓	______
900	____	780	____			______				______

Formulas:

Total Leakages = S + T + M   NI - T = DI
Planned Injections = I + G + X   DI = C + S

3. Compare and contrast the Classical School, Keynesian Economics, and Supply-side Economics.

"The Aggregate Expenditures Model"

REVIEW PROBLEMS

1a. Fill in the table below and graph the consumption and savings curves separately.
b. Determine the break-even point (label on the graph).

DI	C	S	APC	APS	MPC	MPS
100	120	____	____	____		
					____	____
120	130	____	____	____		
					____	____
140	140	____	____	____		
					____	____
160	150	____	____	____		
					____	____
180	160	____	____	____		

2. Determine the Equilibrium NI Level (2 techniques)
   Technique #1 — Keynesian Cross

(AS) = NI	C	I	G	(Xn)	AD
1800	1400	200	200	100	____
2000	1550	↓	↓	↓	____
2200	1700	↓	↓	↓	____
2400	1850	↓	↓	↓	____
2600	2000	↓	↓	↓	____

Technique #2 — Leakages -Injections Approach

NI	DI	C	S	T	(M)	Total Leakages	I	G	X	Planned Injections
1800	____	1400	____	200	25	____	200	200	125	____
2000	____	1550	____	↓	↓	____	↓	↓	↓	____
2200	____	1700	____	↓	↓	____	↓	↓	↓	____
2400	____	1850	____	↓	↓	____	↓	↓	↓	____
2600	____	2000	____	↓	↓	____	↓	↓	↓	____

a. Fill in the tables above.
b. Determine the Equilibrium NI level using both techniques.
c. Prepare two graphs—one for each technique (AS = AD and Total Leakages = Planned Injections).
d. Compare the equilibrium NI using the two techniques.

Formulas:

Xn = X - M
AD = C + I + G + (Xn) Total Leakages = S + T + M
AS = 45 degree reference line Planned Injections = I + G + X
DI = NI - T DI = C + S

"The Aggregate Expenditures Model"

Self-Test

1. Which of the following is not a leakage?
   a. imports
   b. government spending
   c. savings
   d. taxes

2. Which of the following is not an injection?
   a. exports
   b. government spending
   c. investment
   d. taxes

3. For an economy without a public sector, when savings exceeds investment (S > I):
   a. actual income is less than equilibrium income
   b. actual income is greater than equilibrium income
   c. income will decrease
   d. both b and c

4. Households propensity to save is influenced by their desire to:
   a. provide for retirement security
   b. meet unforeseen emergencies
   c. earn interest income
   d. all of the above

5. If the full employment-noninflationary GDP is $400 billion, and equilibrium occurs to the right of that point there exists:
   a. a recessionary gap
   b. an inflationary gap
   c. the economy is now at the new full employment-noninflationary level
   d. a deflationary gap

6. Planned Savings:
   a. always equals actual investment
   b. always equals potential investment
   c. always equals investment
   d. is an injection into the economy

7. The Keynesian Cross technique for determining the equilibrium GDP or NI level is also called the:
   a. Bathtub Theorem
   b. Aggregate expenditure - domestic output approach
   c. Leakages-Injections approach
   d. Paradox of Thrift

8. The private sector consists of:
   a. households
   b. households and business
   c. households, business, and the government
   d. the government

9. As households attempt to save more at each level of GDP (= NI), they may find that they tried to save more, but ended by saving less! This is known as:
   a. Keynes Law
   b. Say's Law
   c. The Paradox of Thrift
   d. the complex multiplier

10. When aggregate demand slips below our capability to produce, the economy will experience
    a. full employment
    b. an expansionary gap
    c. an inflationary gap
    d. a recessionary gap

REVIEW SHEET: UNIT II MACROECONOMICS

ECON 105 – UNIT II REVIEW

Be sure to bring a #2 pencil, graph paper and calculator!

PART I: 40 Multiple Choice questions (2 points each or a total of 80 points)

1. Give several reasons for studying NIA.
2. Know the definition of GDP and how it differs from GNP.
3. Know the difference between "nominal GDP" and "real GDP" and how to calculate "real GDP".
4. Know what is meant by a "final good or service".
5. Know the definition of the "value added approach" and be able to calculate it.
6. Know what is included/excluded when calculating GDP and why.
7. Know how to calculate "per capita GDP" and what it means.
8. Know about the "underground economy".
9. Know how to define and calculate the other NIA accounts": NDP, NI, PI AND DPI.
10. Know how to adjust prices for inflation using a "price index".
11. Know the definition of a "chain-type annual weighted price index".
12. Know whether GDP is a good measure of "social welfare".
13. Know the definition of the "business cycle" and what is meant by the "new business cycle."
14. Know the four phases of the business cycle.
15. Know how a recession effects durable versus nondurable goods.
16. Know the three NBER indicators.
17. Know the definitions of "unemployment" and the "labor force".
18. Know about the four types of unemployment and give examples.
19. Be able to calculate the unemployment rate and how it's under and over stated.
20. Know the full-employment unemployment rate (or "natural rate").
21. Know the two costs of unemployment and know about Okun's Law.
22. Know the definition of "inflation" and the three indexes to measure inflation.
23. Know about the two types of inflation, their causes and graph (ranges).
24. Know why inflation hurts and helps and the redistributive effects of inflation.
25. Know how to calculate real income.
26. Know how the "Phillips Curve" originated and how to move along the curve.
27. Know why the Phillips Curve (and Demand-management) did not explain what happened in the mid-70s and what is meant by the term "stagflation".
28. Know the definition of "supply shocks" and why they caused a shifting of the Phillips Curve (according to Supply-side Economists).
29. Explain why the Long-run Phillips Curve is vertical.
30. Be able to calculate APC, APS, MPC AND MPS from a table or graph.
31. Be able to locate the consumption curve, reference line and the break-even income level.
32. Know the difference between "autonomous" and "induced" consumption and locate on the consumption curve.
33. Know that the "consumption" and "savings" curves shift in opposite directions.
34. Know the definitions of "Investment" and the "Investment-Demand Curve".
35. Know the definition of "Aggregate Expenditure (AE) = Aggregate Demand (AD)"
36. Know what's meant by the "multiplier effect", how to calculate and when to use the "Simple Multiplier (M)", "Tax Multiplier (Mt)", and "Balanced-Budget Multiplier (BBM)" in word problems.
37. Know the definition of "GDP GAP".
38. Know the definition of the "paradox of thrift".

REVIEW SHEET: UNIT II MACROECONOMICS

PART II: Problems (10 points each or a total of 20 points)

Answer only TWO of the FOUR problems, listed on the exam.
Problem #1: National Income Accounting (NIA Sheet) — EX: WB pg. 54, #1.
Problem #2: Consumption and Savings Table and Graphs — EX: WB pgs. 79, #1 and 94, #1.
Problem #3: Draw the Phillips Curve and explain what it illustrates, how the government moves along the curve and the effect of "stagflation", etc. Also, draw the Demand – Pull Inflation Graph and explain.
Problem #4: Table using a Price Index – Ex: WB pg 55, #3

FORMULA SHEET: WORKBOOK PAGE 98

REVIEW TEXTBOOK, CLASS NOTES (ON WORKSHEET), WORKBOOK, CANVAS (QUIZZES AND PP SLIDES)

Any questions please contact your Instructor or visit our "Learning Commons" located in the Bankier Library.

GOOD LUCK!!

UNIT II FORMULAS

$$\text{Unemployment rate} = \frac{\text{\# of unemployed workers}}{\text{Civilian Labor Force}} \times 100$$

Civilian Labor Force = # unemployed + # employed

$$\text{Per Capita GDP} = \frac{\text{Real GDP}}{\text{Population}}$$

Nominal GDP = Price x Quantity

$$\text{Real GDP} = \frac{\text{Nominal GDP}}{\text{GDP Deflator or chain-weighted price index}} \times 100$$

$$\text{Real or Constant \$} = \frac{\text{Nominal or Current \$ GDP}}{\text{Price Index}}$$

$$\text{Price Index} = \frac{\text{Each year's price}}{\text{Base year's price}}$$

$$\text{Inflation (\%)} = \frac{P_2 - P_1}{P_1} \times 100$$

DI = C + S

$$APC = \frac{C}{DI} \qquad APS = \frac{S}{DI} \qquad APC + APS = 1.0$$

$$MPC = \frac{\blacktriangle C}{\blacktriangle DI} \qquad MPS = \frac{\blacktriangle S}{\blacktriangle DI} \qquad MPC + MPS = 1.0$$

$$\text{Simple Multiplier (M)} = \frac{1}{MPS}$$

$$\text{Tax Multiplier } (M_1) = \frac{MPC}{MPS} = M - 1$$

Balanced Budget Multiplier (BBM) = 1

MACROECONOMICS

Unit III

"Classical, Keynesian and Supply-side Economics"

Chapter Orientation

They say "history repeats itself" so we will take a walk through history exploring the School of Thought: Classical School, Keynesian, and Supply-side Economics. A page has been devoted in your workbook, comparing these three economic schools of thought. In addition, be sure to check out the "Last Word" on Keynesian Economics in your textbook!

Three areas to keep in mind while studying these theories are (1) What was the time period? (2) What event caused the theory to lose credibility? (3) What was the role of the government (laissez-faire or to fine-tune)?

Since we know that business cycles (fluctuations) are recurrent, and that history repeats itself, (Supply-side economics is an outgrowth of the Classical School), it is imperative that we study the past to help predict the future. . .

Economists began to wonder if there were ways to improve supply conditions. Ways were sought to control inflationary expectations, increase saving and investing, increase productivity, deregulation, etc. These ideas were not new (outgrowth of the Classical School), but they reflected an awareness that demand management was only half of a balanced policy -- not the whole!

Ronald Reagan won the presidency on a platform of cutting taxes to eliminate the deficits and getting the economy back on track. We will examine the foundations of Reaganomics, including the Laffer curve.

Lastly, we will examine the changes made by the Clinton and Bush administrations.

Learning Objectives

After studying this chapter in the text, and completing the exercises in this concepts book, you should be able to:

1. Explain the relationship between short-run and aggregate supply and long-run and aggregate supply.
2. Discuss how to apply the "extended" AD-AS model to inflation, recessions, and economic growth.
3. Explain the relationship between tax rates, tax revenues, and aggregate supply.
4. Know the differences among the three Economic Schools of Thought: Classical, Keynesian, and Supply-side.
5. Know about Reaganomics, and how it differed from Supply-side Economics.
6. Know about the "Laffer Curve" (relationship between tax rates and tax revenues).
7. Define the Employment Act of 1946, and how Keynesian employment theory played a major role.
8. What are the major provisions of the Economic Recovery Tax Act (ERTA) of 1981?
9. Know the changes the Clinton administration made to the marginal tax rates and the federal budget deficit.
10. Know the changes the Bush administration made to the marginal tax rates and the federal budget deficit.

"Classical, Keynesian and Supply-side Economics"

Chapter Highlights

I. From Short-run to Long-run Aggregate Supply

A. Definitions: Short-run and Long-run

1. The short-run is a period in which input prices (wages) remain fixed in the presence of a change in the price level.
   a. Workers are unaware of price changes
   b. Employee contracts are "fixed wage contracts".
2. The long-run is a period in which input prices (wages) are fully responsive to changes in the price level.

B. Short-run Aggregate Supply

1. The short-run AS Curve slopes upward because, assuming input prices are fixed, as the price level increases, profits increase, and therefore, real output increases. Likewise, when the price level decreases, profits decrease, and therefore, real output decreases.

C. Long-run Aggregate Supply

1. In the long-run, a price level increase, will result in an increase in nominal wages and thus a leftward shift of the short-run AS curve. Likewise, a decrease in the price level will produce a decline in nominal wages and a rightward shift of the short-run AS curve. The long-run AS curve is, therefore, vertical.

II. Long-Run Equilibrium in the AD-AS Model

A. Demand-Pull Inflation in the extended AD-AS Model

1. Occurs when an increase in aggregate demand pulls up the price level.
2. In the short-run, demand-pull inflation will drive up the price level and increase real output; in the long-run, only the price level will rise.

B. Cost-Push Inflation in the Extended AD-AS Model

1. Arises from factors (or resources) which increase the cost of production at each price level – AS shifts leftward.
2. If the government attempts to maintain full-employment (under cost-push inflation) an inflationary spiral is likely to occur.

C. Recession and the Extended AD-AS Model

1. If the government takes a hands-off approach to cost-push inflation, a recession will probably occur.

III. The Historical Backdrop (See Chart) on next page (and chapter introduction)

A. Foundations of Classical Economics and Keynesian Economics

1. Say's Law: supply creates its own demand
   See chart pg 103 – "History of Economic Thought"
2. Adam Smith, Father of Economics
   a. Wealth of Nations (1776)
3. The Great Depression
4. Government should "fine line" the economy
5. John Maynard Keynes, Father of Modern Economics
   a. General Theory of Employment, Interest, and Money (1936)

B. Introduction: Keynesians vs. Supply-siders

1. Keynesians
   a. The government should fine-tune the economy using fiscal tools (government spending and taxing).
   b. Government should "prime the pump" to stimulate employment, savings, and investment.
2. Supply-siders
   a. Low tax rates and low government spending to stimulate employment, savings, and investment.
   b. Government should not compete with the private sector (crowding out).

HISTORY OF ECONOMIC THOUGHT

Classical School	Keynesian Economics	Supply-side Economics
Introduction	**Introduction**	**Introduction**
1. Time period-mid 18th C. to the 1930s. 2. Lost credibility due to the Great Depression (10 yrs.).	1. Time period - 1930s to the mid 1970s. 2. Lost credibility due to "stagflation".	1. Time period - mid 1970s to the early 1990s. 2. Lost credibility due to high budget deficits and recession.
Foundation	**Foundation**	**Foundation**
3. Say's Law: supply creates its own demand.	3. Demand creates its own supply.	3. Rebirth of classical economics - policies to stimulate production.
4. Automatic tendency toward full-employment equilibrium. - Invisible hand concept - Self-interest concept	4. The economy could remain at less than a full-employment level indefinitely. - Keynesian cross (AE = NP) - Leakages-Injection approach	4. Use of incentives: - Cut personal income tax rates - Cut corporate income tax rates - Accelerated depreciation allowance - Investment tax credits; Incentives for saving - Deregulation of industries and markets
5. Emphasis on long-run adjustments in the market.	5. Emphasis on short-run adjustments or "fine-tuning", by the Government (fiscal policy).	5. Tight monetary control to curb inflation. Tax reduction to increase spending and output.
6. Aggregate Expenditure equals Aggregate Income (or output).	6. Aggregate Expenditure may not equal full-employment and aggregate income.	6. Advocate permanent low tax rates and low Government spending.
7. All savings are invested at full-employment because of interest rates, which are flexible.	7. Savers and investors have different goals, therefore, interest rates may fail to bring about equality.	7. Increase productivity, which will increase output.
8. Price-wage flexibility.	8. Most wages and price are not flexible. (Example: Unions and minimum-wage).	8. Laffer Curve (relationship between tax rates and tax revenues
9. Real output remains stable while prices fluctuate to changing market conditions. (Classical view).	9. The price level remains stable while real output fluctuates to changing market conditions. (Keynesian view).	9. "Trickle-down" economics.
10. Government should be laisse-faire or else it will do more harm than good.	10. Government needed to adjust Aggregate Expenditure.	10. Government macroeconomics policies shape the business environment and sets the stage for growth in Aggregate Supply. Massive fiscal policy will dampen AS
Adam Smith - The Wealth of Nations (1776) David Ricardo, Jean Baptiste Say	John Maynard Keynes -The General Theory of Employment, Interest and Money. (1936)	Arthur Laffer, Ronald Reagan (Reaganomics)

"Clintoneconomics" and "Obamanomics" are an outgrowth of Keynesian Economics; "Bush Economics" an outgrowth of supply-side economics.

C. Legislative Mandates
   1. Introduction: After the Great Depression, Keynesian economics was gaining widespread acceptance. As a result, a stronger role for Government was emerging. Keynesian employment theory played a major role in influencing legislative action.
   2. Employment Act of 1946
      a. Definition - passed as a result of economic conditions in the United States after World War II. The act authorizes the federal government to favorably influences aggregate economic performance. The goal of high employment is specified and the goal of price stability is implied.
         1. The act created a Council of Economic Advisors (CEA) to assist and advise the President on matters relating to economic policy making.
         2. The act created a Joint Economic Committee (JEC) of the Congress, which investigates economic problems of national interest.

IV. Taxation and Aggregate Supply (text pgs. 812-817)

A. Taxes and Incentives to Work
   1. Supply-side economics contend that aggregate supply must be recognized as an active force in determining both the level of inflation and unemployment.

B. Incentives to Save and Invest
   1. Taxes and transfer payments have negative effects upon incentives to work, invest, innovate, and assume entrepreneurial risks.
   2. Taxes, according to the supply-siders, are a business cost and shifted forward to consumers in the form of higher prices. Most taxes are a "wedge" between costs of resources and the price of a product.

C. The Laffer Curve
   1. The Laffer Curve (developed by supply-sider Arthur Laffer on a dinner napkin) depicts the relationship between tax rates and tax revenues. His curve shows that if the economy is in the upper range (high tax rates), a decrease in tax rates will increase tax revenues. This forms the foundation for supply-side economics.
   2. Criticisms of the Laffer Curve
      a. Impact of a tax reduction upon incentives will be minimal.
      b. Tax reductions would increase AD (relative to AS) and, thereby creating large budget deficits and rapid inflation.
      c. Position on the Laffer Curve?
      d. Income inequality will increase substantially.

D. Rebuttal and Evaluation
   1. Overregulation - by government has adversely affected productivity and long-run aggregate supply
      a. "Industrial regulation" - protects firms from competition (inefficient)
      b. "Social regulation" - regulations imposed concerning pollution, safety, etc. (which have led to increased costs).
   2. Reaganomics (based upon the elements of supply-side economics) reflects the following four points in the "Economic Recovery Program" of early 1981, which led to high deficits.
      a. Reduce government spending (except defense expenditures).
      b. Reduce government regulation of private businesses.
      c. Prevent the growth in the money supply from being inflationary.
      d. Reduce the personal and corporate income tax rates (from 50 to 28%).
   3. The Clinton administration increased marginal tax rates from 31 to 39.68, to address these deficits.
   4. The Bush administration reduced them to a high of 35%, as well as reducing capital gains tax to 15%.
   5. Financial crisis of 2007-2009 led to highly expansionary fiscal policy and budget deficits have soared.
   6. Supply-side economics has contributed to how economists and policy makers design and implement fiscal policy.

"Classical, Keynesian and Supply-side Economics"

V. Last Word "Say's Law, the Great Depression, and Keynes" (text pg. 653)
VI. Web-based Question/Problem (see your Instructor)

Key Terms

aggregate demand (expenditures)
aggregate supply
closed economy
laissez-faire
classical school
Say's Law
Adam Smith
full employment equilibrium
price-wage flexibility
Keynesian economics
aggregate demand
aggregate supply
demand-pull inflation
cost-push inflation
premature inflation
incomes policies
supply-side economics
tax-transfer disincentives
Economic Recovery Tax Act (ERTA)
devalued dollar

John Maynard Keynes
expected rate of net profits
real rate of interest
investment-demand schedule
autonomous investment
induced investment
noninterest determinants of investment
market policies
wage-price (incomes) policy
wage-price guideposts
wage-price controls
Reaganomics
Laffer Curve
short-run
long-run

“Classical, Keynesian and Supply-side Economics”

PROBLEMS

1. On graph paper, draw the short-run and long-run aggregate demand (AD) curves and the aggregate supply (AS) curves. State what the AD and AS curves illustrate.

2. Explain the difference between demand-pull and cost-push inflation using the AD-AS model (draw two graphs).

3. Draw and explain the “Laffer Curve”. List some of the criticisms.

4. Given that demand-management policies are ineffective in coping with “stagflation”, what are our options?

5. Distinguish between the short-run and the long-run as they relate to macroeconomics.

6. What are the major provisions of the Economic Recovery Tax Act (ERTA) of 1981? What do the critics have to say about ERTA?

7. Discuss the history of economic thought, specifically including the role of government.

"Classical, Keynesian and Supply-side Economics"

Self-Test

1. With the AD curve held constant, a leftward shift of the AS curve will cause:
   a. demand-pull inflation
   b. cost-push inflation
   c. falling unemployment
   d. decreasing prices
2. According to supply-side economists, lower tax rates can increase tax revenues because:
   a. lower tax stimulate incentives to work
   b. lower taxes motivate workers to come out of the underground economy
   c. lower taxes encourage savings and investment
   d. all of the above
3. "Reaganomics" advocates:
   a. reduction in government spending
   b. reduction in government regulation
   c. reduction in personal and corporate income tax rates
   d. all of the above
4. In the Keynesian expenditure-output model, it is impossible for the economy to experience:
   a. full-employment
   b. inflation
   c. unemployment and inflation
   d. full-employment and stable prices
5. In the upper range of the Laffer Curve:
   a. reductions in the tax rate will increase tax revenues
   b. increases in the tax rate will increase tax revenues
   c. reductions in the tax rate will decrease tax revenues
   d. increases in the tax rate will not change tax revenues

"Fiscal Policy, Deficits, and Debt"

Chapter Orientation

This concept analyzes the role of government (the public sector) in our equilibrium national output, and national income model. The Federal government uses budgetary actions to try to "stimulate the economy" or "rein in inflation".

Remember that according to Keynesian Economics, the government's role is to "fine-tune" the economy. As problems in employment, price levels, etc. arise, the government should be there to "prime the pump" and therefore, stimulate the economy through its ability to spend (G) and/or tax (T). The government spending and taxing greatly influences aggregate expenditures, income, and employment -- by a magnified amount (the multiplier). Government purchases of goods and services are included in aggregate demand; and changes in taxes either increases or decreases disposable income, which influences consumption and savings. In addition, the net export effect also works through international trade to reduce the effectiveness of fiscal policy.

EXAMPLES OF THE U.S. GOVERNMENT'S USE OF FISCAL POLICY

1960s	-	Cut taxes to increase sluggish growth
1970s	-	Placed a 10% surcharge on corporate and personal income to curb inflation
1980s (early)	-	Cut tax rate by 25%, over 3 years, to encourage growth
1990s (early)	-	Increased taxes to reduce large budget deficits (yearly surpluses in '99, '00, '01).
2001	-	Major tax reduction package. Increased government spending on war abroad and Homeland Security
2003	-	Major tax reduction - $350 billion over several years
2009	-	$787b stimulus program designed to lift U.S. economy out of "Great Recession" (the American Recovery and Reinvestment Act of 2009)

Discretionary fiscal policy requires that Congress, use its discretion or "good judgment", to vote on appropriate changes in government spending and taxing. (Example: Congress raising or lowering taxes). Nondiscretionary or "built-in stabilizers are already in place in our system and are automatically triggered when appropriate -- no action on the part of Congress is necessary.

There are many concerns and problems in using fiscal policy: timing and political problems, government debt raising the interest rates and "crowding out" the private sector, and lastly, the government may have only small changes in output and employment at the expense of inflation.

Over the years, budget deficits have greatly exceeded budget surpluses, leading to a large public debt. Currently our nation's federal debt is over 18 trillion dollars. What impact does that amount have on the economy -- interest rates, employment, inflation, income, etc.? Is the federal debt a serious problem? What impact does the deficit financing have on our future generations? If we buy now, who pays later? What should our budget philosophy reflect? What has been the foreign reaction to our debt? What are the recent laws and proposals designed to reduce or eliminate the budget deficit? These questions will be examined in this chapter.

Learning Objectives

After reading this chapter in the text, and completing the following exercises in this concepts book, you should be able to:

"Fiscal Policy, Deficits, and Debt"

1. List and explain the legislative changes, following the Great Depression that resulted from Keynesian employment theory.
2. Define fiscal policy.
3. Discuss "Discretionary Fiscal Policy" and the assumptions invoked.
4. Find the equilibrium real GDP in an economy in which the government purchases goods and services and imposes taxes when given the necessary data.
5. Explain the courses of action for the government to follow during expansionary fiscal policy and contractionary fiscal policy.
6. List the ways the government can finance a debt and distribute surplus.
7. Describe how nondiscretionary (or built-in) stabilizers reduce pressures in the economy.
8. Discuss the limitations of nondiscretionary fiscal policy.
9. Discuss the problems of implementing discretionary fiscal policy.
10. Distinguish among progressive, proportional and regressive tax systems.
11. Distinguish between a cyclical deficit and structural deficit.
12. Define the "crowding out effect" and its impact on real output and employment including graphically.
13. Discuss the full employment budget and the actual budget.
14. Discuss the "net export effect" on expansionary fiscal policy and contractionary fiscal policy.
15. Define budget deficit (and surplus).
16. List and explain the three budget philosophies.
17. State the dollar amount of the debt, the percentage of the debt to GDP, the annual dollar amount of the interest payments, the principle causes of the debt, and the impact of accounting and inflation on the debt.
18. Contrast the effects of internal debt with external debt.
19. State two "myths" surrounding the public debt and explain their implications.
20. Explain the effects of the public debt on income distribution and investment.
21. Compare the crowding-out effect of borrowing to finance the budget deficits, on future generations, as compared to raising taxes to finance the debt.
22. Discuss the implications of a large deficit, which have increased interest rates, and increased the demand for American Securities, which has increased the value of the dollar, making our exports more expensive (cause and effect chain).
23. Define four remedies to reduce or eliminate budget deficits.
24. Explain why the debt plays a positive role in a growing and expanding economy.

<u>Chapter Highlights</u>

I. Fiscal Policy and the AD-AS Model

A. Definition of Discretionary Fiscal Policy - requires that Congress use its discretion or good judgment to vote on appropriate changes in government spending and taxing. It is often initiated on the advice of the President's Council of Economic Advisors (CEA) - a group of three appointed advisors to the President.

B. Fiscal policy over the cycle

1. <u>Expansionary</u> fiscal policy -- used during a recession:
   a. Increased government spending (G)
   b. Lower taxes (T)
   c. Combination of G and T
2. <u>Contractionary</u> fiscal policy -- used during a demand-pull inflation:
   a. Decreased government spending (G)
   b. Higher taxes (T)
   c. Combination of G and T

"Fiscal Policy, Deficits, and Debt"

II. Nondiscretionary Fiscal Policy: Built-in Stabilizers

A. Definition -- changes are automatically triggered in the economy without legislative action.

B. Examples of built-in stabilizers

1. Tax receipts (progressive, proportional and regressive tax systems)
2. Unemployment benefits
3. Corporate dividend policy
4. Welfare payments
5. Subsidies to farmers

C. Effects of fiscal stabilizers:

1. Increases the deficit (or reduces surplus) during a recession.
2. Increases surplus (or reduces the deficit) during inflation.

D. Limitations of built-in stabilizers

1. Reduces, but cannot eliminate cyclical fluctuations.
2. Creates a "fiscal drag" problem (tendency of a high-employment economy to be held back from its full growth potential because of incurring budgetary surpluses which trigger a contractionary impact.
3. Requires that the full employment budget be utilized to determine the federal budget's surplus or deficit throughout the year, as opposed to the actual budget surplus or deficit.

III. Evaluating How Expansionary or Contractionary Fiscal Policy is Determined

A. Full Employment Budget (also called the "Cyclically Adjusted Budget"

1. Definition - measures when the Federal budget deficit or surplus would be with existing tax and government spending structures if the economy were at full-employment throughout the year.
2. Structural deficit vs. cyclical deficit - "cyclical deficit" relates to changes due to the business cycle. "Structural deficit relates change to discretionary fiscal policy.
3. Historical comparison - compares deficits and surpluses in full-employment budget with the actual budget.

IV. Recent and Projected U.S. Fiscal Policy

A. Recent U.S. Fiscal Policy

1. Fiscal Policy from 2000 to 2007
   a. In 2000 "dot.com" bubble burst, U.S. economy went into recession → tax cuts.
   b. 2007, "Mortgage Loan Crisis" → stimulus packages (2008 stimulus package of $152 billion and then later passed the American Recovery and Reinvestment Act of 2009).
2. Budget deficits and projections
   a. The CBO projects budget deficits over the next few years (www.cbo.gov).

V. Problems, Criticism, and Complications

A. Timing problems:

1. Recognition lag -- the time it takes to identify a cyclical turning point.
2. Administrative lag -- the time from when a need is recognized and the time of action by Congress.
3. Operational lag -- the time it takes for the action to effect output, employment, income, or prices.

B. Political considerations:

1. Public choice problems: political business cycles - legislators seeking reelection will often adopt policies designed to achieve favorable short term results regardless of what the unfavorable long term consequences will be (James McGill Buchanan won the 1986 Nobel Memorial Prize in Economic Science, for his contributions to the theory of economics and political decision making).
2. Political Business Cycles -- it is politically popular to spend (budget deficits) rather than cut or raise taxes (budget surplus).

C. Future Policy Reversals
   1. If households expect a future reversal of policy then fiscal policy may fail to achieve its goal – called "consumption smoothing."

D. Offsetting State and Local Finance
   1. State and local finance – frequently pro-cyclical (worse in a recession) because most states must balance the budget by year-end (legally)

E. Restrictive effects: crowding-out
   1. Crowding-out can occur when the federal government pursues expansionary fiscal policy and borrows heavily to finance the debt. This causes interest rates to rise and impacts upon investment spending. As a result, the negative multipliers will reduce the positive multipliers arising from fiscal policy.
   2. The crowding-out effect may not be as large as many economists perceive. The money supply may be increased which would offset any increases in the interest rate (the crowding-out effect would be zero).

F. Current thinking on Fiscal Policy
   1. Some prominent economists believe due to the complications and uncertainty that we should not engage in discretionary fiscal policy at all. Mainstream economists generally agree that monetary policy is the best month-to-month stabilization tool.

IV. The Public Debt: Facts and Figures

A. The U.S. National debt, or "public debt" is the accumulation of all past Federal deficits and surpluses.

B. Causes of the debt
   1. Wars -- deficit financing of wars has added tremendously to our debt. (Examples: World War I and World War II)
   2. Recessions -- built-in stability of an economy generates budget deficits automatically. (Examples -- the oil crisis of 1974-1975, 1980-1982, 1990-1991; 1991 and 1993 due to S&L bailout and 2001.)
   3. Tax cuts -- part of the Economic Recovery Act of 1981, were not offset by reductions in government spending.
   4. Lack of Fiscal Discipline — in 1993, Congress and the President passed a deficit-reduction package. As a result of this package and strong economic growth, the annual deficit began to shrink. However, by 2002, we had an annual deficit of $158 billion, and today it continues to grow!

C. Ownership (Quantitative Aspects)
   1. Currently, the public debt is in excess of $18 trillion (2015). Up from $3.2 trillion 25 years before
   2. Public debt, as a percentage of GDP was 70% in 2012 and has been rising dramatically since 2008.
   3. Other industrial nations have public debts similar to, or greater, than the U.S.
   4. Since the early 1970's, the interest payments on the debt have increased tremendously (because of the increases in size of the debt and the interest rates); as a percentage of GDP it has been a dramatic decrease. Annual interest payments were $360 billion in 2012.
   5. The public debt is held by (2012):
      a. 40% Federal agencies and the Fed.
      b. 60% others (state and local governments, private individuals, banks, insurance companies, corporations, etc.).
      c. Approximately, 33% is held by foreigners (external debt).
   6. Social Security and Medicare considerations
      a. Governmental accounting procedures may not reflect the government's actual financial position. For example the American population is getting older and will be relying on Social Security (major public retirement program) and Medicare (U.S. health program for those over age 65). Both these programs are underfunded.

"Fiscal Policy, Deficits, and Debt"

V. False Concerns

A. Government bankruptcy

1. Refinancing: Debt cannot bankrupt the government because the government simply refinances the debt ("borrow from Peter to pay Paul") and has been doing so for over 50 years.
2. Taxation: The government can always levy and collect taxes.
3. The government can always print or create new money.

B. Burdening future generations

1. If the debt was incurred to cushion a period of unemployment, to the extent that resources would have remained idle are thereby put to work, there is no added burden -- society has benefited from the increased production, and some of the output has added to the nation's capital stock (inherited by our future generations).
2. In the case of financing war, those people who lived during the war had to do without many civilian goods for military goods (the production-possibilities curve). Spending on a war lessens the amount of capital goods, which is not replaced as quickly as they are used up. However, this burden is independent of debt financing.
3. In 1960, about 5% of our public debt was held by foreigners (external debt). In 1970, the figure was less than 10%. Today, about 33% of our public debt is held by foreigners. Usually the public debt is not a means of shifting economic burden to future generations. We still owe 67% Americans to Americans.

VI. Substantive Issues

A. Income distribution-payment of interest on the debt probably increases income inequality (bondholders are from the wealthier class).

B. Raising taxes, to finance the interest payments, may <u>not</u> motivate people to take risks, to innovate, to invest, and to work (dampens economic growth).

C. External debt may impose a burden, if the payment of interest to foreigners, results in the money not being spent in the United States.

D. An increase in government spending may or may not impose a burden on future generations:

1. If the government crowds-out investment, then this will indeed lower the capital stock and be a burden to our future generations.
2. If government spending is primarily investment-type outlays (bridges, harbors, etc.) or human-capital investments (education, research and development, etc.) these expenditures will increase the future productive capacity.
3. If government spending occurs at less than full-employment of resources, then the economy can move to full-employment without sacrificing capital accumulation.

VIII. Last Word: Social Security and Medicare Shortfalls

IX. Web-based Question/Problem (see your Instructor)

"Fiscal Policy, Deficits, and Debt"

<u>Key Terms</u>

Fiscal Policy
Keynesian economics
Supply-side economics
Employment Act of 1946
Council of Economic Advisors (CEA)
Joint Economic Committee (JEC)
net export effect
discretionary fiscal policy
lump sum tax
Keynesian Cross
Leakages-Injections approach
simple multiplier (M)
tax multiplier (Mt)
balanced-budget multiplier (BBM)
expansionary fiscal policy
contractionary fiscal policy
crowding-out effect
structural deficit
budget surplus
national debt
crowding-out
external debt (public)
cyclically adjusted budget
U.S. Government Securities

progressive tax system
proportional tax system
regressive tax system
net export effect
target level
financing the deficit
returning the surplus
impounding
nondiscretionary fiscal policy
built-in stabilizers
fiscal drag
actual budget
full-employment budget
recognition lag
administrative lag
operational lag
public choice problems
political business cycle
aggregate supply effects
cyclical deficit
budget deficit
public debt
Social Security Trust Fund
internal debt (public)
public investments

“Fiscal Policy, Deficits, and Debt”

PROBLEMS

1. Currently, how much is the U.S. debt? What are the interest payments on this debt? What has been the trend over the last twenty years?

2. How does externally held public debt differ from internally held public debt? Why is this distinction important?

3. What are the government’s fiscal policy options for ending severe demand-pull inflation? What are the options for ending a severe recession?

4. Briefly state and evaluate the problem of time lags in enacting and applying fiscal policy.

5. Define the cyclically adjusted budget, explain its significance, and state why it may differ from the actual budget?

"Fiscal Policy, Deficits, and Debt"

Self-Test

1. Our current debt is approximately:
   a. $1.6 trillion   b. $18 trillion   c. $139.8 trillion   d. $6.6 billion

2. The "crowding-out effect" suggests that:
   a. most employees would rather work for the federal government in civil service which causes shortages in labor for the private sector
   b. when net exports is a negative number, the U.S. economy starts to contract
   c. when the government borrows money to finance the debt, interest rates increase and causes a decrease in investment
   d. the fiscal tools -- spending and taxing cancel each other out or weaken the multiplier

3. The Federal Government budget is in surplus whenever:
   a. it spends more than it receives in taxes
   b. it spends less than it receives in taxes
   c. it spends the same amount it receives in taxes
   d. it pays out a lot of money in welfare benefits

4. The largest portion of the public debt is held by:
   a. Federal agencies
   b. Federal Reserve
   c. others (individuals, state, insurance, etc.)
   d. foreign investors

5. Which of the following is <u>not</u> a problem of the public debt?
   a. income inequality
   b. external debt
   c. dampens economic growth
   d. absorbs the saving done in a growing economy at full employment

6. A cyclically adjusted budget means that:
   a. every person in the economy, over age 16, will be employed.
   b. there is an automatic tendency toward full-employment GDP.
   c. the size of the federal budget's surplus or deficit when the economy is operating at full employment.
   d. discretionary fiscal policy will cause inflation and, therefore, lower interest rates and tax revenues.

7. The restrictive effects of fiscal policy:
   a. may cause crowding-out
   b. can occur when the federal government pursues expansionary fiscal policy
   c. can cause the level of investment to decline
   d. all of the above

8. A $1 increase in government spending (injection) will have a greater impact on GDP than will a $1 decline in taxes (leakage) because:
   a. a portion of the tax cut may be saved
   b. government spending and taxing have different multipliers
   c. part of the reduction in taxes may leak out of the economy
   d. all of the above

9. Which of the following is <u>not</u> a source of financing the deficit?
   a. money creation
   b. borrowing money
   c. taxation
   d. impounding

10. Which of the following is <u>not</u> a timing problem for fiscal policy?
    a. recognition
    b. administrative
    c. political considerations
    d. operational

"Money, Banking and Financial Institutions"

Chapter Orientation

This concept discusses one of our favorite topics -- MONEY. We work hard to earn and spend money. According to the Federal Reserve, the story of money began when people learned they could trade for things they wanted -- but it was often difficult. For example, a fisherman couldn't get wheat from a farmer who didn't like fish.

So, prized ornaments -- beads, shells, stones, furs, etc. were items used as money. Because of the ease of carrying, and for its durability, "metal" money became popular. About 2,500 B.C. the Egyptians produced one of the first types of metal money in the form of rings. The Chinese used gold cubes about 400 years later. In Lydia, (western Turkey), the first metal coins were struck about 700 B.C. . . . some of the world's most beautiful coins were struck during the Golden Age of Greece -- 400 to 300 B.C. For centuries, coins remained the favored medium of exchange.

Paper money is related to the clay tablets on which the Babylonians wrote due bills and receipts about 2,500 B.C. Marco Polo reported that the Chinese Emperor Kubla Khan issued mulberry bank paper notes bearing his seal and the signatures of his treasurers in 1273 A.D.

Metal coins lost some of their appeal during the Middle Ages as travel became more common. Their weight and the fear of robbery made coins impractical. Instead, travelers went to goldsmiths to exchange their coins for receipts that were valueless to a robber. The receipts could be exchanged for coins with a designated goldsmith in another city (paper money at work).

Our coins and coinage have changed many times since the Coinage Act of 1792, which adopted the dollar as our standard monetary unit and established the country's first Mint -- at Philadelphia (the Federal Reserve, "Coins and Currency"). We will explore our new currency, as well as "E-cash" and "Smart-cards".

What are the functions of money? What is the U.S. money (stock) supply? What is the framework of the U.S. financial system? What is happening to our banking system and where are we headed? These questions will be addressed in this concept.

Learning Objectives

After reading this chapter in the text and completing the following exercises in this concepts book, you should be able to:

1. Discuss the earliest beginnings of money.
2. List and explain the three functions of money.
3. Define the money supply, M1.
4. Identify the four kinds of checkable deposits; and the four principal kinds of depository institutions.
5. Give examples of near-monies.
6. Define M2 and MZM.
7. Explain what "back" the money supply in the United States.
8. Discuss why money has "value".
9. Explain the relationship between the value of money and the price level.
10. Explain how the government keeps the value of money relatively stable.
11. Discuss the framework of the American financial system.
12. Explain the roles of the district banks.
13. list items that have been used as money (history).

14. Describe six functions of the Federal Reserve System and indicate which is the most important.
15. Discuss the recent developments in the banking industry.

Chapter Highlights

I. **The Functions of Money**
   A. Medium of exchange -- use to execute transactions.
   B. Unit of Account -- used as a yardstick for dollars.
   C. Store of value -- holds purchasing power until you spend it.

II. **The Components of the Money (Stock) Supply**
   A. Liquid Assets
      1. Liquid assets are assets, which can be quickly turned into cash, with little loss of value. Cash is 100% liquid, therefore has a key advantage for spendability.
   B. Money Definition M1
      1. M1 -- highly liquid, consists of currency (coins and paper) plus checkable deposits (deposits in which checks can be drawn). It is the narrowest definition of the U.S. money supply.
      2. All coins in circulation in the U.S. are "token money" (the value of the metal contained in the coin is less than its face value) and are issued by the U.S. Treasury. The coins are minted by the U.S Mint. Paper money consists of Federal Reserve notes issued by "The Fed" and printed by the Bureau of Engraving and Printing.
      3. Institutions Offering Checkable Deposits:
         a. Commercial banks (primary depository institutions)
         b. Thrift institutions:
            (1) Savings and loan associations
            (2) Mutual savings banks
            (3) Credit unions
      4. Safety and convenience has made "checkable deposits" the largest component (55%) of M1. The types of checkable deposits are:
         a. Demand deposits (checking accounts).
         b. Automatic transfer of saving (ATS) accounts in commercial bank
         c. Negotiable order of withdrawal (NOW) accounts in savings and loans.
         d. Share drafts in credit unions.
      5. Currency and checkable deposits owned by the government, the Federal Reserve Banks, commercial banks, or other financial institutions are <u>excluded</u> from M1 or any other broad measure of the money supply.
   C. Near-monies: M2 and MZM
      1. Near-monies are highly liquid assets that do not function directly or fully as a medium of exchange, but can be readily converted into currency or checkable deposits. Examples include: deposits in savings accounts, time deposits, short-term government securities, money market mutual fund shares, overnight repurchase agreements, small (under $100,000) time deposits.
      2. M2 = M1 + savings deposits, including MMDAs + small-denominated (<$100,000) time deposits + MMMFs held by individuals.
      3. M2 is a broader measure of the money (stock) supply.
      4. MZM (money zero maturity) focuses exclusively on monetary balances that are immediately available, at zero cost, for household and business transactions.
      5. MZM = M2 - Small Time Deposits + MMMFs held by businesses
      6. The Federal Reserve stopped publishing M3, in March 2006.

7. Credit cards or plastic money, are not money -- they are a loan (credit).

III. What Backs the Money (Stock) Supply

A. Money as Debt
   1. In the U.S. and other advanced economies, all money is "backed" (guaranteed) by the government's ability to keep the value of money relatively stable.
   2. Paper money is the circulating debt of the Federal Reserve Banks. Checkable deposits and the debts of commercial banks and thrift institutions.
   3. Relative Scarcity
      a. The value of money depends on supply and demand.

B. Value of money
   1. Acceptability -- confidence that we can exchange our money for goods and services when we choose to spend it.
   2. Legal tender -- designated by the government.
      a. Fiat money ("play money") is money because the government says its money -- not because it is backed by a precious metal.
      b. The advantages of "fiat" money include: easily controlled by the government, less costly, and can possess all of the characteristics of "commodity" money (money which has value in addition to what it will buy).

C. Money and Prices
   1. The value of money is inversely related to the price level. (As prices increase, the value of a dollar decreases or loses purchasing power).
      a. Runaway inflation may significantly depreciate the value of money (Germany's WWI) – called "hyperinflation," discussed in Chapter 27.

D. Stabilization of Money Value
   1. The government's responsibility in stabilizing the value of money (since it is not "backed" by any precious metal).
      a. The application of appropriate fiscal policies.
      b. The effective control over the supply of money.

IV. The Federal Reserve and the Banking System

A. Historical Background
   1. Early in the twentieth century, Congress decided that centralization and public control were essential for efficiency. In 1907, the country experienced a severe banking crisis, a commission (the National Monetary Commission) was established to study the banking problems and recommend a new structure. The result was The Federal Reserve Act of 1913, which created our banking system.

B. Framework of the Federal Reserve System (The "Fed") see "Organization Chart of the Fed"
   1. Introduction
      a. At 6:00 p.m. on December 23, 1913, President Woodrow Wilson entered his office -- he was smiling . . . The President then sat down at his desk and, using four gold pens, signed into law the Federal Reserve Act . . . With this law, Congress established a central banking system which would enable the world's most powerful industrial nation to manage its money and credit far more effectively than ever before . . . the political and legislative struggle to create the Federal Reserve System was long and often extremely bitter, and the final product was the result of a carefully crafted yet somewhat tenuous political compromise. (The Federal Reserve Bank of Boston, "Historical Beginnings . . . the Federal Reserve").
      b. The independence of the Fed is a matter of continuing discussion.

2. Structure of the Fed
   a. Board of Governors -- seven members, with fourteen-year terms staggered every two years -- appointed by the President with the confirmation of the Senate, which helps keep the Fed independent of the administration. The prime function of the Board is the formulation of monetary policy by determining reserve requirements and approving changes in the discount rate. The Board supervises and regulates member banks and bank holding companies. In addition, it oversees the 12 Federal Reserve Banks. The Chairman and the Vice Chairman of the Board are named for four-year terms by the President.
   b. Federal Open Market Committee -- is made up of the seven members of the Board plus five of the president's of the Federal Reserve Banks (one of whom is the president of the Federal Reserve Bank of New York; the other Bank presidents serve one-year terms on a rotating basis). Open market operations (buying and selling of government securities), are the principal instrument used by the Fed to implement monetary policy.
   c. Advisory Councils - The Councils confer with the Board of Governors on economic and banking developments and make recommendations regarding Monetary Policy. They have no policy-making power.
      1. Federal Advisory Council (12 commercial bankers)
      2. Thrift Institution Advisory Council (representatives from S&L, C.U. and Savings Banks.)
      3. Consumer Advisory Council (30 members from financial, academic and legal backgrounds.)
   d. Twelve Federal Reserve Banks -- for the purpose of carrying out day-to-day operations of the Federal Reserve System -- the U.S. has been divided into 12 districts, each with a Federal Reserve Bank. Branches of Reserve Banks have been established in twenty-five cities. Many of the services performed by the Reserve Banks for depository institutions **("Bankers' Banks")** for a fee are similar to services performed by banks and thrifts for the public. These services include issuing currency, and processing checks, holding cash reserves and making loans, redeeming government securities, and act as fiscal agent for the U.S. Government. They supervise and examine member banks for soundness and take primary responsibility for setting the Bank's discount rate (subject to review by the Board of Governors). District banks are **quasi-public** banks in that they are a blend of private ownership and government control. They are not motivated by profit, as each year they return to the U.S. Treasury all earnings in excess of Federal Reserve operating and other expenses and statutory dividends paid on stock owned by member banks. "The Fed" is the "lender of last resort" to the banking system.
3. Commercial Banks and Thrifts
   a. Commercial Banks: There are approximately 6,000 commercial banks.
      (1) Roughly three-fourths are state banks -- private banks operating a under state charter.
      (2) Roughly one-fourth are national banks -- private banks operating under a Federal charter and three-quarters are state banks.
   b. Thrift institutions: There are approximately 8,500 (most are credit unions) thrift institutions.
      (1) Thrift Institutions are regulated by agencies separate from the Board of Governors and the District Banks. For example, credit unions are regulated and monitored by the National Credit Union Administration (NCUA).
      (2) Thrift institutions are subject to the same reserve requirements as other depository institutions.

C. Fed Functions and the Money Supply
   1. Issuing Currency
   2. Setting Reserve Requirement and holding reserves
   3. Lending Money and serving as an emergency lender of last resort.
   4. Providing Check Collection

5. Acting as fiscal agent
6. Supervising banks
7. Controlling the money supply

D. Federal Reserve Independence
1. Congress purposely established the Fed as an independent agency of government. The objective was to protect the Fed from political pressures, such as special interest groups.
2. The Fed can take actions to increase interest rates when higher rates are needed to stem inflation.

V. The Financial Crisis of 2007 and 2008

During late 2007 and 2008, the U.S. financial system faced its most serious crisis since the Great Depression of the 1930s. The financial crisis soon spread to the entire economy, culminating in the "Great Recession" of 2007-2009. The following explains what led up to the crisis, how severe and how it changed the structure of the U.S. financial services industry.

A. The Mortgage Default Crisis
1. In 2007 a major wave of defaults of home mortgage loans threatened our financial institutions. A majority of these mortgage defaults were on subprime mortgage loans (high-interest-rate loans to home buyers with higher-than-average credit risk).
2. The Federal government had encouraged banks to make these types of loans as part of an effort to broaden home ownership to more Americans.
3. Financial institutions thought that a new concept "mortgage-backed securities" (bonds backed up by mortgage payments) would eliminate most of the bank exposure to mortgage defaults—BIG MISTAKE!
4. Causes: government programs encouraging subsidized home ownership for former renters; declining real estate values after a long boom; bad incentives provided by the mortgage-backed securities.

B. Securitization
1. Definition—the process of slicing up and bundling groups of loans, mortgages, corporate bonds or other financial debts into distinct new securities ("bundling").
2. Several large insurance companies offered polices to insure against losses from defaults (EX: AIG) called "collateralized default swaps".
3. Securitization is so widespread and so critical to our financial system it is sometimes referred to as the "shadow banking system".
4. The "perfect storm" occurred: homeowners defaulted, major financial institution plunged, and the insurers (like AIG, which is the largest in the U.S. and the world) did not have enough resources to finance the claims.

C. Failures and Near-Failures
1. As a result of the above, first the big mortgage lenders faced demise, then the securities firms and investment banks, and then the insurance companies.
2. Many felt that the U.S. financial system might collapse

D. The Treasury Bailout: TARP
1. In late 2008, Congress passed the Troubled Asset Relief Program (TARP), which allocated $700 billion to the U.S. Treasury to make emergency loans to critical financial institutions, and other U.S. firms.
2. TARP saved several financial institutions, which would have derailed other firms and frozen credit throughout the economy.
3. This brings up the question of "moral hazard", which is the tendency for financial investors and financial services firms to take on greater risks because they assume they are at least partially insured against losses.

E. The Fed's Lender-of-Last-Resort Activities
1. The Fed is the "lender of last resort" to financial institutions in times of financial emergencies.
2. The Fed performed this vital function following the 9/11 terrorist attacks (lent $45 billion).
3. In addition to TARP and the use of standard tools, the Fed designed and implemented several creative facilities to pump liquidity into the financial system.

a. Primary Dealer Credit Facility (PDCF)
b. Term Securities Lending Facility (TSLF)
c. Asset-Backed Commercial Paper Money Market Mutual Fund Liquidity Facility
d. Commercial Paper Funding Facility (CPFF)
e. Money Market Investor Funding Facility (MMIFF)
f. Term Asset-Backed Securities Loan Facility (TALF)
g. Interest Payments of Reserves

VI. The Post crisis U.S. Financial Services Industry

A. The financial services industry has been evolving into fewer, larger firms, each offering a wider spectrum of services. In 1999, Congress ended the Depression-era prohibition against banks selling stocks, bonds, and mutual funds.

B. The financial crisis of 2007-2008 generated introspection about what went wrong and how to prevent this happening again in the future. In addition, legislation was passed to help homeowners who were "underwater" (owed more on mortgage loan than property is worth) on mortgage loans remain in their homes.

C. Wall Street Reform and Consumer Protection Act

1. In response to the financial crisis, Congress passed the Wall Street Reform and Consumer Financial Protection Act of 2010.
2. This legislation includes more oversight and provisions to help eliminate repeating the financial "meltdown" that occurred in 2007-2008.

VII. Last Word: "Too Big to Fail, Too Big to Jail?"

VIII.Web-based Question/Problem (see your Instructor)

"Money, Banking and Financial Institutions"

Key Terms

medium of exchange
unit of account
store of value
money supply
M1
currency
paper money
checkable deposit
Money market
Board of Governors
Open Market Committee
Federal Advisory Committee
Federal Reserve Bank
central bank
bankers' bank
quasi-public bank
dual-banking system
commercial bank
state bank
national bank
member bank
reserve requirement
discount rate
E-cash
smart cards
MZM
Securitization
Troubled Asset Relief Program (TARP)

fiat money
commodity money
depository institution
value of money
FDIC
FSLIC
token money
ATS
NOW
share draft
commercial bank
thrift institution
liquid asset
intrinsic value
face value
F.R. Note
time deposit
overnight RPs
checking account
near-money
plastic money
M2
noncheckable savings account
legal tender
MMDA
MMMF
subprime mortgage loans
moral hazard
Wall Street Reform and Consumer Protection Act

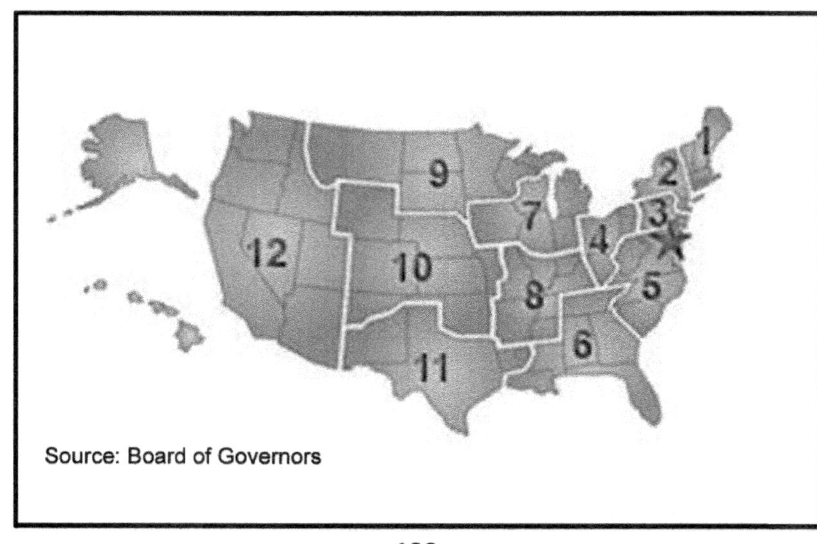

Source: Board of Governors

The Federal Reserve System

Board of Governors

Seven members appointed by the President

- Sets reserve requirements and approves the discount rate as part of monetary policy
- Supervises and regulates member banks, bank holding companies and foreign-owned banks operating in the United States
- Establishes and administers protective regulations governing consumer credit
- Oversees Federal Reserve Banks

The Board exercises general supervision over the Reserve Banks.

The members of the Board, along with five presidents from the Reserve Banks, compose the Federal Open Market Committee.

These councils advise the Board on various issues.

Federal Open Market Committee

Board of Governors and five Reserve Bank Presidents

- Directs open market operations (the buying and selling of U.S. Government securities), the primary tool of monetary policy.

Advisory Councils

- Consumer Advisory Council
- Federal Advisory Council
- Thrift Institutions Advisory Council

Twelve District Banks serve as the operating arms of the central bank. Five presidents from the Reserve Banks sit on the Federal Open Market Committee.

Federal Reserve Banks

Twelve district Banks serve as the operating arms of the central bank. Five presidents of the Reserve Banks sit on the Federal Open Market Committee

- Propose discount rate
- Hold reserve balances for depository institutions and lend them at the discount window
- Furnish currency and coin
- Collect, clear, and transfer funds for depository institutions
- Act as fiscal agent for Treasury Department

Source:
Board of Governors

“Money, Banking and Financial Institutions”

PROBLEMS

1. Describe the earliest beginnings of money.

2. List and explain the three functions of money.

3. Define the money stock: M1 and M2.

4. What “backs” the U.S. dollar?

5. Name the four principal types of financial institutions and explain the role of each.

6. Why do households and businesses need money?

7. Define “MZM” and describe the function.

8. Describe the “Mortgage Default Crisis”.

9. Discuss the framework of the Federal Reserve. Explain the role for each area.

10. Why is the Fed, the lender of last resort?

11. What is “securitization”? Why is it important to our financial system?”

12. Define and explain TARP and the Wall Street Reform and Consumer Protection Act.

"Money, Banking and Financial Institutions"

Self-Test

1. The major component of the money supply (M1) is:
   a. currency
   b. coins
   c. gold certificates
   d. demand deposits
2. Which of the following items is a function of money?
   a. medium of money
   b. Unit of account
   c. marketable good
   d. medium of barter
3. Which of the following is considered "near-money"?
   a. a commercial bank time deposit
   b. a commercial bank demand deposit
   c. a General Motors bond
   d. a gold watch
4. Currently, the U.S. money supply is "backed" by:
   a. gold
   b. silver
   c. copper
   d. faith in the U.S. Government
5. The value of money is:
   a. directly related to the price level
   b. inversely related to the price level
   c. proportionally related to the price level
   d. equally related to the price level
6. MZM (money zero maturity) focuses on:
   a. monetary balances immediately available
   b. monetary balances at zero income
   c. MMMFs held by businesses only
   d. currency and checking accounts
7. When the quantity of money demanded is less than the quantity supplied:
   a. the interest rate will rise
   b. the interest rate will fall
   c. the market demand curve will shift to the left
   d. the money supply curve will shift to the right
8. "Moral hazard" is defined as:
   a. tendency to take on greater risk because you assume losses are partially insured
   b. the "bundling" of assets to be sold in open market
   c. the "Shadow banking system"
   d. loans made to insure financial stability
9. The policy making arm of the Federal Reserve System is:
   a. the FOMC
   b. the Board of Governors
   c. the Federal Advisory Council
   d. the Federal District Banks
10. District banks are "quasi-public" banks because:
    a. they are a blend of private ownership and government control
    b. they deal only with foreign nations and do not have direct control with the American public
    c. they are able to earn and retain all net earnings
    d. they deal only with the thrift institutions and not the general public

"Money Creation"

Chapter Orientation

In the last concept, money was defined by the components of the money (stock) supply. The most liquid form of money, M1, is currency in circulation plus the checkable deposits in depository institutions — commercial banks have the largest volume. The examples in the chapter involve commercial banks, but remember that thrift institutions also provide checkable deposits.

What happens when a bank receives a demand deposit? Since, the United States operates under a fractional reserve banking system, some fraction of percentage less than 100% (called the required reserve ratio) must be legally held in reserve at the Federal Reserve District Bank or in vault cash. The balance is then placed into excess reserves, until it is invested or loaned out. For example, if a bank receives a demand deposit of $100, and has a 10 percent required reserve ratio, $10 will be the legal or required reserve and $90 would be placed into excess reserves until it is loaned out. Total (actual) reserves equals required reserves plus excess reserves.

Commercial banks create money whenever they increase the net amount of their loans. Monetary authorities (Board of Governors of the Federal Reserve System) utilize reserve requirements to influence the lending ability of commercial banks. Remember that a single commercial bank can expand (or contract) the money supply only by the amount of its excess reserves; the commercial banking system can expand the money supply by a magnified (money multiplier) amount.

We will examine the effects of various transactions on the quantity of money. The basic working tool is the "T" account, which gives us a simple step-by-step process on both the asset and liability sides of bank balance sheets.

Learning Objectives

After reading this chapter in the text and completing the following exercises in this concepts book, you should be able to:

1. Discuss the reason why Congress decided a "banking system" was needed by the early twentieth century.
2. Explain how banks "create" money.
3. Calculate a bank's required and excess reserves given the necessary balance-sheet information.
4. Discuss what is meant by a "fractional reserve system".
5. Explain the function or purpose of required reserves. Are the required reserves adequate to cover all depositors?
6. Describe how a check drawn against a bank and deposited in another bank, effects both the reserves and demand deposits for each bank.
7. Explain why commercial bank reserves are an asset to the commercial bank, but are a liability to the Federal Reserve Bank holding them.
8. Illustrate what happens to the money supply when a commercial bank grants a loan (or buys securities); and what happens to the money supply when a loan is repaid (or a bank sells securities).
9. Explain what happens to a commercial bank's reserves and demand deposits after it has made a loan, a check has been written on the newly created demand deposit, deposited in another commercial bank, and cleared. What happens to the reserves and demand deposits of the commercial bank in which the check was deposited?
10. Describe what would happen to a commercial bank's reserves if it made loans (or bought securities) in an amount greater than its excess reserves.
11. Explain the differences in the money-creating potential of a single commercial bank vs. the banking system.
12. Calculate the money multiplier (M$) and the total loan or investment potential, when given the necessary information.
13. List and explain the two leakages, which effect the money-creating potential of the banking system.
14. Explain the need for monetary control.

"Money Creation"

Chapter Highlights

I. The Fractional Reserve System

A. Definition -- a portion (fraction) of checkable deposits are backed up by cash in bank vaults or deposits at the central bank.

B. Illustrating the Idea: The Goldsmiths

1. History of the goldsmiths. Traders stored gold with the goldsmiths (in their vault).The goldsmith would issue a receipt. Soon people were paying for goods with these receipts.

C. Significant characteristics of fractional reserve system of banking

1. Money creation and reserves - banks create money through lending. They are regulated to keep a reserve on hand.
2. Bank "panics" and regulation - to avoid bank "panics" or "runs", banking systems are regulated and must have deposit insurance.

II. A Single Commercial Bank

A. Definition -- the purpose of a balance sheet is to show the assets, liabilities, and net worth (equity) of a bank. In practice, total assets should equal total liabilities plus net worth. Assets = Liabilities + Net Worth

B. Steps in organizing a single commercial bank:

Step 1. Creating a bank

a. Secure a national or state charter
b. Sell shares of stock in return for cash ("vault cash" or "till money").

Step 2. Becoming a going concern ("reality")

a. Purchase property and equipment needed to run the bank

Step 3. Accepting deposits

a. Depository cash in the bank does not change the total supply of money -- it merely changes the composition from currency in circulation (decreases) to demand deposits (increase).

Step 4. Depository reserves in a Federal Reserve (District) Bank

a. All depository institutions with checkable deposits will have:

(1) Required (legal) reserves -- some fraction less than 100% of the total deposit must be kept at the Federal Bank or vault cash. Required legal, or reserves, cannot be used for meeting unexpected cash withdrawals. Its purpose is a means in which the Board of Governors can influence the lending ability of commercial banks.
(2) The reserve ratio (R) is a specified percentage that banks use to calculate legal reserves.
(3) The actual reserves are the deposits of a commercial bank at the Federal Reserve Bank.
(4) The excess reserves (E) equal the actual (total) reserves minus the required reserves.
(5) Commercial bank reserves are an asset to the commercial bank; but are a liability to the Federal Reserve Bank holding them.

Step 5. A check is drawn against the bank

a. Effects -- whenever a check is drawn against a bank and deposited in another bank, the first bank loses (transfers) both reserves and deposits and the second gains both reserves and deposits.

III. Money-Creating Transactions of a Commercial Bank

Step 6. Granting a loan

a. A single commercial bank in a multibank banking system can lend only an amount equal to its initial preloan excess reserves.
b. Whenever a bank grants a loan, it creates money -- they create a demand (checkable) deposits, which are money. This increases the bank's deposit liabilities and the supply of money.

c. When the loan is repaid, the bank's deposit liabilities and the supply of money decrease (currency held by bank is excluded from the money supply).

d. Repaying a loan

   a. Money is credited when banks make a loan and it vanishes when bank customers pay off loans.

Step 7. Buying government securities

a A bank's balance sheet reflects the tradeoff between profits (making loans; purchasing securities) and safety (liquidity such as having excess reserves or vault cash). The Federal funds rate is the rate banks lend to each other, usually overnight.

1. When a commercial bank purchases securities, it increases its own deposit liabilities and the supply of money (when the securities dealer draws and clears the check, the bank will lose reserves and deposits in that amount).
2. The selling of securities to the public will reduce the bank's deposit liabilities and the supply of money.

IV. Banking System: Multiple Deposit Expansion

A. The Monetary (money) multiplier $(M\$) = \frac{1}{R}$

1. A single bank in a banking system can only lend the amount of its excess reserves. The banking system can lend (create money) a multiple of its excess reserves or (excess reserves x M$) because the reserves lost by a single bank are not lost to the banking system as a whole.
2. Three underlying assumptions are made: D = E x M$ ("D" is the maximum checkable – deposit creation)
   a. Uniform reserve ratio
   b. All banks are "loaned up" no excess reserves
   c. Checks for the entire amount of the loan will be written and deposited.

B. Reversibility – The Multiple Destruction of Money

1. The Money Multiplier (M$) works in both directions, it applies to money destruction from the payback of loans as well as the money creator from the making of loans.

C. Some modifications

1. Additional leakages
   a. Currency Drains - Borrowers choose to be paid in cash (rather than a demand-deposit).
   b. Excess Reserves - Bankers choose to hold excess reserves (rather than lend the excess).

D. Need for Monetary Control

1. During prosperity, banks happily extend credit to the maximum of their excess reserves. Borrowers are working, the economy is expanding, so the thought of default is minimized.
2. During a recession or depression, banks are extremely cautious in lending money (because of fear of default) and therefore retreat to the safety of liquidity (excess reserves) even at the expense of interest income.
3. As a result of banks intensifying the business cycles, the Federal Reserve must use its "monetary tools", which are anticyclical, to stabilize the money supply.

V. Last Word: Banking, Leverage and Financial Instability

VI. Web-based Question/Problem (see your Instructor)

"Money Creation"

Key Terms

balance sheet
assets
liabilities
net worth (capital stock)
fractional reserve system
vault cash
legal (required) reserve
reserve ratio
actual reserve
excess reserve
reversibility
FDIC
lending potential
monetary (money) multiplier(M$)
loaned-up
leakages
anticyclical
procyclical
promissory note
monetary tools
federal funds rate

Notes:

"**Money Creation**"

PROBLEMS

1. Discuss the process (steps) involved in forming a commercial bank.

2. Explain the differences in the money creating potential for a single commercial bank vs. the banking system as a whole.

3. Explain the function or purpose of required reserves. Are the required reserves adequate to cover all depositors?

4. Describe how a check drawn against a bank and deposited in another bank, effects both the reserves and demand deposits for each bank.

5.

Simplified Bank Balance Sheet

Assets			Liabilities and Net Worth	
Total Reserves:		$__________	Demand Deposits	$10,000
Required	__________			
Excess	0			
Loans		$ 8,000		__________
Total Assets		$ 10,000	Total Liabilities and Net Worth	$10,000

a. Fill in the Balance Sheet above.

$$R = \frac{\text{Required Reserves}}{\text{Demand Deposits}}$$

b. What is the required reserve ratio (R)?__________

c. If this bank received $15,000 in new deposits, its required reserves would become __________.

d. Construct a new balance sheet for part "c" above.

e. If all banks had the same required reserve ratio, what would the money multiplier (M$) be? __________

f. Therefore, this additional $15,000 in NEW deposits would expand NEW loans and investments in the banking system, by __________.

PROBLEMS

6. Suppose Bank #1 receives $20,000 as a new deposit in Olivia's checking account. Assuming a 20% reserve requirement, complete the balance sheet below.

BANK #1

Assets		Liabilities and Net Worth	
Total Reserves:	$__________	Demand Deposits	__________
Required __________			
Excess __________			
Loans	$__________		
Total Assets	$__________	Total Liabilities and Net Worth	__________

7. At this point, how much can Bank #1 loan out? __________

8. Suppose Victoria borrows this entire amount from Bank #1 to pay for a painting she is buying from Erica. Show the new balance sheet after the loan has been withdrawn.

BANK #1

Assets		Liabilities and Net Worth	
Total Reserves:	$__________	Demand Deposits	__________
Required __________			
Excess __________			
Loans	$__________		
Total Assets	$__________	Total Liabilities and Net Worth	__________

PROBLEMS

9. Erica deposits the money which she received from the painting in her checking account in Bank #2. Assume she has the only account and the reserve requirement ratio (R) is 20%, complete the balance sheet below.

BANK #2

Assets			Liabilities and Net Worth	
Total Reserves:		$ ______	Demand Deposits	______
Required	______			
Excess	______			
Loans		$ ______		
Total Assets		$ ______	Total Liabilities and Net Worth	______

10. At this point, how much can Bank #2 loan out? ______

11. Suppose Erin borrows this entire amount to buy a car from Jim. Show the new balance sheet after Erin's money has been withdrawn from Bank #2.

BANK #2

Assets			Liabilities and Net Worth	
Total Reserves:		$ ______	Demand Deposits	______
Required	______			
Excess	______			
Loans		$ ______		
Total Assets		$ ______	Total Liabilities and Net Worth	______

"Money Creation"

Self-Test

1. Commercial banks increase the money supply when:
   a. they accept deposits
   b. the amounts of new loans exceed the old loans being paid off.
   c. the amounts of old loans exceed the new loans being made.
   d. they sell government securities.
2. If $1 of cash in a bank's vault (or at the Fed) can be used by a commercial bank to support $5 of new deposits:
   a. the reserve ratio is .5.
   b. the reserve ratio is .25.
   c. the reserve ratio is .20.
   d. every $1 reduction of cash must reduce reserves by .5.
3. If you borrow $1,000 from your local bank to buy a fur jacket, the transactions alone will:
   a. increase the money supply by $1,000.
   b. increase the money supply by more than $1,000.
   c. increase the money supply by less than $1,000.
   d. not change the money supply.
4. If the First National Bank has $10,000 in excess reserves and the reserve ratio is 25%, the bank must have:
   a. $100,000 in demand deposits and $35,000 in total (actual) reserves.
   b. $100,000 in demand deposits and $25,000 in total (actual) reserves.
   c. $40,000 in demand deposits and $10,000 in total (actual) reserves.
   d. $50,000 in demand deposits and $5,000 in total (actual) reserves.
5. The purpose of a reserve requirement is:
   a. to cover the demand-deposits.
   b. to protect depositors.
   c. to insure liquidity in the system.
   d. for the Fed to control the money supply.
6. Commercial banks create money when they:
   a. hold their excess reserves.
   b. collect checks through the Fed.
   c. increase the net amount of their loans.
   d. accept repayment on a loan.
7. When commercial banks loan the maximum amount:
   a. legal reserves will be zero.
   b. legal reserves will equal actual reserves.
   c. excess reserves will equal zero.
   d. all of the above.
8. Practicing fractional reserve banking:
   a. increases liabilities of the bank.
   b. reduces profits for the bank.
   c. attracts depositors to the bank.
   d. increases profits for the bank.
9. Assume that $20,000 is deposited at a commercial bank which has a 25% reserve requirement and is fully loaned up. What is the total amount of new loans which can be made in the banking system?
   a. $80,000
   b. $60,000
   c. $20,000
   d. $10,000
10. A bank's balance sheet reflects the tradeoff between:
    a. assets and liabilities.
    b. profits and safety.
    c. what you have and what you owe.
    d. all of the above.

"Interest Rates and Monetary Policy"

Chapter Orientation

Now we have a dilemma to solve -- banks actually intensify the business cycle (procyclical). As a result, the Board of Governors (policy-making arm) of the Federal Reserve System, must reverse or counteract these fluctuations by utilizing the major and minor monetary controls (tools) available. For example, what actions would the Fed take to counteract inflation? or recession? These questions will be addressed in this chapter.

In addition, the Cause-effect chain of how monetary policy works will be presented step-by-step. The goal of monetary policy (and fiscal policy) is to stabilize the economy—to achieve a full-employment, noninflationary level of output. The effectiveness of monetary policy is determined by comparing the strengths and shortcomings of this system. Because monetary policy is implemented by the 12 Federal Reserve Banks, a consolidated balance sheet is examined.

This chapter is a good "wrap-up" chapter for Fiscal and Monetary Policy because it reviews both and reaches the conclusion that although they are different, fiscal and monetary policy should be coordinated to maximize the goal of stabilizing the economy at a full-employment, non-inflationary level.

Lastly, it focuses on the Federal Funds Rate, now being targeted by the Fed as well as the international flows ("net export effect"). The current chair of the Federal Reserve's Board of Governor's (Janet Yellen) has a tremendous influence on monetary policy.

Learning Objectives

After reading this chapter in the text, and completing the following exercises in this concepts book, you should be able to:

1. Explain the objectives of monetary policy.
2. Discuss the cause-effect chain between monetary policy and output and employment.
3. Explain the impact of interest rates on consumer investment (saving).
4. List and explain the two major assets and the three major liabilities of the Federal Reserve Banks.
5. Identify the three tools (or techniques) employed by the Board of Governors of the Federal Reserve System and explain how each can expand or contract the money supply.
6. State the most important (effective) tool that the Fed utilizes.
7. List and explain the three selective controls, which supplement the major instruments of monetary policy.
8. Draw the demand and supply curves for money. Show how a change in the money supply will effect the interest rate, investment-demand, and equilibrium GDP.
9. Explain how the shape of the demand for money and the investment-demand curves influence the impact of a change in the money supply and on the equilibrium GDP.
10. Using the AS - AD model show the effect of changes in monetary policy.
11. Explain the three strengths and four shortcomings of monetary policy.
12. State the policy (or target) dilemma faced by the Fed and explain why it faces this dilemma.
13. Discuss the recent focus of the Federal Funds Rate by the Federal Reserve.
14. Explain how changes in monetary policy will produce a "net export effect".

"Interest Rates and Monetary Policy"

Chapter Highlights

I. Interest Rates

A. Definition - the price paid for the use of money

B. The Demand for Money

1. Households and businesses need money for:

   a. Transactions demand -- for cash-flow purposes -- day-to-day spending activities.

      1. Influenced by the level of money (income) or nominal GDP (rather than by changes in the interest rate).
      2. The transactions demand for money varies directly with nominal GDP.
      3. Transactions demand for money (Dt) is shown as a vertical line because it is independent (unrelated) to changes in the interest rate. See Figure 1.

   b. Asset demand -- money functions as a store of value. Included as part of a portfolio of investments.

      1. The asset demand for money varies inversely with the rate of interest (when the interest rate is low, people will hold a large amount of money as assets; (when the interest rate is high, people will hold a small amount of money). See below.

   c. The total demand for money (D$) is the sum of the transactions demand and the asset demand.

   d. Where the total demand curve intersects the money supply curve is the equilibrium interest rate in the money market of the economy. See — Figure 1.

      1. Adjustment to a Decline or Increase — The Money Supply

         a. Shortage — When the supply of money is reduced, people will make up for this shortage by selling financial assets. Example, lower bond prices are associated with higher interest rates.

         b. Surplus — When the supply of money is increased, people will try to rid themselves of money by purchasing more bonds. Example, higher bond prices are associated with lower interest rates.

         c. Interest rates and bond prices are inversely related

FIGURE 1

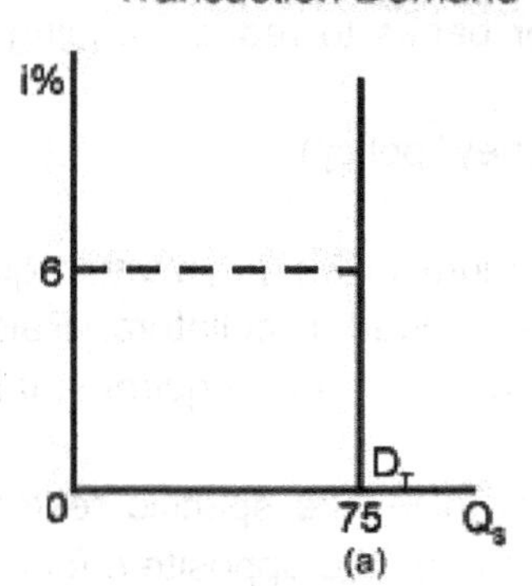

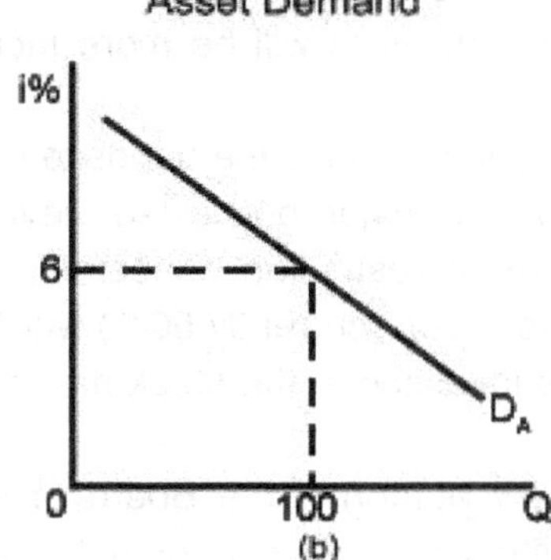

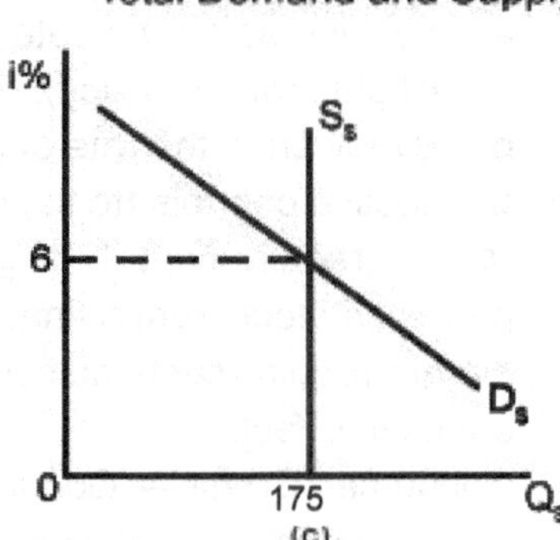

"Interest Rates and Monetary Policy"

II. Consolidated Balance Sheet of the 12 Federal Reserve Banks

A. Assets
   1. Securities (government bonds to adjust commercial bank reserves and therefore their ability to create money).
   2. Loans to commercial banks (commercial banks increase their reserves in exchange for IOUs).

B. Liabilities
   1. Reserves of commercial banks (deposits).
   2. Treasury deposits (enables the Treasury to draw checks and pay obligations.
   3. Federal Reserve Notes outstanding (our paper money supply consists of Federal Reserve Notes).
      a. Federal Reserve Notes in circulation are liabilities for the Fed banks.
      b. Those notes out of circulation (resting in the vault of the Fed) are neither an asset nor a liability.

III. Tools of Monetary Policy

A. Major tools (Four)
   1. Open-market operations -- (discussed under FOMC) -- the buying and selling of government securities by the Federal Reserve, in the open market to commercial banks and the public.
      a. Buying government securities increases the reserves ("Easy Money").
      b. Selling government securities decreases the reserves ("Tight Money").
   2. The Reserve ratio -- the percentage of deposit liabilities that a bank must maintain with the Federal Reserve Bank and vault cash.
      a. Raising the reserve ratio reduces excess reserves and the money multiplier putting downward pressure on the money supply ("Tight Money").
      b. Lowering the reserve ratio has the opposite effect (from 2a), "Easy Money".
   3. The Discount rate -- the percentage charged on loans from the Federal Reserve Banks.
      a. Raising the discount rate discourages borrowing (which discourages excess reserves) "Tight Money".
      b. Lowering the discount rate encourages borrowing (which encourages excess reserves and loans to the public) "Easy Money".
   4. Interest on reserves – in 2008, federal law was changed to allow the Federal Reserve to pay back interest on their reserves held at the Fed.
      a. By increasing the rate of interest, there will be more incentive for banks to reduce lending money ("tight money" policy).
      b. By lowering the rate of interest, it will cause the opposite ("Easy Money" policy).

B. Minor selective controls (to supplement the major tools listed previously)
   1. Margin requirement -- a government restriction concerning the minimum down payment required to purchase stock from a financial institution (currently 50%) with the stock pledged as collateral. Raising the margin requirements discourages investing in the stock market; lowering the margin requirement has the opposite effect.
   2. Consumer Credit -- Congress may authorize the Board of Governors to invoke specific restraints on consumer credit. Tightening credit discourages spending; loosening credit has the opposite effect.
   3. Moral suasion -- monetary authorities can use "jawboning" (oral statements) to influence lending policies of commercial banks.

C. Relative Importance
   1. Open market operations are clearly the most important of the tools over the business cycle.

IV. Targeting the Federal Funds Rate

A. Introduction
   1. Definition of "Federal Funds rate" - the interest rate that banks charge each other on overnight loans of reserves.

2. The Fed communicates changes in monetary policy by announcing changes it targets for the Federal funds interest rate.
3. In the past two decades, the Fed has been successful in utilizing "tight" and "easy" money policies. (see Table 4)

B. Easy Money and Tight Money
1. "Easy Money"—to make credit cheaply and easily available. To increase AE and employment. (Buy securities, reduce R, lower the Discount rate)
2. "Tight Money"—to tighten the supply of money to reduce spending and control inflation. (Do opposite of above.)

C. The Taylor Rule - The Fed appears to roughly follow a rule by Economist, John Taylor of Stanford - assumes a 2% target rate of inflation and has three parts:
1. When GDP = Potential GDP and inflation is 2%, federal funds target should be 4%.
2. For each 1% increase of real GDP above potential GDP, raise real federal funds rate by .5%.
3. For each 1% increase in the inflation rate above 2% target, raise real federal funds by .5%.

V. Monetary Policy, Real GDP and the Price Level

A. Cause-Effect Chain: (see Table 4)
1. Influencing the size of excess reserves which
2. Influences the supply of money
3. Influences the interest rate and bank credit which
4. Influences investment spending, output, employment, and the price level.

B. The Board of Governors directs the Federal Reserve Banks to increase (or decrease) the excess reserves of commercial banks -- this starts the ball rolling . . .

C. Investment effect
1. The impact of the interest rate
   a. Investment spending is very sensitive to change in the interest rates (long-term purchases are "locked-in").
   b. Consumer spending is not quite as sensitive to changes in the interest rates (can refinance or "stretch" most payments over a longer time period).

D. Equilibrium GDP
1. Investment spending is a component of aggregate demand (AD) which influences equilibrium.

E. Effects of Expansionary ("Easy $") or Restrictive ("Tight $") Monetary Policies

VI. Monetary Policy: Evaluation and Issues

A. Strengths of monetary policy over fiscal policy
1. Speed and flexibility -- monetary policy can be more quickly altered than fiscal policy.
2. Isolation from Political Pressure -- monetary policy is more subtle and more politically conservative than raising taxes.

B. Recent U.S. Monetary Policy: The Fed has been highly active in its use of monetary policy in recent decades.
1. <u>The 2001 Recession</u> – although the Fed cut the federal funds rate by 1%, the economy entered a recession in March of 2001. The Fed again lowered the rate by 2.5% by August. In the three months following the terrorist attacks on 9/11, the rate was lowered again to 1.75% and held that rate until Nov. 2002. Economists give the Fed high marks for helping to keep the recession relatively mild.
2. <u>The 2007-2009 Recession</u> – the mortgage default crisis (discussed in Chapter 32) posed a grave threat to the financial system. In response, the Fed lowered the discount rate by .5% and lowered the target for the federal funds rate to 2%. The Fed kept lowering the federal funds target rate and finally it was near-zero targeted range. This dropped the prime interest rate to only 3.25%. Economists are divided on the Fed's performance.

3. After the Great Recession – the economy did NOT bounce back from the Great Recession, especially in terms of employment. Therefore, the Fed undertook a series of innovative monetary policy initiatives designed to stimulate GDP and employment growth:
   a. Zero Interest Rate Policy (ZIRP) – The Fed aimed to keep short-term interest rates near zero to stimulate the economy.
   b. Zero Lower Bound Problem – after ZIRP was implemented, growth remained weak. There, the Fed had to deal with the zero lower bound problem, which happened when the Fed could not lower interest rates below zero.
   c. Quantitative Easing (QE 1 & 2) – The Fed's response was "quantitative easing." QE is when the Fed buys bonds solely with the intention of increasing the quantity of reserves in the banking system. Interest rates remain at the same levels to avoid the zero lower bound problem. But with bank reserves increased, the hope is that the economy will be stimulated through increased lending. The first round began in March 2009 and involved the Fed purchasing $1.75 trillion worth of bonds. The second round began in November 2010 and involved purchasing $600 billion.
   d. Forward Commitment – Under QE2, the Fed engaged in forward commitment, preannouncing exactly how much and when it was going to buy. This was a drastic change in policy from being vague about Fed initiatives.
   e. Operation Twist – the Maturity Extension Program began in September of 2011. The Fed preannounced that by the end of 2012, it would purchasing $677 billion in long-term government bonds while simultaneously selling an equivalent dollar amount of short-term government bonds. This was to spur investment and consumption. Although long-term interest rates dropped, short-term stayed near zero.
   f. QE3 – When economic growth remained weak in 2012, the Fed decided that the lack of effectiveness of QE2 and Operation Twist might have been due to limited time durations. Thus, the Fed committed itself to utilizing ZIRP until either the jobs situation dramatically improved or inflation started rising too high. By May of 2013, the Fed's balance sheet reached $3.3 trillion and was continuing to grow by $85 billion per month. New Fed Chair, Janet Yellen announced that QE3 would end in October of 2014 (with a Fed balance sheet of $3.5 trillion – roughly equal to the size of the German economy). The Fed's decision in 2013 was to gradually reduce the monthly boost...a plan called "the taper." The taper began in December 2013 and ended with a final $15 billion purchase in October 2014. There was much speculation as to the global reaction, but markets rebounded, interest rates stayed low and the Fed stuck with its plan. After the taper, the Fed has continued to hold interest rates near zero and has hinted at holding onto the bonds for years and reinvesting the proceeds.

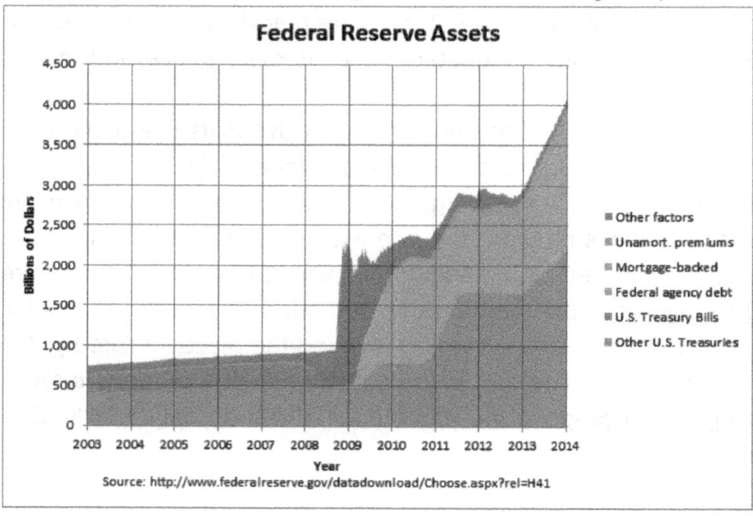

C. Problems and Complications
   1. Recognition lag, administrative lag and operational lags – complicate the timing of monetary policy (discussed under fiscal policy)
   2. Cyclical Asymmetry and the Liquidity Trap -- the power of a "tight money" policy <u>may</u> be greater than that of an "easy money" policy (Fed cannot <u>force</u> "easy money"). During severe recession banks are reluctant to lend excess reserves. The Fed cannot be certain of achieving its goal due to "Liquidity Trap: (adding more liquidity to banks has little or no impact – it is up to the banks to lend).
      a. Some economists believe that monetary policy only has a small impact upon investment spending in the economy. For example, a severe recession may undermine business confidence so investment decreases even with "easy money" policy.

Table 4

Monetary Policy and the Net Export Effect

(1) Expansionary Monetary Policy Easy Money Policy	(2) Restrictive Monetary Policy Tight Money Policy
Problem: recession, slow growth	*Problem:* inflation
↓	↓
Easy money policy (money supply rises) (lower interest rate)	Tight money policy (money supply falls) (higher interest rate)
↓	↓
Investment spending increases	Investment spending decreases
↓	↓
Decreased foreign demand for dollars	Increased foreign demand for dollars
↓	↓
Dollar depreciates	Dollar appreciates
↓	↓
Net exports increase (aggregate demand increases, strengthening the easy money policy)	Net exports decrease (aggregate demand decreases, strengthening the tight money policy)

D. Monetary Policy and the International Economy (See Table 4 above)
   1. Net Export Effect - International flows of financial capital in response to interest rate changes in the U.S., strengthen domestic monetary policy.
   2. "Easy Money" Policy is compatible with the goal of correcting a trade deficit.
   3. "Tight Money" Policy conflicts with the goal of correcting a balance of trade deficit.

VII. The Big Picture

A. Fiscal Policy (See Table 4 above)
   1. Definition -- using the government's tools of spending and taxing to correct "problems" in the economy.
   2. Discretionary and "built-in" stabilizers are part of fiscal policy

B. Fiscal and monetary policy
   1. Interrelated and should be coordinated to maximize the effectiveness.

VIII. Last Word: Worries about ZIRP, QE and Twists

IX. Web-based Question/Problem (see your Instructor

<u>Key Terms</u>

monetary policy
cause-effect chain
monetarists
treasury deposits
Federal Reserve Notes
open-market operations
easy money – expansionary policy
tight money – restrictive policy
reserve ratio
margin requirement
Federal Funds Rate
Taylor Rule
operation lag
interest
transactions demand for money
asset demand for money
total demand for money
discount rate
selective controls
moral suasion or jawboning
money market
cyclical asymmetry
liquidity trap
cost-push inflation
fiscal policy
discretionary stabilizers
built-in stabilizers
prime interest rate
net exports effect
recognition lag
interest on reserves
zero interest rate policy (ZIRP)
quantitative easing (QE 1&2)
quantitative easing (QE 3)
forward commitment
operation twist

"Interest Rates and Monetary Policy"

X. Monetary Policy Worksheet

Directions: Circle the appropriate answer for the following scenarios.
Check answer with Table 4 in workbook or text.

Problem: Recession, (slow growth)

Solution: Easy or Tight MP

↓

Higher or lower interest rate

↓

Increase or decrease investment

↓

Increase or decrease foreign demand for dollars

↓

Dollar appreciates or depreciates

↓

Net Exports increase or decrease

↓

Expanding or contracting the economy

Problem: Inflation (too much spending)

Solution: Easy or Tight MP

↓

Higher or lower interest rate

↓

Increase or decrease investment

↓

Increase or decrease foreign demand for dollars

↓

Dollar appreciates or depreciates

↓

Net Exports increase or decrease

↓

Expanding or contracting the economy

PROBLEMS

1a. Fill in the table below, based upon the correct policy actions by the Fed during a recession or during inflation.

Tool	"Easy $" Stimulate Economy RECESSION	"Tight $" Slow-down Economy INFLATION
1. FOMC	________	________
2. Reserve ratio	________	________
3. Discount rate	________	________
4. Interest on reserves	________	________
5. Margin requirement	________	________
6. Consumer credit	________	________
7. Moral suasion or jawboning	________	________

b. What is the most frequently used tool that the Fed utilizes?

2. Below is the demand schedule for money.

TABLE 1
Demand for Money (millions)

Rates of interest	Asset demand for money	Total
20%	$25	$________
18%	$50	$________
16%	$75	$________
14%	$100	$________
12%	$125	$________
10%	$150	$________

a. If the transactions demand is $50, calculate the total demand for money.

b. On graph paper, plot the total demand for money (D$) at each rate of interest.

c. Assume the money supply (S$) is $150 million, plot this curve on the graph (in "b").

d. What is the equilibrium rate of interest?____________

e. If the money supply increased by $25 million, at each rate of interest, what is the new equilibrium rate of interest? Show this change on the graph (also in "b").

3. Given the following: Year 1: $1 = 90 yen Year 2: $1 = 120 yen

a. Has the dollar appreciated or depreciated against the yen from year 1 to year 2? ________________

b. Fill in the blanks:

IMPORTING JAPANESE CARS TO THE U.S.

	Price of Car in Yen	Price of Car in Dollars	U.S. Imports	Japanese Exports
Year 1	10,000 yen	$________		
Year 2	10,000 yen	$________	________ (increase or decrease)	________ (increase or decrease)

c. Fill in the blanks

EXPORTING U.S. PLASTICS TO JAPAN

	Price of Plastic in Yen	Price of Plastic in Dollars	U.S. Exports	Japanese Imports
Year 1	________ yen	$75		
Year 2	________ yen	$75	________ (increase or decrease)	________ (increase or decrease)

d. Describe what happened above by completing the following statement:

"If the value of the dollar ____________________________ (appreciates or depreciates), U.S. imports will ____________________________ (increase or decrease) and U.S. exports will ____________________________ (increase or decrease)."

e. Given the change in the value of the dollar indicated in part "A" of this question, what will be the positive and negative effects on the U.S. economy?

Positive:

Negative:

"Interest Rates and Monetary Policy"

4. List and explain the two major assets and three major liabilities of the Federal Reserve Banks.

5. Discuss the cause-effect chain between monetary policy and output and employment.

6, Draw the demand and supply curves for money. Show how a change in the money supply will effect the interest rate, investment-demand the equilibrium.

7. Discuss the strengths and shortcomings of monetary policy. Why is it easier to conduct than fiscal policy?

8. Discuss the close relationship between the Federal Funds rate and the prime interest rate.

9. Explain how changes in monetary policy will produce a "net export effect".

10. Describe the Fed's action to combat the recessions of 2001 and 2007 – 2009.

11. Comment on the diagram shown in the "Key Graph" at the end of Chapter 34 in the textbook.

"Interest Rates and Monetary Policy"

Self-Test

1. The Federal Reserve controls the level of __________ and hence greatly influences the __________.
   a. bank reserves; money supply
   b. income; money supply
   c. prices; level of investment
   d. prices; inflationary gap
2. A decrease in the money supply __________ the interest rate, and the new interest rate __________ investment spending.
   a. lowers; lowers
   b. raises; lowers
   c. raises; raises
   d. lowers; raises
3. The __________ the demand for money curve, and the __________ the investment-demand curve, the greater the effect on equilibrium GDP.
   a. steeper; flatter
   b. flatter; steeper
   c. constant; more vertical
   d. more horizontal; more vertical
4. Which of the following determines the position of the supply curve for money?
   a. The Board of Governors of the Federal Reserve, through its control over bank reserves by monetary policy.
   b. Congress, through control of the federal appropriations and its Money and Banking Committee.
   c. The president of the Federal Reserve Banks who sit as a committee to formulate monetary policy.
   d. The Council of Economic Advisers, through recommendations to the Congressional money and banking committees.
5. Which of the following is a true statement about the total demand for money?
   a. The total demand for money is equal to the transaction demand plus total vault cash.
   b. The total demand for money is equal to the asset demand plus the transaction demand for money.
   c. The total demand for money is equal to the asset demand plus total vault cash.
   d. The total demand for money is equal to the difference between transaction demand and asset demand for money.
6. If a commercial bank has demand deposits of $100, total reserves of $75 and a required reserve ratio of 20%, it has excess reserves of:
   a. $75
   b. $55
   c. $20
   d. $100
7. The most important monetary tool used by the Fed over the business cycle is:
   a. the discount rate
   b. the margin requirement
   c. the reserve ratio
   d. open-market operations
8. To establish a "tight money" policy, the Board of Governors of the Federal Reserve may:
   a. increase the discount rate and lower the reserve ratio
   b. increase the reserve ratio and sell government securities in the open market
   c. increase the reserve ratio and lower the discount rate
   d. sell government securities in the open market and lower the discount rate
9. Changing the required reserve ratio may be ineffective as an "easy money" policy because:
   a. it takes large changes in the reserve ratio to offset a recession
   b. banks are required to maintain a legal reserve
   c. banks may hold excess reserves
   d. Congress may overrule the Fed's decision
10. Which of the following is <u>not</u> considered an asset to a Federal Reserve bank?
    a. Gold certificate account
    b. Federal Reserve Notes
    c. Loans to depository institutions
    d. U.S. government securities

REVIEW SHEET: UNIT III MACROECONOMICS

ECON 105 – UNIT III REVIEW

Be sure to bring a #2 pencil, graph paper and calculator!

PART I: 40 Multiple Choice questions (2 points each or a total of 80 points)

1. Know the differences among the three Economic Schools of Thought: Classical, Keynesian and Supply-side (WB pg. 103).
2. Know about "Reagonomics" and how it differs from "Supply-side Economics".
3. Know about the "Laffer Curve" — tax rates and tax revenues.
4. Know about the changes the Clinton administration made to the marginal tax rate and the federal budget deficit.
5. Know about the changes the Bush administration made to the marginal tax rate and the federal budget deficit.
6. Know the fiscal policy (expansionary, contractionary, discretionary, nondiscretionary (automatic or "built-in stabilizers) and when to use.
7. Know how the government finances debt and the implications.
8. Know the "problems" in applying fiscal policy: timing, political & "crowding-out".
9. Know the differences among "budget deficit", "balanced budget" and "budget surplus".
10. Define the budget philosophy: "Cyclically Adjusted Budget."
11. Know how large the total U.S. debt is; what are the causes/implications and why we are the "largest debtor nation".
12. Know several "solutions" to the budget deficit and the current policy.
13. Know the three functions of money and be able to give examples.
14. Know what comprises the money (stock) supply and their definitions.
15. Know the difference between "money" and "near monies".
16. Know the difference between "commodity money" and "flat money".
17. Know about the transactions demand and the asset demand for money.
18. Know who sets the supply of money and the impact on impact on interest rates, when the supply of money curve shifts to the right ("Easy Money") and to the left ("Tight Money").
19. Know what happens to interest rates when: D$ > S$ or D$ < S$.
20. Know about the "value of the dollar" and exchange rates.
21. Know about appreciation/depreciation of a currency and the effect on exports.
22. Know the framework of the "Federal Reserve System".
23. Know the definitions of "quasi public" and "banker's banks".
24. Know why the Fed is the "Lender of Last Resort".
25. Know what caused the financial crises of 2007-2009 and 2001.
26. Know about bank balance sheets: definition, terms (required or legal reserves, reserve ratio, total or actual reserves and excess reserves) and how to make changes on the balance sheet, or in a word problem.
27. Know how to do a "Money Multiplier (M$)" problem in the banking system.
28. Know about how much money a single bank can loan out and the effect on the banking system.
29. When the Reserve Ration (R) is ↑ or ↓, what is happening to Excess Reserves (E).
30. Know the Monetary Policy tools (major and minor) and what to do during a recession or during inflation.
31. Know the "Cause-Effect Chain".
32. Know the strengths and weaknesses of Monetary Policy.
33. Know the definitions and impact of the "federal funds rate", "prime rate" and "discount rate".
34. Know how "Easy Money" or "Tight Money" policies effect interest rates, foreign investment and demand for the dollar.
35. Know why both "Fiscal" and "Monetary" policies should be coordinated.
36. Know the "American Recovery and Reinvestment Act of 2009."
37. Discuss the tools the Fed used when the economy did not bounce back from the Great Recession.

38. Discuss ZIRP and how it can create a “zero lower bound problem.”
39. Know why the U.S. dollar appreciates, what happens to the value of the other currency.
40. Know the breakdown of who owns the U.S. debt.

PART II: Problems (10 points each or a total of 20 points)

Answer only TWO of the THREE problems, listed on the exam.
Problem #1: Essay on the “Structure of the Federal Reserve System”.
Problem #2: Define monetary policy tools and know what to do during a recession or inflation in the economy.
Problem #3: Bank Balance Sheet Problem (WB pg. 130, #5).
Problem #4: Foreign Exchange Problem (WB pg. 143).

FORMULA SHEET: WORKBOOK PAGE 148

REVIEW TEXTBOOK, CLASS NOTES (OR WORKSHEET), CANVAS (QUIZZES and PP SLIDES)

Any questions please contact your Instructor or visit our new “Learning Commons” located in the Bankier Library.

GOOD LUCK!

UNIT III

FORMULA SHEET

$$\text{Reserve Ratio (R)} = \frac{\text{Required (Legal) Reserves}}{\text{Demand Deposits}}$$

Required (Legal) Reserves = Reserve Ratio x Demand Deposits

Total (Actual) Reserves = Required Reserves + Excess Reserves

$$\text{Money Multiplier } (M_\$) = \frac{1}{R}$$

Δ Money Supply = Δ Excess Reserves x Money Multiplier ($M_\$$)

$$\text{Price of a good in dollars} = \frac{\text{Price of Good in Foreign Currency}}{\text{Foreign Currency Equivalent of \$1}}$$

M I C R O E C O N O M I C S

Unit I

MICROECONOMICS CONCEPTS OF

"GRAPHING AND INTRODUCTORY TERMS",

THE FIVE FUNDAMENTAL QUESTIONS

AND DEMAND, SUPPLY, AND EQUILIBRIUM

ARE FOUND WITHIN THE MACROECONOMICS

SECTION OF THIS WORKBOOK

"Elasticity"

Chapter Orientation

One way to study the behaviors and decisions of consumers and sellers is through the concept of "elasticity." The study of elasticity is a refinement of supply and demand. Do you think it is important to know your customer's reaction if you raise or lower the price? (It is, if you are interested in maximizing your profits). Price elasticity means "sensitivity" or "responsiveness" to price changes.

When a product is sensitive to a price change, we say the product is "elastic" (a small change in price will greatly effect the quantity). When a product is insensitive to changes in price (substantial price changes cause only a small change in quantity), we say the product is "inelastic". When raising (or lowering the price) brings in the same total revenue, we say the product is "unit elastic", (borderline). Price elasticities are utilized in analyzing consumer response, as well as seller response, in business and in the government. We will examine each of these in depth.

The government measures price elasticity of a product(s) in order to determine which item(s) to tax and which to subsidize, for the greatest impact. Also, when a tax is imposed, the price elasticity of the buyer and the seller, determine which one, or both, will bear the burden of the tax.

In addition, two other types of elasticities are presented in this chapter. They are "income elasticity (Ey)" and "cross elasticity (Exy)". Income elasticity (Ey) measures the responsiveness of a change in demand to a change in one's income. Cross elasticity (Exy) measures the responsiveness of a change in demand for one good to a change in price of a different good.

Learning Objectives

After reading this chapter in the text and completing the following exercises in this concepts book, you should be able to:

1. Define the Law of Demand and the Law of Supply.
2. Determine the equilibrium price and quantity.
3. Define the price elasticity of demand (Ed) and explain the two techniques for calculating (Ed).
4. Calculate the price elasticity of demand (Ed) and determine whether the product is elastic, inelastic, or unit elastic.
5. Define elasticity of supply and compute (Es).
6. Explain how time influences the elasticity of supply.
7. List at least three factors that influence price elasticity.
8. Explain how elasticity of price influences the incidence of an excise tax.
9. Define and calculate income elasticity of demand (Ey).
10. Define and calculate cross elasticity of demand (Exy).

"Elasticity"

Chapter Highlights

I. **Price Elasticity of Demand (E_d)**

A. Definition: the percentage change in quantity demanded resulting from a one percent change in price. It measures consumers' sensitivity to change in price.

B. Price-Elasticity Coefficient and Formula

1. Mathematical formula

$$E_d^* = \frac{\% \blacktriangle \text{ in } Q_d}{\% \blacktriangle \text{ in } P} = \frac{\dfrac{Q_2 - Q_1}{Q_2 + Q_1}}{\dfrac{P_2 - P_1}{P_2 + P_1}}$$

When $E_d > 1$ Elastic (sensitive)
$E_d < 1$ Inelastic (not sensitive)
$E_d = 1$ Unit elastic (borderline)

Q_1 (Old Quantity) P_1 (Old Price)
Q_2 (New Quantity) P_2 (New Price)

*(take the absolute value or omit negative sign in the final answer)

2. The total revenue test (TR Test)
   a. Total revenue = price x quantity demanded
   b. The way total revenue changes with price changes, determines the price elasticity of a product. (See below).

↑P ↓TR or ↓P ↑TR	Elastic (opposite directions)
↑P ↓P = same TR	Unit Elastic (same TR)
↑P ↑TR or ↓P ↓TR	Inelastic (same direction)

C. Characteristics of Elasticity
1. Elasticity varies over different price ranges
2. Elasticity is not measured by the slope

D. Determinants of price elasticity of demand:
1. Number of substitutes
2. Proportion of income
3. Luxuries vs. necessities
4. Time period

E. Applications (examples of price elasticity of demand):
1. Bumper crops (large crop yields)
2. Excise taxes
3. Decriminalization of illegal drugs

II. **Price Elasticity of Supply (Es)**

A. Definition: the percentage change in quantity supplied resulting from a one percentage change in price. It measures the sellers' sensitivity to price changes. The main determinant is the amount of <u>time</u>, which a producer has to respond.

B. Way to measure (Es)

1. Mathematical formula:

$$E_s^* = \frac{\% \blacktriangle \text{ in } Q_s}{\% \blacktriangle \text{ in } P} = \frac{\dfrac{Q_2 - Q_1}{Q_2 + Q_1}}{\dfrac{P_2 - P_1}{P_2 + P_1}}$$

When $E_s > 1$ Elastic (sensitive)
$E_s < 1$ Inelastic (not sensitive)
$E_s = 1$ Unit elastic (borderline)

Q_1 (Old Quantity) P_1 (Old Price)
Q_2 (New Quantity) P_2 (New Price)

*(take the absolute value or omit negative sign in the final answer and be sure to use <u>quantity</u> supplied)

C. Factors that influence price elasticity of supply (E_s)
   1. Market period (immediate)
   2. Short-run
   3. Long-run

D. Applications of price elasticity of supply:
   1. Antiques and reproductions
   2. Volatile gold prices

III. Cross Elasticity and Income of Demand

A. Cross Elasticity of Demand (E_{xy})
   1. Definition: measures the responsiveness of a change in demand for one good to a change in price of another good.
   2. Way to calculate (E_{xy}):
      a. Mathematical formula:

$$E_{xy} = \frac{\%\blacktriangle \text{ in Q Product X}}{\%\blacktriangle \text{ in P Product Y}} = \frac{\dfrac{Q_{X2} - Q_{X1}}{Q_{X2} + Q_{X1}}}{\dfrac{P_{Y2} - P_{Y1}}{P_{Y2} + P_{Y1}}}$$

$E_{xy} > 0$ Substitute good
$E_{xy} < 0$ Complementary good
$E_{xy} = 0$ Independent good

IV. Income Elasticity of Demand (E_y)

1. Definition: measures the responsiveness of a change in demand to a change in income (judges the importance of a product).
2. Way to calculate E_y:
   a. Mathematical formula:

$$E_y = \frac{\%\blacktriangle \text{ in Q}}{\%\blacktriangle \text{ in Y}} = \frac{\dfrac{Q_2 - Q_1}{Q_2 + Q_1}}{\dfrac{Y_2 - Y_1}{Y_2 + Y_1}}$$

$E_y > 1$ superior
$E_y = 0\text{-}1$ normal
$E_y < 0$ inferior

V. Last Word: Elasticity and Pricing Power: Why Different Consumers Pay Different Prices

VI. Web-based Question/Problem, (see your Instructor)

Key Terms

law of demand
law of supply
equilibrium price and quantity
price elasticity
elastic demand/supply
inelastic demand/supply
unit elastic demand/supply
total revenue
elasticity of supply
elasticity coefficient
total revenue test
short-run
long-run
increasing-cost industry
decreasing-cost industry
constant-cost industry
tax incidence
tax shifting
subsidy
income elasticity of demand
cross elasticity of demand
market period

"Elasticity"

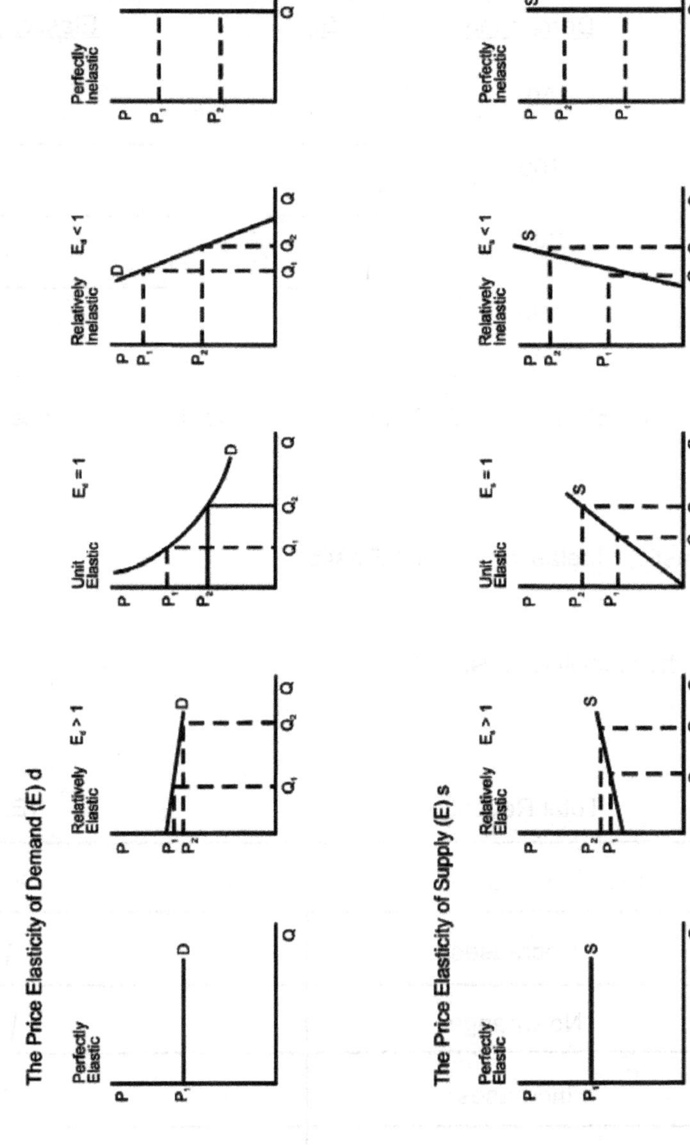

The Spectrum of Elasticity of Price
The Price Elasticity of Demand (E) d
Perfectly Elastic
Relatively Elastic $E_d > 1$
Unit Elastic $E_d = 1$
Relatively Inelastic $E_d < 1$
Perfectly Inelastic
The Price Elasticity of Supply (E) s
Perfectly Elastic
Relatively Elastic $E_s > 1$
Unit Elastic $E_s = 1$
Relatively Inelastic $E_s < 1$
Perfectly Inelastic

"Elasticity"

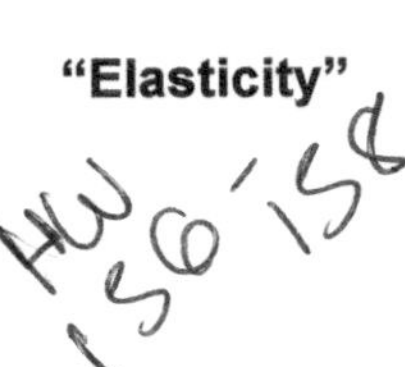

$$E_d = \frac{\frac{Q_2 - Q_1}{Q_2 + Q_1}}{\frac{P_2 - P_1}{P_2 + P_1}}$$

PROBLEMS

1. A GM dealer in Chicago cut her prices by 10 percent and sold 22 percent more cars. What is the Elasticity of Demand (E_d) __2.2__? Label your answer "Elastic," "Inelastic," or "Unit Elastic" __elastic__.

2. Suppose we are given the following demand schedule for a commodity:

Points	Price	Quantity Demanded	Coefficient E_d	(El, Inel, Unit El) Elasticity
A	.20 P_1	50 Q_1		
			2.32	elastic
B	.15 P_2	100 Q_2		
			1.5	elastic
C	.10	200		
			1	unit elastic
D	.05	400		

a. Calculate the (E_d) between points A and B; B and C; C and D. Enter the price elasticity coefficient into the table above.

b. Label your answers "Elastic," "Inelastic," or "Unit Elastic."

3. Fill the blank cell in each of the following rows:

Price	Total Revenue	(E_d)
Increases	Decreases	>1
Decreases	Decreases	<1
Decreases	No Change	=1
increases	Increases	<1
increase	Decreases	>1
Increases	no change	=1

PROBLEMS (continued)

4. Assume that the Fisher family purchases the amounts shown of five commodities before and after Ms. Fisher gets a raise.

Income per Week	Chicken	Peanut Butter	Steak	Hamburger	Bread
	Quantity Purchased per Month (all in pounds)				
$1,200	10.0	5.0	3.0	9.0	5.0
$1,600	11.4	4.5	5.2	11.0	5.0
E_y					

a. Calculate the income elasticity of demand (E_y) for each commodity and enter it in the table above.

b. Which goods (if any) are superior, which (if any) are normal, and which (if any) are inferior — enter it in the table above.

5. After Ms. Fisher received the raise, the price of hamburger, which had been $2.00/lb., went up to $2.10/lb. Ms. Fisher adjusted her purchases of all commodities as shown below.

Price per lb. of hamburger	Chicken	Fish	Ketchup	Tofu	Hamburger Buns (doz.)
	Quantities of Goods Purchased Other Things Remaining the Same				
$2.00	11.4	4.5	3.0	5.0	4.0
$2.10	12.0	4.7	2.5	5.5	3.5
E_{xy}					

a. Calculate the cross elasticity of demand (E_{xy}) for each product and enter it in the table above.

b. Which goods are complements to, which are substitutes for, and which are independent of hamburger—enter it in the table above.

PROBLEMS (continued)

6. Fill in the table below and check to see if the total revenue test and the price elasticity of demand (E_d) yield the same results.

E_s	Quantity Supplied	Price	Quantity Demanded	TR	(El, Inel, Unit El) TR Test	E_d
4.4	100	$12	80	$960	el	1.25
3.5	70	$11	90	$990	el	1.1
6.4	50	$10	100	1000	inel	.9
8.5	25	$9	110	990	inel	.7
	10	$8	120	960		

Total Revenue (TR) = Price x QTY. Demanded

"Elasticity"

Self-Test

1. If the government imposes a tax on a commodity to obtain tax revenues, what type of product should be selected to obtain the highest revenue?
   a. Elastic
   b. Inelastic
   c. Unit elastic
   d. Unable to determine

2. If the government subsidizes a product in order to increase output, it would be the most successful if the supply curve is:
   a. Elastic
   b. Inelastic
   c. Unit elastic
   d. Unable to determine

3. If the price of a product increases, and total revenue decreases then:
   a. the demand for this product must be elastic
   b. the demand for this product must be inelastic
   c. the supply of this product must be elastic
   d. the supply of this product must be inelastic

4. If the cross elasticity for Products B and D is 2.6, then these products are:
   a. complementary
   b. substitutes
   c. independent
   d. normal

5. If the income elasticity for Products J and K is -1.7, then these products are:
   a. inferior
   b. superior
   c. independent
   d. complementary

6. If the price elasticity of demand for products M and N is .8, then these products are:
   a. Elastic
   b. Inelastic
   c. Unit elastic
   d. Substitutes

7. If the price of DVDs falls from $8.00 to $6.00 and the quantity demanded increases from 500 to 750, we can conclude that:
   a. demand is Elastic
   b. demand is Inelastic
   c. demand is Unit elastic
   d. unable to determine

8. If the demand for ice cream is relatively elastic, a 5% decline in the price will:
   a. increase the amount demanded by <u>less</u> than 5%
   b. decrease the amount demanded by <u>less</u> than 5%
   c. increase the amount demanded by <u>more</u> than 5%
   d. decrease the amount demanded by <u>more</u> than 5%

9. If the management of a theater wishes to lower the ticket prices for their plays, they are assuming that the demand for tickets is:
   a. Inelastic
   b. Elastic
   c. Unit elastic
   d. shifting to the right

10. Assume the demand for wine is highly inelastic and the supply is highly elastic, who will bear the burden of the specific tax?
    a. primarily by the consumer
    b. primarily by the seller
    c. shared equally by consumers and sellers
    d. the wholesaler

"Consumer Behavior and Utility Maximization"

Chapter Orientation

We learned from the law of demand, as the price of a good falls, consumers will purchase a higher quantity by substituting the cheaper good for something else (substitution effect). Also, when the price of a good decreases, your income will stretch further due to increased purchasing power (income effect) The opposite occurs when the price increases.

Utility analysis further clarifies the law of demand by explaining consumer decision making. How does the consumer choose among goods, services, and savings? It depends on the price of the product, the consumer's income, and how much he/she wants the product. We assume that every consumer wants to maximize his/her satisfaction. Utility is the ability or power of a good to satisfy a want -- not a need or usefulness. A "util" is a unit by which utility is measured. Determining how large one util of satisfaction is can be a difficult concept to quantify. But if you realize that we choose a starting point (how much satisfaction do you receive when you purchase a new DVD) and then compare the satisfaction you feel when you purchase another item (a movie ticket). The concept is relative to the starting point.

As more and more of a product (or service) is consumed during a certain time period, total satisfaction (total utility) increases but at a slower and slower rate. This means that although your total satisfaction may increase, the extra satisfaction is less. This concept is known as "Diminishing Marginal Utility." The word marginal means a small increment change (or consuming one more).

Given your income, what combination of goods should you purchase to maximize satisfaction (consumer equilibrium)? You will be calculating this optimal solution, using the Utility Maximizing Rule.

Do consumers really use this approach? Do we go into the mall shopping and say to ourselves, "how many "utils" does this pair of shoes give me?" Probably not, however don't you say to yourself, "given the money I have to spend, do I really want these shoes? Maybe I'll buy the shoes; but then again maybe I'll buy a pair sneakers instead -- or can I afford both? The wallets are on sale, maybe I'll purchase one since the price is so reasonable and I can afford it." We may not call this "utility analysis", but we are indeed trying to get the most out of our hard-earned dollar.

Learning Objectives

After studying this chapter in the text, and completing the following exercise in this concept book, you should be able to:

1. Define and distinguish between the income effect and the substitution effect as a result of a price change.
2. Define utility and state how it is measured.
3. Explain the concept of diminishing marginal utility.
4. List the four assumptions that are made in explaining consumer behavior.
5. Define the utility maximizing rule (or consumer equilibrium).
6. Derive a demand curve from data given.
7. Explain how real world applications can be explained by applying the theory of consumer behavior.
8. Calculate the consumer expenditure and surplus in dollars and in utils.

"Consumer Behavior and Utility Maximization"

Chapter Highlights

I. Law of Diminishing Marginal Utility

A. Definition - during a certain time period, as you consume successive units, eventually, the extra satisfaction decreases.

II. Terminology

A. Definition of Utility - The ability or power of a good to satisfy a want. It is measured in "utils" of satisfaction

1. Not usefulness
2. Subjective
3. Difficult to quantify

III. Total Utility and Marginal Utility

A. Total Utility (TU)

1. Definition - the total amount of satisfaction or pleasure a person derives from consuming some specific quantity of a good or service.

B. Marginal Utility (MU)

1. Definition - the extra satisfaction a consumer realizes from an additional unit of the good or service.

C. Relationship of TU and MU

1. When TU is at a maximum point, MU is equal to zero.
2. MU is the slope of the TU curve.

D. Relationship to Demand and Elasticity

1. If successive units yield smaller and smaller amounts of extra (marginal) satisfaction, the consumer will only purchase additional units of a product if the price falls (demand curve).

IV. Theory of Consumer Behavior

A. Consumer Choice and Budget Constraint

1. Rational behavior
2. Preferences
3. Budget constraint
4. Prices

B. Utility Maximizing Rule (or Consumer Equilibrium)

1. Definition - The consumer's money income should be allocated so that the last dollar spent on each product purchased yields the same amount of extra (marginal) utility.
2. Marginal Utility per Dollar
   a. To maximize your satisfaction, allocate your income such that

$$\frac{MUA}{PA} = \frac{MUB}{PB} = \frac{MU\$\ Saved}{P\$ = \$1}$$

When $\frac{MUA}{PA} > \frac{MUB}{PB}$ Choose more of "A"

3. Decision-making process
4. Word problems and table format

V. Utility Maximization and the Demand Curve

A. Deriving the Demand Schedule and Curve

B. Substitution and Income Effects (revisited)

1. Income effect (change in purchasing power)
2. Substitution effect (replace more expensive good with a cheaper good)

VI. Calculation of Consumer Expenditure and Consumer Surplus (in dollars and in utils)-See below

Consumer Expenditure and Surplus

DEMAND CURVE

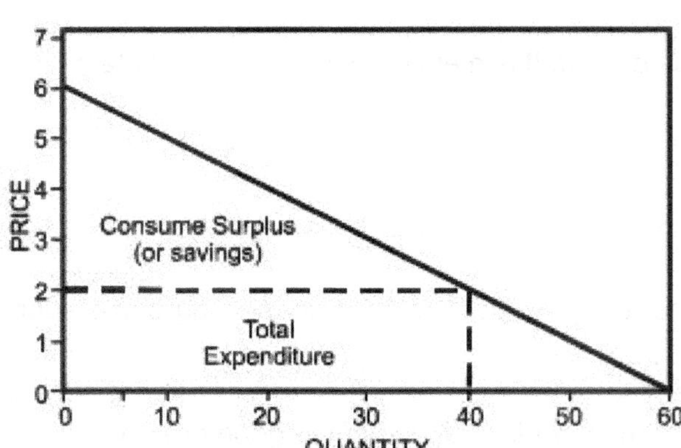

UTILITY CURVE

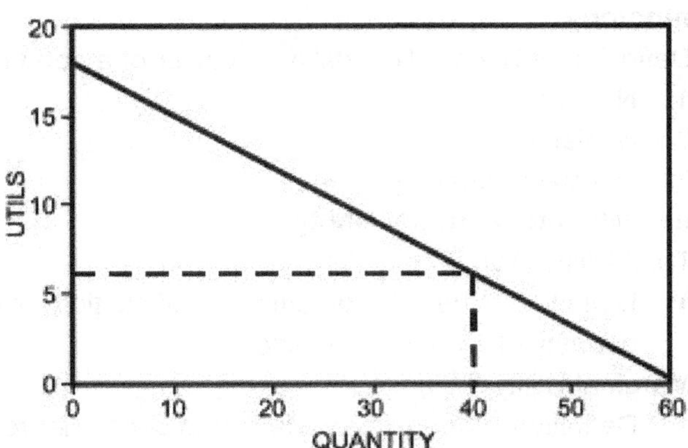

VII. Applications and Extensions

A. iPads
   1. Preference Changes
   2. iPad Prices

B. The Diamond - Water Paradox
   1. Diamonds (a nonessential) is priced much higher than water (an essential to life).
   2. Water is in great supply as compared to diamonds.
   3. Water with its low price causes consumers to purchase a large quantity, the opposite holds true for diamonds.

C. Opportunity Cost and the Value of Time
   1. Time is a valuable economic resource.
   2. Time must be taken into account (the retiree has more time than a corporate executive).

D. Medical Care Purchases
   1. Americans who have health insurance usually pay a fixed premium and 20%. When ill they will purchase lots of medical services (they only pay 20%)

E. Cash and Noncash Gifts
   1. Noncash transfers may be less efficient than cash transfers because the specified user may not match the recipient's preferences.
   2. This logic also applies to noncash private gifts to others.

"Consumer Behavior and Utility Maximization"

VIII. Last Word: Criminal Behavior
IX. Appendix: Indifference Curve Analysis
XI Web-based Question/Problem (see your Instructor)

Key Terms

income effect
substitution effect
utility
utils
law of diminishing marginal utility
marginal utility
total utility
prospect theory
anchoring
endowment effect
behavorial economics
budget restraint
consumer optimum mix
utility maximizing rule
consumer expenditure
consumer surplus
loss averse
framing effect
mental accounting

"Consumer Behavior and Utility Maximization"

PROBLEMS

1. a. Fill in the following table:

Number of protein bars consumed per week	Total utility (in utils)	Marginal utility (in utils)
0	0	
		________
1	5	
		________
2	12	
		________
3	20	
		________
4	26	
		________
5	31	
		________
6	34	
		________
7	33	
		________
8	30	

b. Construct a graph of total utility (top half of graph paper).

c. Construct a graph of marginal utility (bottom half of graph paper).

d. When TU is at a maximum, MU is ____________.

e. MU is the ___________ of the TU curve.

$$MU^* = \frac{\blacktriangle TU}{\blacktriangle Q}$$

* graph at the midpoints

PROBLEMS (continued)

CONSUMER EQUILIBRIUM

Definition: To maximize your utility allocate, so MU per dollar spent on two commodities is equal. (Don't spend more $ than you earn).

Rule I: $\frac{MUa}{Pa} = \frac{MUb}{Pb} = \frac{MU\$ \text{ (saved)}}{P\$}$

Rule II: Spend and/or save all of your income

2. Two goods are available, pizza and suntan lotion, and money has no utility. A pizza pie costs $3 and suntan lotion costs $2 per bottle. Your income is $35. How should you allocate your income?

#Pies/Bottles	MU Pizza	÷3	MU Lotion	÷2
4	24	8/,	20	10 per 1
5	21	7	18	9
6	18	6	16	8
7	15	5	10	5
8	12	4	8	4
9	9	3	4	2
10	3	1	2	1

3. Assume that it is the day before payday, and all you have in your wallet is $10.00. You decide to meet some friends at a local happy-hour. A glass of wine costs $2.00/glass; a mug of beer costs $.50/mug; and a glass of soda costs $3.00 each. The last column—MU$ shows your MU for savings. To maximize your utility, what is your optimal combination? How much will you save?

Units/$	MU Wine	÷2	MU Beer	÷.5	MU Soda	÷3	MU $ (saved)	÷1
1	20	10	10	20	3	1	14	14
2	16	8	8	16	1.5	.5	12	12
3	10	5	6	12	0	0	10	10
4	6	3	4	8	-1.5	-.5	8	8
5	2	1	2	4	-3	-1	6	6

EXHIBIT I

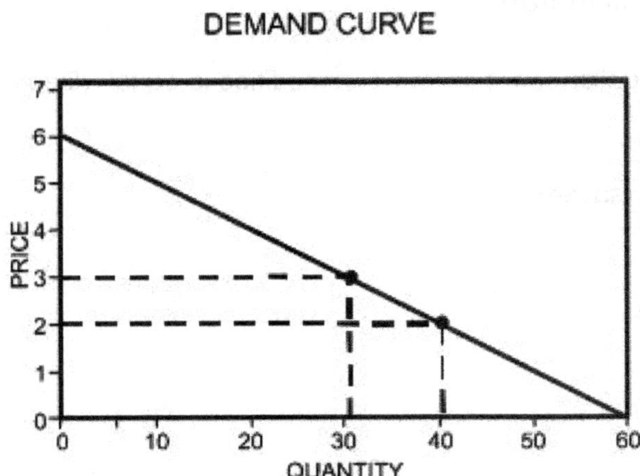

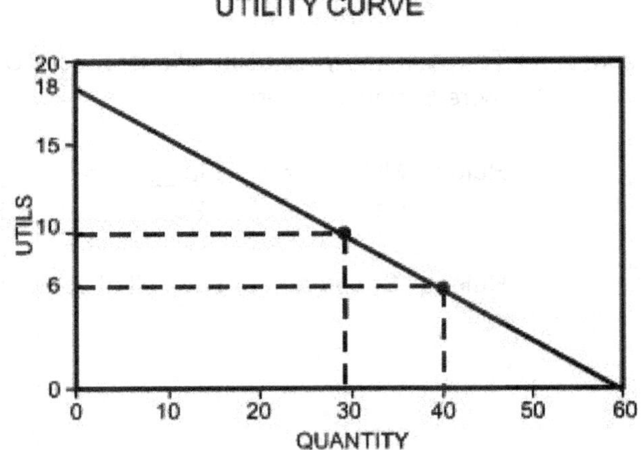

4. Answer the following questions, based upon Exhibit I.

   a. What is the total expenditure (in dollars and in utils) if the consumer purchases 40?

   b. What is the consumer surplus (in dollars and in utils) if the consumer purchases 40?

   c. Determine the total expenditure (in dollars and in utils) and the consumer surplus (in dollars and in utils) if the consumer purchases 30 units.

Formulas:

Area of a rectangle = LW

Area of a triangle = ½ (BH)

"Consumer Behavior and Utility Maximization"

Self-Test

Answer questions 1 - 4 based upon Exhibit II (below).

EXHIBIT II

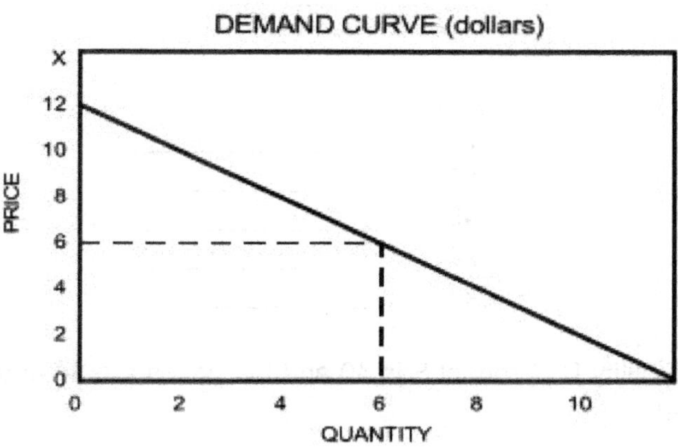

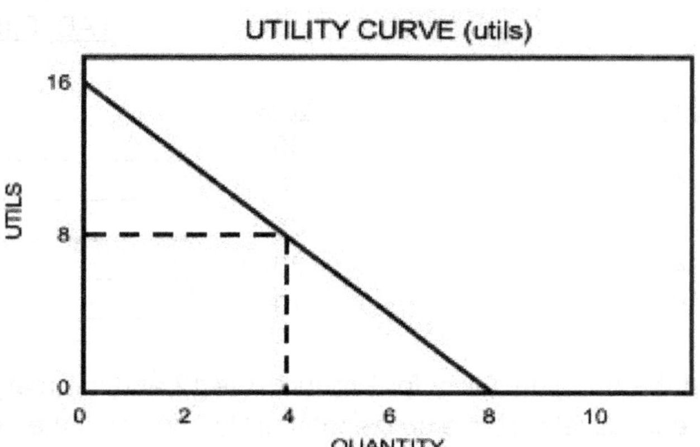

1. At a quantity of 6, the consumer expenditure in dollars is:
   a. $24
   b. $36
   c. $48
   d. $30
2. At a quantity of 6, the consumer surplus in dollars is:
   a. $96
   b. $108
   c. $18
   d. $36
3. At a quantity of 4, the consumer expenditure in utils is:
   a. 32 utils
   b. 24 utils
   c. 48 utils
   d. 16 utils
4. At a quantity of 4, the consumer surplus in utils is:
   a. 36 utils
   b. 24 utils
   c. 32 utils
   d. 16 utils

Self-Test (continued)

5. Assume your income is $48.00 and the price of product A is $5.00 each and the price of product B is $7.00 each. Assume saving money has no utility (satisfaction). What is your optimal combination (mix) to maximize your utility?

TABLE II

Units	MUa		MUb	
1	60		77	
2	50		56	
3	35		49	
4	20		28	
5	10		21	

6. If the marginal utility for Product A is 12 and the marginal utility for Product S is 40 and the prices are $4 and $10 respectively. To maximize total utility, the consumer would:
   a. buy more of Product A
   b. buy more of Product S
   c. buy equal amounts of each product
   d. unable to determine

7. When total utility is at a maximum; marginal utility is:
   a. increasing
   b. proportional
   c. zero
   d. unable to determine

8. We define utility as:
   a. how much we need a good
   b. how useful we find a good
   c. how much satisfaction a good gives us
   d. what the price of the product is

9. The income effect states that:
   a. as income increases, we purchase more goods and services
   b. when the price of a good falls, we purchase more of the cheaper good
   c. we replace the expensive good with the cheaper good
   d. our purchasing power is affected by changes in price

10. The "law of diminishing marginal utility" is defined:
    a. as the price of a product increases, we buy a smaller quantity
    b. as the price of a product decreases, we buy a larger quantity
    c. that at some point, we start experiencing less and less extra satisfaction from additional units of a product
    d. once we purchase a product, we are less and less happy with it and want to purchase something else

REVIEW SHEET: UNIT 1 MICROECONOMICS

ECON 106 – UNIT I REVIEW

Be sure to bring a #2 pencil, graph paper and calculator!

PART I: 40 Multiple Choice questions (2 points each or a total of 80 points)

1. Know a definition of "Economics".
2. Know the difference between Macro and Micro Economics.
3. Know how to determine direct and inverse relationships (table and graph).
4. Be able to calculate the slope of a straight line.
5. Know what is meant by "ceteris paribus".
6. Know the Five Fundamental Questions in Economics.
7. Know the definition of "opportunity cost".
8. Know what is meant by the "Fallacy of Composition".
9. Know what the demand and supply curves and schedules illustrate.
10. Know the difference between and what would cause a movement along the demand and supply curves, and a shifting of the curves (emphasis on word problems and graphs — superior/normal, inferior, substitute and complementary goods).
11. Know what the "Law of Demand" and the "Law of Supply" state.
12. From a graph of supply and demand, calculate the surplus or shortage.
13. Know where a price ceiling and a price floor are located in relation to the equilibrium price and explain the reasoning behind them.
14. Know how to graphically determine changes in equilibrium price and quantity.
15. Know what "elasticity coefficient" means.
16. Be able to calculate elasticity coefficients and interpret what the value means for PRICE, INCOME AND CROSS ELASTICITIES.
17. Know the determinants of elasticity for both demand and supply.
18. Know how to calculate price elasticity of demand using both the formula method and the "TR TEST".
19. Know about elasticity and taxes (and graphically determine whether the buyer or the seller must bear the greatest burden of the tax).
20. Know about the "Income and Substitution Effects".
21. Know the definition of "Utility".
22. Know about the "Law of Diminishing Marginal Utility" and calculate.
23. Know how to calculate "Consumer Equilibrium" utilizing "utils", prices and income) in a word problem or table.
24. Be able to determine whether a consumer should buy more or less of a product to maximize their utility.
25. Know how to calculate "consumer expenditure" and "consumer surplus" in dollars and in utils of satisfaction.

REVIEW SHEET: UNIT 1 MICROECONOMICS

<u>PART II:</u> Problems (10 points each or a total of 20 points)

Answer only <u>TWO</u> of the THREE problems, listed on the exam.
Problem #1: Supply and Demand (Example: Workbook page 27, #1)
Problem #2: Elasticity Table (Example: Workbook page 158, #6)
Problem #3: Utility Table (Example: Workbook page 165, #3).

FORMULA SHEET: WORKBOOK PAGE 171
ELASTICITY REVIEW SHEET: WORKBOOK PAGE 172

<u>REVIEW TEXTBOOK, CLASS NOTES, (ON WORKSHEET), WORKBOOK, CANVAS (QUIZZES AND PP SLIDES)</u>

Any questions please contact your Instructor or visit our new "Learning Commons" located in the Bankier Library.

GOOD LUCK!!

REVIEW SHEET: UNIT 1 MICROECONOMICS

FORMULA SHEET

$$\text{SLOPE} = \frac{\Delta Y}{\Delta X} = \frac{\text{rise}}{\text{run}} = \frac{Y_2 - Y_1}{X_2 - X_1}$$

$$E_d = \frac{\dfrac{Q_2 - Q_1}{Q_2 + Q_1}}{\dfrac{P_2 - P_1}{P_2 + P_1}} = E_s$$ #2 elasticity table

$$E_y = \frac{\dfrac{Q_2 - Q_1}{Q_2 + Q_1}}{\dfrac{Y_2 - Y_1}{Y_2 + Y_1}}$$ income

$$E_{xy} = \frac{\dfrac{Qx_2 - Qx_1}{Qx_2 + Qx_1}}{\dfrac{Py_2 - Py_1}{Py_2 + Py_1}}$$

$$MU = \frac{\Delta TU}{\Delta Q} \qquad \frac{MUa}{Pa} = \frac{MUb}{Pb} = \frac{MU\$ \text{ saved}}{P\$ = \$1}$$

$TR = (P) X (Q_d)$

Area of Triangle = 1/2 (BH)

Area of Rectangle = LW

REVIEW SHEET: UNIT 1 MICROECONOMICS

Elasticity Review Sheet

I. Price Elasticity of Demand (E_d)

A. Definition: the percentage change in quantity demanded, resulting from a one percent change in price.

B. Ways to calculate (Ed):

1. $E_d* = \frac{\% \blacktriangle \text{ in } Q_d}{\% \blacktriangle \text{ in } P} = \frac{\frac{Q_2 - Q_1}{Q_2 + Q_1}}{\frac{P_2 - P_1}{P_2 + P_1}}$

When $E_d > 1$ Elastic (sensitive)
$E_d < 1$ Inelastic (not sensitive)
$E_d = 1$ Unit elastic (borderline)

*take the absolute value (or omit negative sign) in the final answer

2. The total revenue test (TR test)

Total revenue = price x quantity demanded = (P x Q_d)

↑P ↓TR or ↓P ↑TR	Elastic (opposite directions)
↑P ↓P = same TR	Unit Elastic (same TR)
↑P ↑TR or ↓P ↓TR	Inelastic (same direction)

II. Price Elasticity of Supply (Es)

A. Definition: the percentage change in quantity supplied resulting from a one percentage change in price.

B. Way to measure (Es)

$E_s* = \frac{\% \blacktriangle \text{ in } Q_s}{\% \blacktriangle \text{ in } P} = \frac{\frac{Q_2 - Q_1}{Q_2 + Q_1}}{\frac{P_2 - P1}{P2 + P1}}$

When $E_s > 1$ Elastic (sensitive)
$E_s < 1$ Inelastic (not sensitive)
$E_s = 1$ Unit elastic (borderline)

*(take the absolute value) or omit negative sign in the final answer
be sure to use quantity supplied

III. Income Elasticity of Demand (E_y)

A. Definition: measures the responsiveness of a change in demand to a change in income.

B. Way to measure (E_y):

$E_y = \frac{\% \blacktriangle \text{ in } Q}{\% \blacktriangle \text{ in } Y} = \frac{\frac{Q_2 - Q_1}{Q_2 + Q_1}}{\frac{Y_2 - Y_1}{Y_2 + Y_1}}$

$E_y > 1$ superior
$E_y = 0\text{-}1$ normal
$E_y < 0$ inferior

IV. Cross Elasticity of Demand (E_{xy})

A. Definition: measures the responsiveness of a change in demand for one good to a change in price of another good.

B. Way to calculate (E_{xy}):

$E_{xy} = \frac{\% \blacktriangle \text{ in Q Product X}}{\% \blacktriangle \text{ in P Product Y}} = \frac{\frac{QX_2 - QX_1}{QX_2 + QX_1}}{\frac{PY_2 - PY_1}{PY_2 + PY}}$

$E_{xy} > 0$ Substitute good
$E_{xy} < 0$ Complementary good
$E_{xy} = 0$ Independent good

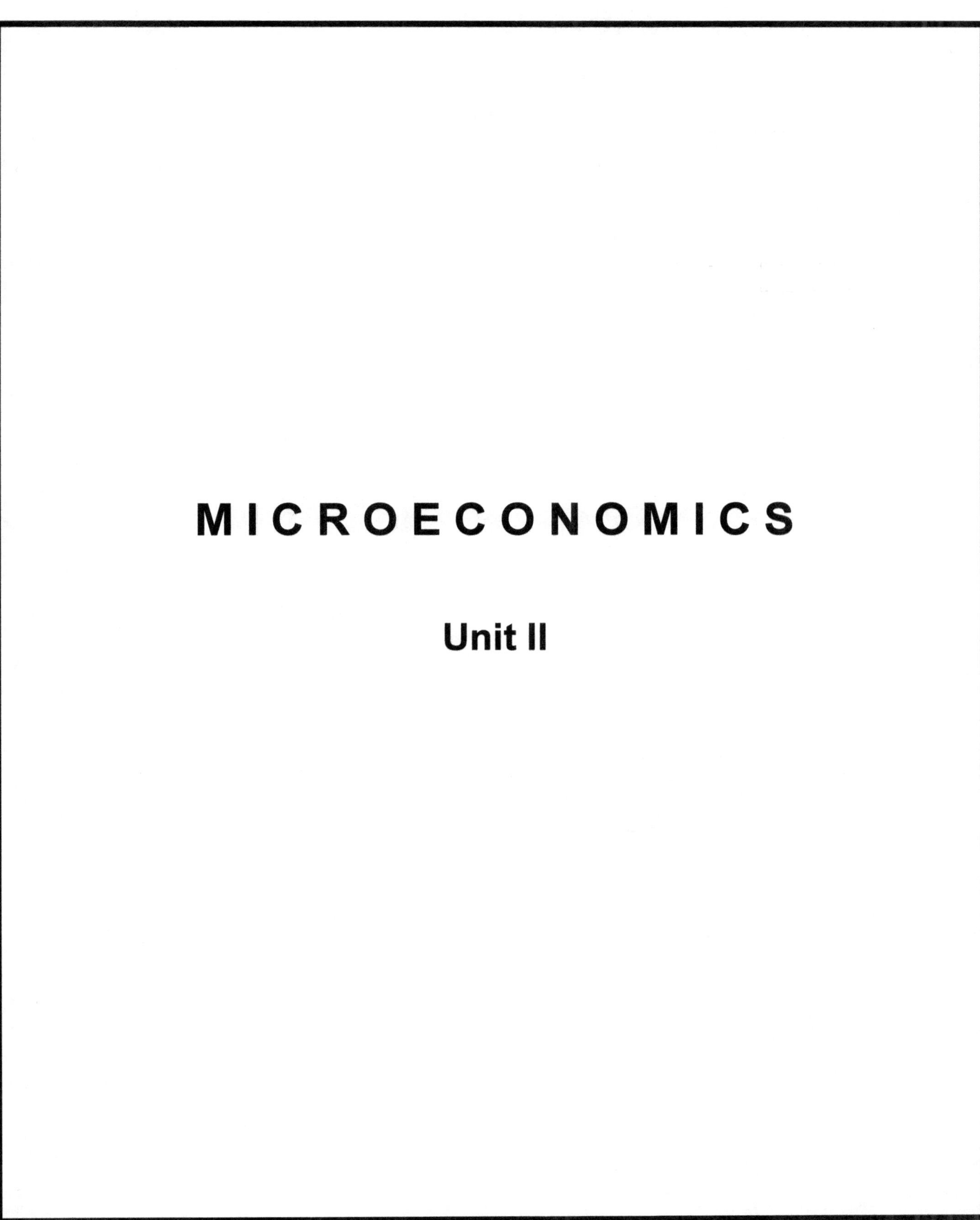
MICROECONOMICS
Unit II

"Businesses and the Costs of Production"

Chapter Orientation

Economists have long been interested in the market and in what determines value. Since market prices reflect value, they seek to analyze the facts that influence the relative market prices of goods and services. These prices also give us information about the allocative efficiency of our economy.

The market price is determined by the forces of supply and demand. In previous chapters, factors which influence consumer demand were examined. This concept focuses on the seller or supplier. Supply was defined previously as the amount of a commodity that the sellers are willing and able to make available for sale, at alternative prices, during a certain time period, all other things remaining the same.

Supply depends upon the costs of production (cost is a sacrifice, whether tangible or intangible). Economists view costs quite differently from expenses in accounting, because they include opportunity cost (value of the best alternative -- what you gave up). We will be computing and graphing costs in both the short-run and long-run.

For the most part, the goal of business is to maximize profit. Profit is the difference between total revenue (price x quantity) received by a firm and the total costs (fixed plus variable) incurred. As a profit maximizer, a business needs to know when diminishing returns begins and where the most efficient level of production is located.

This concept serves as a foundation for analyzing the four markets structures -- pure competition, pure monopoly, monopolistic competition, and oligopoly. Therefore, it is extremely important that you have a clear understanding of all the terms, and be able to explain the shape of each of the cost curves in both the short-run and the long-run.

Learning Objectives

After reading this chapter in the text, and completing the following exercises in this concepts book, you should be able to:

1. Define opportunity cost (economic cost).
2. Distinguish between implicit and explicit costs.
3. Explain the difference between normal profit and economic profit.
4. Explain why normal profit is a cost but economic profit is not a cost.
5. Define the law of diminishing returns.
6. Distinguish between the short-run and the long-run in economics.
7. Using the Input/Output Model, compute and graph average product (AP) and marginal product (MP)
8. Explain the relationship between MP and AP.
9. Define the total costs: fixed costs, (TFC), variable costs, (TVC) and total costs, (TC). Graph each curve and explain the shape of each curve.
10. Define the average costs: average fixed costs (AFC), average variable cost (AVC), average total cost (ATC).Graph each curve and explain the shape of each curve.
11. Define the marginal cost curve (MC) and graph an MC curve and explain its shape. Compare the MP curve with the MC curve.
12. Compute TFC, TVC, TC, AFC, AVC, ATC, and MC when given the necessary data.
13. State the relationship between AVC and AP.
14. Explain the shape of the long-run average total cost curve based upon economies and diseconomies of scale.
15. Indicate the relationship between economies and diseconomies of scale and the size and number of firms (competitiveness) in an industry.
16. Discuss how the "planning curve" in the long-run determines the most efficient level of production.

"Businesses and the Costs of Production"

Chapter Highlights

I. Economic Costs

A. Definition of opportunity cost -- the value of the benefit that is given up to produce one economic good as opposed to another.

B. Definition of economic cost -- payments a firm must make to secure resources.

1. Explicit costs -- tangible expenses; out-of-pocket expenditures such as wages, materials, telephone, etc.
2. Implicit costs -- nonexpenditures which include a "normal" profit such as foregone wages, interest, rental income, etc.
3. Economic Cost = Explicit Cost + Implicit Cost

C. When the total revenue received by a firm, equals the economic cost, a normal profit has been realized.

1. A normal profit is a cost, because without it, resources cannot be secured.

D. Economic (pure) profits are surplus or excess profits.

1. Economic profits are not a cost because they are over-and-above what is needed to secure the resource.
2. Economic profits differ from accounting profits because economic profits include implicit costs.
3. Total Revenue

- Explicit Cost	or	Total Revenue
Accounting Profit		- Economic Costs
- Implicit Cost		Economic Profit*
Economic Profit		

* when economic profit equals zero, a normal profit has been realized.

E. Short-run vs. long-run costs

1. The short-run refers to a period of time where at least one cost is fixed and there is not enough time to change plant capacity.
2. The long-run refers to a period of time where all costs are variable including plant capacity.

II. Short-run Production Relationships

A. Law of Diminishing Returns -- a property of a production process which states that when one factor is fixed, adding successive units of a variable resource will result in declining output (returns) beyond some point.

B. The "Production Function" or "Input/Output Model

1. Total product (TP)--combining output at each level of input.
2. Marginal product (MP) -- how much output was achieved by adding one more worker (input).

$$MP^* = \frac{\blacktriangle TP}{\blacktriangle \text{ units of labor}}$$

* graphed at the midpoints

3. Average product (AP) -- shows the output per worker (per unit)

$$AP = \frac{TP}{\text{units of labor}}$$

4. MP is the slope of the TP curve. When TP is at a maximum, MP is equal to zero.

5. When MP is greater than AP, AP is rising; when MP is less than AP, AP is falling; therefore, MP intersects AP at its maximum point (See below).

Figure 1
"The Production Function"
The Law of Diminishing Returns

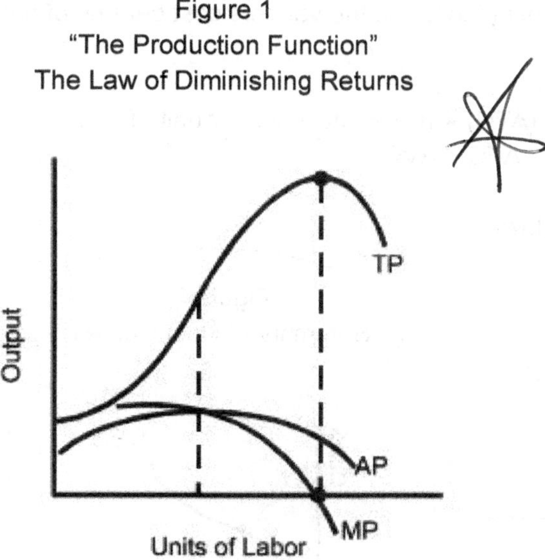

III. Short-run Production Costs

A. Fixed, Variable, and Total Costs

1. Total Fixed costs (TFC) or "sunk costs" are those costs that do not change with output -- starts at zero quantity (overhead costs).
2. Total Variable costs (TVC) are those costs that vary or change with output (operating costs). In the beginning, variable costs will increase at a decreasing rate (volume), but at some point (diminishing returns), variable costs will switch to an increasing rate.
3. Total cost (TC) is the sum of fixed and variable costs at each level of output.
   TC = TFC + TVC
   Once TFC is satisfied, TC resembles the TVC curve. (See total curves next page).

B. Average or "per unit" Costs
   1. Average Fixed Cost (AFC) -- is the fixed cost per unit of output.
      $\frac{TFC}{Q}$
   2. Average Variable Cost (AVC) -- is the variable cost per unit of output.
      $\frac{TVC}{Q}$
   3. Average Total Cost (ATC) -- is the total cost per unit of output.
      $ATC = \frac{TC}{Q} = AFC + AVC$

(see average curves below)

Figure 2
Summary of Cost Curves

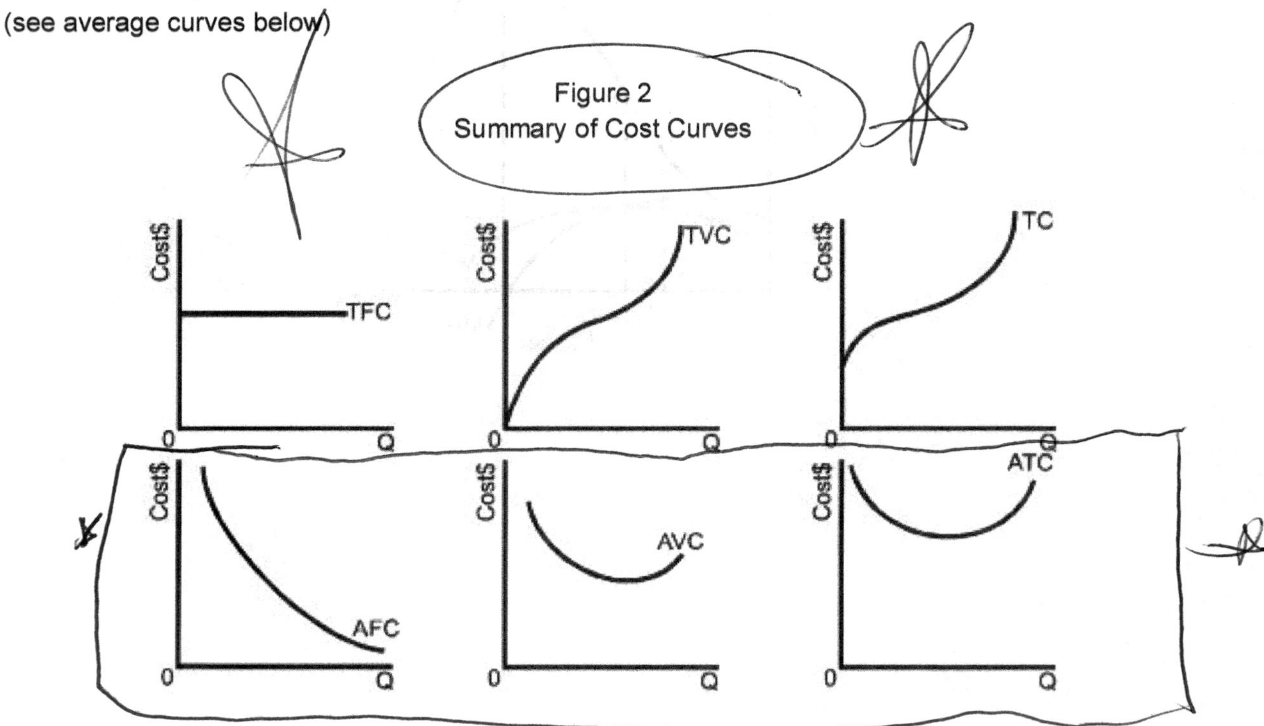

C. Marginal Cost
   1. Definition -- marginal cost is the extra cost incurred in the production of one more unit of output.
      $\frac{\Delta TC}{\Delta Q}$
   2. The marginal cost curve (MC) intersects both ATC and AVC at their minimum points (when the cost of adding one more unit is less than the average, it pulls the average down; when it is greater than the average, it pulls the average up).
   3. The MC curve reflects the law of diminishing returns.
   4. The MC curve is a mirror reflection of the marginal product (MP) curve -- when MP is increasing, MC is decreasing and vice versa.

5. The "most efficient level of production" is where MC = ATC or where ATC is at its minimum point, (at 15 units in Figure 3).
   (See relationships below).

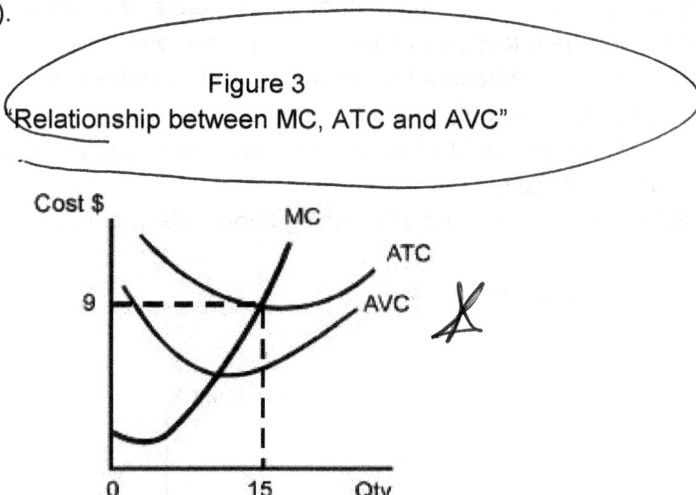

Figure 3
"Relationship between MC, ATC and AVC"

D. Shifting the Cost Curves
   1. Reasons: changes in resource prices or technology will cause costs to change and cost curves to shift.

SHORT-RUN PRODUCTION COSTS

Total	Average	Marginal
Total Product (TP)	Average Product (AP)	Marginal Product (MP)
Total Fixed Cost (TFC)	Average Fixed Cost (AFC)	Marginal Cost (MC)
Total Variable Cost (TVC)	Average Variable Cost (AVC)	
Total Cost (TC)	Average Total Cost (ATC)	

Formulas for the Short-run Production Costs

TP (given) $\quad AP = \frac{TP}{\text{Units of Resource}}$ $\quad MP = \frac{\blacktriangle TP}{\blacktriangle \text{Units of Resources}}$

TFC = TC - TVC $\quad AFC = \frac{TFC}{Q}$

TVC = TC - TFC $\quad AVC = \frac{TVC}{Q}$ $\quad MC = \frac{\blacktriangle TC}{\blacktriangle Q}$

TC = TFC + TVC $\quad ATC = \frac{TC}{Q} = AFC + AVC$

IV. Long-run Production Costs

A. Definition -- the long-run refers to a period of time in which the firm can vary all inputs, as well as plant capacity, in order to produce at the most efficient (profitable) level of output.

1. The long-run average total cost curve (LRATC) is an "envelope" of all the short-run curves for the firm.
   a. The LRATC curve indicates the minimum cost possible (by varying all inputs, including firm size) to produce any given output.
   b. The LRATC curve is U-shaped over an entire range of output, because of economies and diseconomies of scale.
   c. The LRATC curve is the firm's "planning curve". (See below).

Figure 4 Figure 5

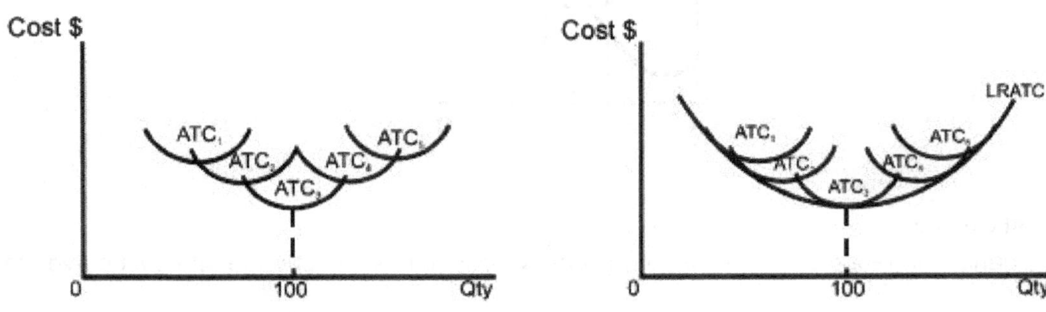

B. Economies and diseconomies of scale

1. Definition -- refers to the effects on unit costs for a firm, as it increases its scale or plant size over the long-run (see Figure 6).
   a. Economies of scale imply decreasing units costs as plant size increases due to increased specialization (labor and management); technological factors (capital goods) and financial advantages (discounts given to larger buyers of resources).
   b. Diseconomies of scale imply increasing unit costs as plant size increases, primarily due to the managerial problems encountered.
   c. Constant returns to scale imply that unit costs stay the same as plant size expands.
2. The LRATC curve can have different shapes (slopes), depending upon the industry. The shape of the LRATC curve can be significant in determining the structure and competitiveness of an industry.

C. MES and Industry Structure

1. The minimum efficient scale (MES) is the smallest level of output which a firm can minimize long-run average total costs.
2. Natural Monopoly - a market situation in which ATC is minimized when only one firm produces the particular good or service.

Figure 6

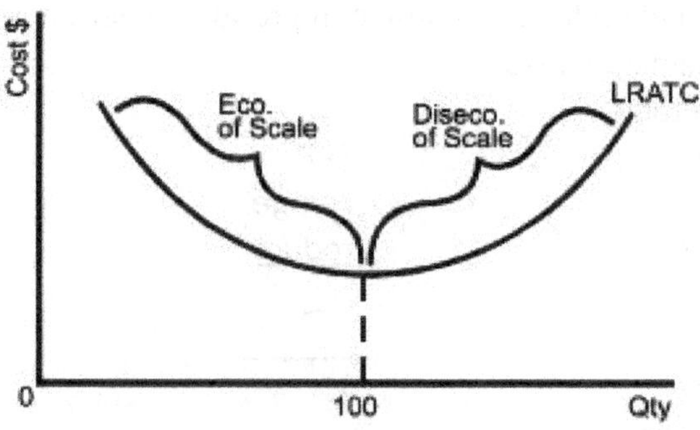

V. Last Word: 3-D Printers

VI. Web-based Question (see your Instructor)

<u>Key Terms</u>

economic cost
explicit cost
implicit cost
accounting profit
economic profit
normal profit
tangible
intangible
short-run
long-run
Law of diminishing returns
production function
total product (TP)
average product (AP)
marginal product (MP)
fixed cost(TFC)
variable cost (TVC)
total cost (TC)
average fixed cost (AFC)
average variable cost (AVC)
average total cost (ATC)
marginal cost (MC)
planning curve (LRATC)
economies of scale
diseconomies of scale
by-product
minimum efficient scale (MES)
natural monopoly

"Businesses and the Costs of Production"

PROBLEMS

1. You are given the following information for a firm that can produce different levels of output by varying the amount of one input, all other inputs remaining constant.
Fill in the last two columns of the table.

(Q) Units of Resource	(TP) Total Product	(AP) Average Product	(MP) Marginal Product
0	0		
1	3		
2	8		
3	15		
4	20		
5	23		
6	20		

a. Plot all three product curves.

b. Answer the following questions with reference to the graphs you have drawn:

(1) When marginal product is greater than average product, average product is (rising/constant/falling).

(2) When marginal product is less than average product, average product is (rising/constant/falling).

$$AP = \frac{TP}{Q}$$

$$MP = \frac{\Delta TP}{\Delta Q}$$

(3) Label the three phases on the graph and on the table.

PROBLEMS (continued)

2. The Fiasco Company is a perfectly competitive firm whose costs of production in the short-run are as follows:
   a. Total Fixed Costs are $14 per day

Output per day (Q)	TFC	TVC	TC	ATC	AVC	MC
0		0				
1		2				
2		4				
3		6				
4		10				
5		16				
6		24				
7		34				
8		46				
9		60				
10		76				

   b. Fill in the chart above and on graph paper plot and label the average variable cost (AVC), average total cost (ATC) and marginal cost (MC) curves.

   c. How would you interpret the vertical distance between the average total cost and the average variable cost curves?

   d. Why does average total cost (ATC) decline first, and then start rising?

   e. Where is the most efficient level of production? ____________

*Formulas are on the next page (Problem 3)

PROBLEMS (continued)

3. Assume a firm has Total Fixed Costs (TFC) of $80 and Total Variable Costs (TVC) as indicated below:

QTY.	TFC	TVC	TC	AFC	AVC	ATC	MC
0		$0					
1		110					
2		150					
3		180					
4		220					
5		270					
6		340					
7		440					
8		580					

a. Complete the table above.

b. On graph paper, plot and label the AVC, ATC, and MC curves on one graph.

c. What is the most efficient level of production? ______________

d. Shade in the AFC area (on graph).

$TC = TFC + TVC$

$AVC = \frac{TVC}{Q}$

$MC^* = \frac{\blacktriangle TC}{\blacktriangle Q}$

$AFC = \frac{TFC}{Q}$

$ATC = \frac{TC}{Q} = AFC + AVC$

*graphed at midpoint

"Businesses and the Costs of Production"

Self-Test

1. Implicit costs:
   a. are utilized by accountants to calculate total expenses
   b. are regarded as costs by accountants and by economists
   c. plus explicit costs are equal to economic cost
   d. are an expenditures cost
2. A firm will, in the short-run, incur:
   a. only fixed costs
   b. both fixed and variable costs
   c. only variable costs
   d. only costs related to expanding plant capacity
3. The difference between the average total cost (ATC) and total cost (TC) concepts is that:
   a. TC refers to both fixed and variable cost, while ATC refers to variable cost only
   b. TC refers to losses, while ATC is equivalent to price
   c. TC is the sum of all costs incurred in the production process, while ATC is the cost per unit
   d. TC is a long-run concept, while ATC is a short-run concept

Answer the following four questions based upon Table I below:

Table I

Output	TFC	TVC	TC	AFC	AVC	ATC	MC
0			100				
1			112				______
2			116				______
3			121				______
4			132				______
5			145				______

4. When output increases from 2 to 3, marginal costs is:
   a. 2 c. 5
   b. 4 d. 11
5. When output increases from 4 to 5, marginal cost is:
   a. 4 c. 11
   b. 5 d. 13
6. At an output level of 4, ATC is:
   a. 58 c. 33
   b. 29 d. 112
7. At an output level of 5, AFC is:
   a. 20 c. 50
   b. 25 d. 100

Self Test – (continued)

Figure 7

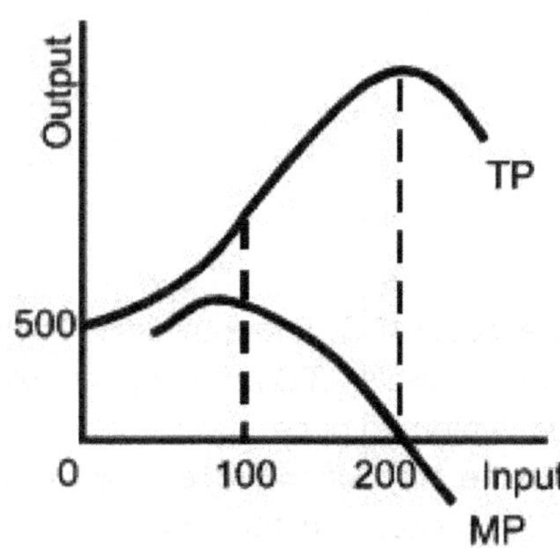

8. In Figure 7 (above), diminishing returns first occurs at ________ and negative returns first occurs at ________.
   a. 0; 100
   b. 100; 200
   c. 100; 0
   d. 200; 100

9. The "most efficient" level of production is where:
   a. MC equals ATC
   b. per unit costs are at their minimum
   c. ATC is at its lowest point
   d. all of the above.

10. Economies and diseconomies of scale help to explain the shape of the:
   a. MC curve
   b. MR curve
   c. AFC curve
   d. LRATC curve

Self Test – (continued)

Figure 8

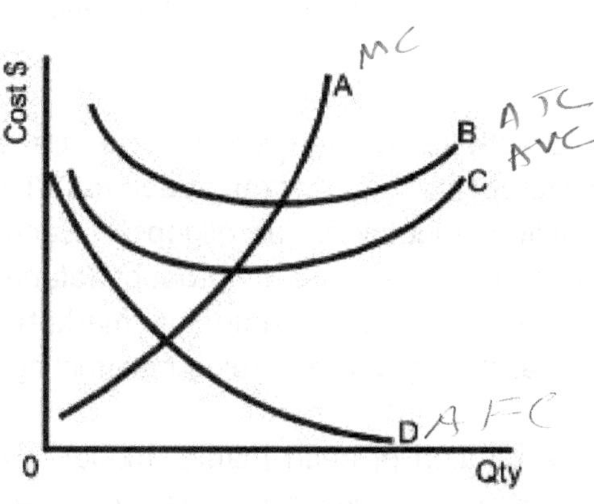

11. In Figure 8 (above), curves A, B, C, and D represent the:
    a. MC, AVC, ATC, and AFC curves respectively.
    b. AFC, AVC, ATC, and MC curves respectively.
    c. MC, ATC, AVC, and AFC curves respectively.
    d. AVC, ATC, AFC, and MC curves respectively.

12. Average fixed cost decreases with increased output because:
    a. output rises as more costs are incurred
    b. total fixed cost is divided by larger and larger numbers
    c. it is always cheaper to produce on a larger scale
    d. none of the above

13. Which of the following would not represent a fixed cost to a firm in the short run?
    a. the rent owed on the plant
    b. salary of the company president
    c. mortgage payments on the land
    d. overtime pay to machine operators

14. A technology company has an output of 1.5 million cell phones in the short-run. During the same period its total variable cost is $450,000. Its average variable cost for a cell phone is:
    a. Three dollars
    b. Thirty cents
    c. Thirty dollars
    d. Three cents

15. The relationship between MC and MP is:
    a. when MP is increasing, MC is increasing
    b. when MP is decreasing, MC is decreasing
    c. when MP is increasing, MC is decreasing
    d. there is no real relationship

ɿɪentation

Now that we have the foundation to calculate the costs of production and an understanding of consumer demand, we can now bring the sellers and the consumers together under various market structures to see how price and output are determined.

Although no two industries are exactly alike (and since there are so many to examine), economists have developed certain basic models or stereotypes of market structures. The four basic market models are: pure competition, pure monopoly, monopolistic competition, and oligopoly. Each model will be analyzed by looking at the number of firms in the market (competition); the type of product (standard or differentiated); control over price (consumers are elastic, inelastic); conditions of entry (into the market); and nonprice competition (advertising). Decisions will be made (in the short-run and long-run) regarding maximizing profit or minimizing loss.

This concept opens with a brief description of each market model to give you an overall idea of the spectrum which will be covered. Then from that point, the chapter moves into the first market model and focuses on pure competition. Although, in the real-world, it is difficult to cite an industry that is operating under all the conditions of pure competition, the concept is important because it provides us with a standard of comparison with real-world market structures.

Learning Objectives

After reading this chapter in the text, and completing the following exercises in this concepts book, you should be able to:

1. List the four basic market structures and explain the major characteristics.
2. Distinguish between the demand curve facing an individual firm and the industry demand curve.
3. Compute total revenue (TR), average revenue (AR) and marginal revenue (MR) when given the necessary data.
4. Graph demand, price, average revenue (AR) and marginal revenue (MR) on one line and explain the relationship.
5. Explain why a "purely competitive" firm is a price-taker.
6. Determine the profit maximizing or loss minimizing output (in the short-run) using the three approaches (techniques).
7. Derive a short-run supply curve under pure competition, using the cost and revenue curves given.
8. Determine the long-run equilibrium price and output given short-run curves.
9. Explain why a firm might stay open, in the short-run, even when incurring a loss.
10. Explain the close (shut) down point.
11. Discuss how the entry and exit of firms in a purely competitive market, determines the long-run equilibrium.
12. Compare the long-run supply curves for constant-, increasing-, and decreasing-cost industries.
13. Distinguish between productive efficiency (P = AC) and allocative efficiency (P = MC).
14. Explain the shortcomings of a purely competitive price system.

Chapter Highlights 

I. Four Market Models

A. Four basic market models (overview)

1. Pure (perfect) competition

a. A very large number of firms, producing a standardized product ("price-taker"). New firms can enter (or exit) the industry easily. No one firm has an impact on market price or output.

"Pure Competition"

2. Pure monopoly
   a. One firm is the sole producer of a unique (differentiated) product and there are no close substitutes ("price-maker"). Entry into the industry is blocked by patents, economies of scale, etc.
3. Monopolistic competition
   a. Many sellers with a differentiated product, which gives each firm a "partial monopoly" (based upon elasticity). Product differentiation lends itself to advertising. Entry (or exit) into (from) the industry is relatively easy.
4. Oligopoly
   a. A few sellers, with either a standardized or a differentiated product. Each firm is affected by the price and output decisions of the other firms (mutual interdependence). Entry into the industry is difficult because of significant obstacles such as licensing boards, zoning, etc.
5. Imperfect competition covers monopoly, monopolistic competition, and oligopoly.

II. Pure Competition: Characteristics and Occurrence

A. Characteristics
   1. Very large number of firms
   2. Standardized product (no need for nonprice competition -- advertising)
   3. "Price-taker" -- no one firm can control price or output in the market
   4. Free entry and exit -- no significant obstacles

III. Demand as Seen By Purely Competitive Seller

A. Perfectly Elastic Demand
   1. One firm -- the demand curve is perfectly elastic (no one firm can control price, as a result, the firm must accept the going-market price. A firm cannot get a higher price by cutting output and it can sell all that it wants at the market price, so there is no need to lower price).
   2. The industry is faced with a downward sloping demand curve (it can only sell a larger quantity by lowering price). See demand curves in Figure 1 below.
   3. For a single firm, therefore, price does not change ($6 in the example below).

Figure 1

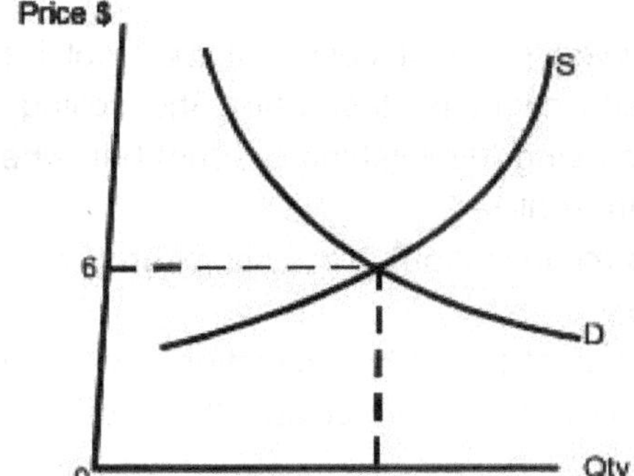

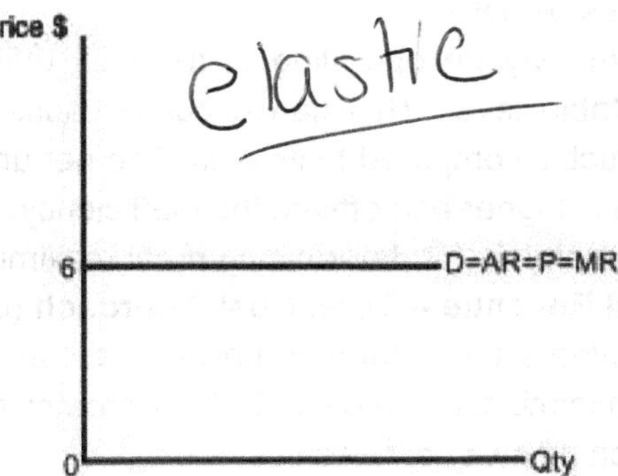

B. Average, Total and Marginal Revenue
1. Total revenue (TR) -- the sum of all the receipts of a firm in a given time period.
   TR = Price x Quantity Demanded
   a. Since the price stays the same for a firm under pure competition, TR increases at a constant rate (linear).
2. Average revenue (AR) -- the "per unit" receipt (money) from each unit sold.
   $AR = \frac{TR}{Q}$
   a. Since the price stays the same, for a purely competitive firm, the "per unit" revenue will be the same as price. ($6 in Figure 1).
3. Marginal revenue (MR) -- the extra receipt (money) from selling one more unit.
   $MR = \frac{\blacktriangle TR}{\blacktriangle Q}$ (graphed at the midpoints)
   a. Since the price stays the same for a purely competitive firm, the money received by selling one more unit will be the same as price ($6 in Figure 1).
4. Under Pure Competition: D = P = AR = MR
5. Total economic profit (or loss) is the difference between TR and TC (also called, "net revenue" or "gross profit").
   Total profit (or loss) = TR – TC = Net Revenue (NR)

Table 1
Formulas for the Short-run Revenue Curves

Total	Average	Marginal
Total Revenue (TR)	Average Revenue (AR)	Marginal Revenue (MR)
TR = P x Q NR = TR - TC	$AR = \frac{TR}{Q}$	$MR^* = \frac{\blacktriangle TR}{\blacktriangle Q}$ *graph at midpoints

IV. Profit Maximization (or loss minimization), in the Short-Run

A. Difference between the "most efficient" level (MC = ATC) and the "most profitable level" of output (three techniques below).
1. A firm may be operating at its most efficient level (lowest per unit cost) but may not be at its most profitable level. This can occur because potential profits might be lost when the selling price of the product is compared to its cost. The per unit cost may be rising (diminishing returns) but, when the selling price is higher and offsets the inefficiency, more profits are realized.

B. Three techniques for determining profit maximization or (loss minimization) in the short-run:
1. **Total Revenue -- Total Cost Approach** (or TR-TC Rule)
   a. Where the difference between TR and TC is the greatest (profit maximization) or the smallest (loss minimization) provided TR is greater than TVC -- a firm more than covers the cost of materials and chips away at fixed cost.
   b. When TR is greater than TC an economic profit is realized; when TR is equal to TC a normal profit is realized; when TR is less than TC a loss is incurred.
   c. A firm will stay open, even when losing money in the short-run, if the firm is minimizing that loss by staying open -- the loss is less than the total fixed cost (if a firm closed-down it would still be responsible for its total fixed costs). See Figure 2.

TR > TC = econ profit
TR = TC = Normal profit

2. **Marginal Revenue -- Marginal Cost Approach (or MC = MR Rule)**
   a. A firm will produce where MR = MC, provided MR (or price) is greater than average variable cost (AVC). If the MR (price) is less than or equal to AVC, the firm will shut-down because it is not helping itself by staying open.
   See Figure 2.
3. **Total economic profit (or loss) approach (or where Net Revenue is at a maximum).**
   a. A firm will produce where total economic profit (or loss) is at its maximum point.
   Total profit (or loss) = TR - TC = NR
   b. This technique is similar to technique 1, but it shows only one curve.
   c. Also called "net revenue" and "gross profit."

Table 2

Three techniques to maximize profit (or minimize loss) in the short-run

1. Total Revenue - Total Cost Approach (or TR-TC Rule)
2. Marginal Revenue = Marginal Cost Approach (or MC = MR Rule)
3. Total Economic Profit (or loss) Approach (or NR at a maximum)

C. Marginal Cost and Short-Run Supply

1. The short-run supply curve for a single firm, under pure competition, follows the path of the MC curve above the shut-down point. (Shut-down occurs where MC = AVC). Another way of describing the short-run supply curve is to say that it is that portion of the MC curve above AVC. (See Figure 2). A step-by-step derivation is found under the "Problems" section of this concepts book.

Figure 2: Short-run Supply Curve under Pure Competition

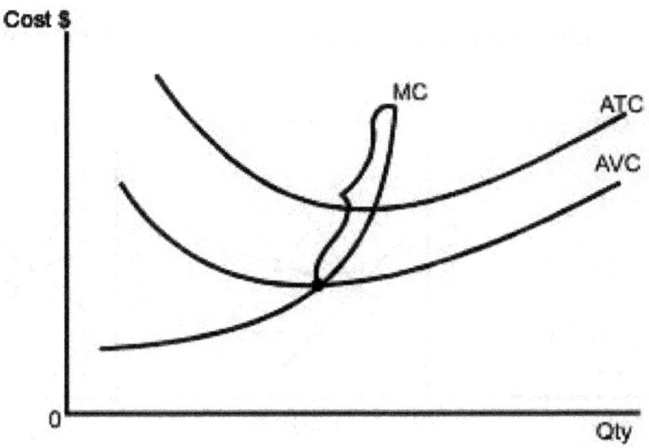

D. Diminishing Returns, Production Costs and Product Supply
   1. Links among concepts

E. Changes in Supply
   1. The industry supply curve (which is the sum of all the individual supply curves) and the total demand for the product, determine the short-run price and equilibrium output for the industry: the firms in the industry may be prosperous (profitable) or unprosperous (loss) in the short-run.

F. Firm and Industry: Equilibrium Price
   1. The actual market equilibrium price will be determined by supply and demand.

V. Profit Maximization, (or loss minimization) in the long-run

A. Long-run Assumptions
   1. Firms in an industry can either expand or contract their plant capacities.
   2. The number of firms in the industry can increase or decrease (entry and exit within the industry) and may have identical costs.

B. Profit and Long-run Equilibrium
   1. The existence of economic profits (when average revenue exceeds average total cost) induces firms to enter an industry. As a result, the market supply increases causing price to decrease (eliminating the economic profits).
   2. Once the economic profits are exhausted, the incentive to enter the industry disappears and long-run equilibrium has been restored.
   3. As a result of declining consumer demand, prices drop (causing losses to be incurred) and when average total cost is greater than average revenue firms exit from an industry.
   4. Competition forces each firm (in the long-run) under pure competition, to end up with an optimum plant size, earning normal profits, (MC = P = MR = AR = ATC = LRATC).

C. The Long-run Supply Curves
   1. The industry's long-run supply curve is shaped by the number of firms entering or exiting the industry.
   2. Equilibrium for the industry (in the long-run) is reached when no firm wishes to enter or leave the industry.
   3. The long-run supply curve in a **constant-cost** industry is horizontal (perfectly elastic) -- no increases in costs as new firms expand the industry and prices remain the same.
   4. The long-run supply curve in an **increasing-cost** industry is upward sloping (positive slope) -- rising costs as new firms expand the industry cause increases in price (the most common characteristic in American industry).
   5. The long-run supply curve in a **decreasing-cost** industry is downward sloping (negative slope) -- costs decline due to economies of scale, causing prices to fall as the industry expands.

The Long-Run Supply Curve under Pure Competition

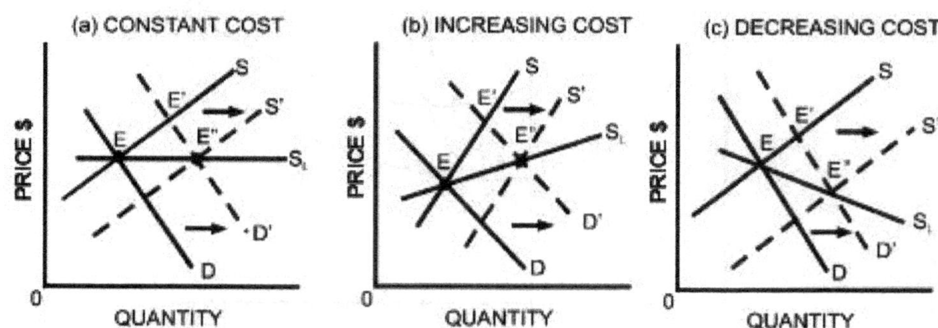

VI. Pure Competition and Efficiency

A. Productive Efficiency: P = Minimum ATC
   1. Profit-seeking sellers will result in efficient utilization of resources. Competition forces firms to produce at the minimum average total cost (LRATC) and charge a price equal to that amount (P = ATC) -- productive efficiency.
   2. Consumers benefit in that resources are allocated so that total satisfaction is maximized (P = MC) -- allocative efficiency. The "invisible hand" guides a competitive market through self-interest.

B. Allocative Efficiency: P=MC
   1. Underallocation P>MC
   2. Overallocation: P<MC
   3. Efficient Allocation

C. Dynamic Adjustments
   1. Market failure: spillovers and public goods -- the price system does not measure spillovers or externalities.
   2. Economics of scale - large-scale producers may be needed for major efficiency.

D. "Invisible Hand" revisited — organizes resources efficiently

E. Technological Advance and Competition
   1. Large-scale production is lost due to the large number of sellers in a competitive market as well as the ability of small firms to keep up technologically.
   2. Range of consumer choice -- since the competitive market structure entails a standardized product, it presents a limited choice for consumers (no product differentiation), and is not progressive in developing new products.
   3. Creative Destruction – as new products and methods destroys the market position of existing firms.

VI. Last Word: "Digging Yourself Out of a Hole" and "A Patent Failure"

VII.Web-based Question (see your Instructor)

Key Terms

pure competition
pure monopoly
monopolistic competition
oligopoly
imperfect competition
price-taker
nonprice competition
total revenue (TR)
average revenue (AR)
marginal revenue (MR)
total economic profit
net revenue (NR)
profit maximization
loss minimization
break-even point
total revenue - total cost approach
externalities (spillovers)
marginal revenue - marginal cost approach
close-(shut) down point
MR = MC rule
short-run supply curve for a single firm
standardized product
short-run equilibrium
total profit approach
industry supply curve
long-run equilibrium
long-run supply curve
constant-cost industry
increasing-cost industry
decreasing-cost industry
productive efficiency
allocative efficiency
self-interest

HW → 195

NR = TR − TC TC = TFC + TVC

TR = P × Q

MR = ΔTR / ΔQ

"Pure Competition"

PROBLEMS

1. **Profit Maximization in the Short-Run**

   a. Fill in the table and determine, as the production manager, how many items you would produce in each of the three cases below. Are you earning a profit or a loss in the short-run?

A.Case 1

QTY	Price	TR	TVC	TFC	TC	MR	MC	NR
0	$5.99	0	$0	$5	5			-5
1	↓	5.99	6	↓	11	5.99	6	5.01
2	↓	11.98	14	↓	19	5.99	8	-7.02
3	↓	17.97	24	↓	29	5.99	10	-11.03
4	↓	23.96	36	↓	41	5.99	12	-17.04

B.Case 2

QTY	Price	TR	TVC	TFC	TC	MR	MC	NR
0	$6.01	0	$0	$5	5			-5
1	↓	6.01	6	↓	11	6.01	6	-4.99
2	↓	12.02	14	↓	19	6.01	8	-6.98
3	↓	18.03	24	↓	29	6.01	10	-10.97
4	↓	24.04	36	↓	41	6.01	12	-16.96

C.Case 3

QTY	Price	TR	TVC	TFC	TC	MR	MC	NR
0	$10.01	0	$0	$5	5			-5
1	↓	10.01	6	↓	11	10.01	6	-.99
2	↓	20.02	14	↓	19	10.01	8	1.02
3	↓	30.03	24	↓	29	10.01	10	1.03 ←
4	↓	40.04	36	↓	41	10.01	12	-.96

184 298

PROBLEM

2.

QTY	Price	TR	TFC	TVC	TC	AFC	AVC	ATC	MC	MR	NR
0	$9	0	1	0	1	1	0	0			-1
1		9	1	8	9	1	8	9	8	9	0
2		18	1	15	16	.5	7.5	8	7	9	2
3		27	1	23	24	.3	7.7	8	8	9	3
4		32	1	33	34	.25	8.25	8.5	10	9	2
5		45	1	44	45	.2	8.8	9	11	9	0
6		54	1	57	58	.17	9.5	9.5	13	9	-4
7		63	1	74	75	.14	10.6	10.7	17	9	-12

A. Complete table.

B. Graph #1 - Graph TR and TC

#2 - Graph MC, MR, and ATC

#3 - Graph NR

C. What is our profit maximum quantity? ___________ Label on graph.

D. What is Total Fixed Cost (TFC) in the above problem? _____________

FORMULAS:

$TR = P \times Q$ $\qquad MR^* = \frac{\Delta TR}{\Delta Q}$ $\qquad NR = TR - TC$

$TC = TFC + TVC$ $\qquad MC^* = \frac{\Delta TC}{\Delta Q}$

$AFC = \frac{TFC}{Q}$ $\qquad AVC = \frac{TVC}{Q}$ $\qquad ATC = \frac{TC}{Q} = AFC + AVC$

*graphed at midpoints

PROBLEM

3. Short Run Supply Curve
   A. Below are the cost and revenue curves for a perfectly competitive firm.
      1. Label the cost curves (AVC, ATC and MC)
   B. For each selling price (MR) determine the following: (show all work)
      1. Label the profit max. (loss min.) price—Pe and quantity—Qe
      2. State whether an economic profit, normal profit, or a loss has occurred and give the per unit and the total dollar amounts.
      3. Should you shutdown?
   C. At what selling price (MR) should you shutdown?
   D. Shade the AFC area.
   E. Where is the short-run supply curve? (highlight on graph)

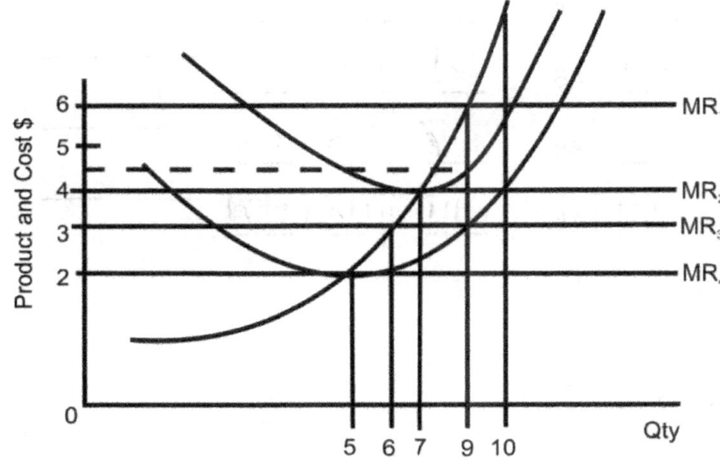

HINTS (if you need them):

Step 1- Determine the profit max.(loss min.) price and quantity-MC=MR Rule

2- Calculate the profit (or loss) per unit:
Pe—Selling price (Demand Curve)
-CP—Cost price (ATC Curve)
Economic Profit (or loss)* when Economic Profit = 0 (normal return)
* loss incurred by staying open.

3- Should the firm shut down when its earning a loss (or are you minimizing losses by staying open)?
AVC—(Average Variable Cost)
+AFC—(Average Fixed Cost)**
ATC—(Average Total Cost)

** Incur the Average Fixed Cost when you shutdown.

"Pure Competition"

Self-Test

Exhibit I

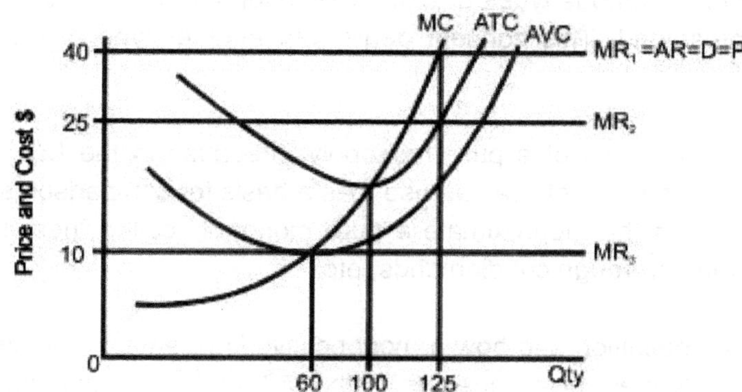

1. In Exhibit I, the firm's total cost of producing at a selling price of $40 is:
   a. $2,200 b. $3,125 c. $2,500 d. $4,500
2. In Exhibit I, the firm's total revenue from the sale at its most profitable level of output is:
   a. $4,000 b. $600 c. $2,200 d. $5,000
3. In Exhibit I, the firm's total economic profits (NR) at its most profitable level of output is:
   a. $1,875 b. $2,200 c. $5,000 d. $600
4. In the short-run, the individual competitive firm's supply curve is that segment:
   a. of the marginal cost curve which lies between the ATC and AVC curves.
   b. of the marginal revenue curve which lies below the demand curve.
   c. of the marginal cost curve which lies above the AVC curve.
   d. of the average variable cost curve which lies below the MC curve.
5. In Exhibit I, the firm will shut down in the short-run if the price is:
   a. $20 b. $25 c. $10 d. $30
6. Under pure competition, the demand curve facing a single firm is:
   a. perfectly inelastic c. downward sloping
   b. perfectly elastic d. vertical
7. A purely competitive firm will stay open, even if it is incurring a loss in the short-run if:
   a. the firm is minimizing that loss
   b. total fixed cost is greater than the loss
   c. MR is greater than AVC
   d. all of the above
8. A purely competitive firm sells its output for $25 when it produces 100 units. At that output MC = $25 and is rising, AVC = $30 and ATC = $50. In this situation, the firm should:
   a. increase output c. maintain output
   b. decrease output d. close- (shut) down
9. A purely competitive industry will earn:
   a. normal profits in both the short-run and long-run.
   b. economic profits in both the short-run and long-run.
   c. economic profits in the short-run and normal profits in the long-run.
   d. normal profits in the short-run and economic profits in the long-run.
10. The long-run supply curve in an increasing-cost industry will be:
    a. negatively sloped. c. perfectly elastic.
    b. positively sloped. d. downward sloping.

"Pure Monopoly"

Chapter Orientation

Economic activity is carried on in various types of market situations. In the last concept, the foundations of pure (or perfect) competition were presented. This concept deals with another type of market model -- the monopoly market.

Although it is difficult to cite examples of a pure monopoly, (because in the U.S. pure monopolies are either regulated or broken up) by studying this model, we can use it as a basis for comparison since it is at the opposite end of the spectrum. There are industries that approximate a pure monopoly called "near monopolies" such as central microprocessors, money order transfer, rough cut diamonds, etc.

"Pure Monopoly" opens with a definition and how a monopolistic firm remains "alone and loving it" (through high barriers to entry); how price and output are determined using the MC = MR rule; and compare the monopoly model to the competitive model.

In addition, the chapter explains how the monopolist discriminates by price to maximize profits. Lastly, since there is no competition in a monopoly market to keep prices in line, the government has a dilemma as to which pricing policy to follow.

Learning Objectives

After reading this chapter in the text, and completing the following exercises in this concepts book, you should be able to:

1. Define pure monopoly and list the key characteristics.
2. List and explain six barriers to entry.
3. Describe the demand curve facing the pure monopolist.
4. Compare the demand curves for pure competition and pure monopoly.
5. Explain why price exceeds marginal revenue under a pure monopoly.
6. State the technique used to determine price and output under a monopoly; locate the equilibrium price and output on a monopoly graph.
7. Describe the effects of pure monopoly on the price of a product, the quantity of a product, and the allocation of resources.
8. Explain why economies of scale and X-inefficiency affects the cost structure.
9. Define technological progress (or dynamic efficiency) in pure competition and pure monopoly.
10. Explain the effects of monopoly on the distribution of income in the economy.
11. Define price discrimination; list the three conditions necessary for successful price discrimination; and explain two economic consequences of price discrimination.
12. Compare the socially optimum (marginal-cost) price; fair return (full-cost) price; and the monopolist's (profit max) price.
13. Explain the dilemma, which the regulatory agencies encounter in setting price.

"Pure Monopoly"

Chapter Highlights

I. An Introduction to Pure Monopoly

A. Market model

1. Definition of pure monopoly -- a market situation in which there is only one seller or producer of a product or service and there are no close substitutes.
2. Characteristics of a pure monopoly
   a. Single seller -- or one-firm industry, therefore the firm and the industry are one and the same.
   b. No close substitutes -- the buyer must purchase the product from the monopolist or do without the product.
   c. "Price-maker" -- the monopolist sets the price by manipulating the quantity supplied.
   d. Blocked entry -- high barriers to entry into the industry such as economic, legal, or technological barriers.
   e. Nonprice competition -- since there is no competition, if a monopolist advertises it will be for public relations or good will.
   f. Examples -- utilities, professional sports teams, Internet access on planes, etc., approximate pure monopolies.
   g. Dual objectives of the study of monopoly — for its own sake and to help understand the other structures.

II. Barriers to entry

A. A natural monopoly exists when economies of scale are so great in an industry that only one firm can efficiently serve the market. As a result, the government grants to the industry exclusive franchises and in return reserves the right to regulate the industry.

B. A monopoly firm might have exclusive ownership or control of a basic new material or other factors of production.

C. A monopoly firm might control patents on production equipment and techniques, or may utilize tying agreements to extend monopoly power. A patent is the exclusive right to control a product for twenty years (new world-wide period).

D. A monopoly firm might engage in unfair competitive practices designed to exclude new or existing competitors, such as Microsoft.

E. The monopolist might be so well established that it might have exceptional advantages or economies arising: from the ability to raise money more easily and cheaply, from long-term advertising, and from efficient policies and personnel.

F. The question of efficiency arises when there is a lack of competition in the market (perhaps too much time is wasted keeping the competition out); so there is a question of "desirability".

III. Determining Price and Output for a Pure Monopolist

A. Monopoly demand

1. Definition—the demand curve for a monopolist is the same as the industry demand curve because the monopoly firm is the only seller in the market.
2. The industry demand curve is a downward sloping because of the inverse relationship between price and quantity (the monopolist must lower prices to increase the quantity demanded).
   a. As a result of lowering price to increase sales, marginal revenue is less than price (= AR) for every level after the first one. The reason for this is because when you drop the price, for example by a dollar, the marginal effect (or change will be a dollar, the average effect will be the dollar divided by the number of units (therefore once the number of units is greater than 1, AR or price will be greater than MR). See Table 1 and Graph 1.

Table 1

Q	Price=AR	TR	AR	MR
1	$ 9	9	9	
				7
2	8	16	8	
				5
3	7	21	7	
				3
4	6	24	6	

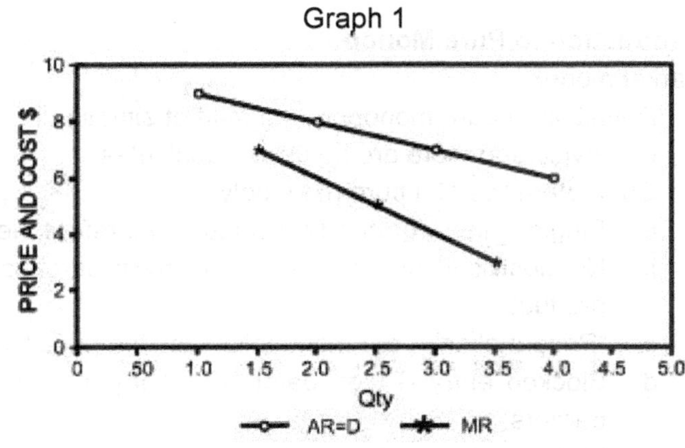

3. All imperfect market firms have a price policy because they can influence total supply which in turn effects price.
4. The monopolist will try to operate in the elastic range of the demand curve. As a rational producer, the monopolist will not produce where an increase in output lowers revenue (inelastic demand).
5. To maximize profit (or minimize loss) in the short-run, the monopolist will produce according to:
   a. MC = MR Rule
   b. TR-TC Rule, where the difference between TR and TC is the greatest (profit maximization) or the smallest (loss minimization).
   c. Total profit (or net revenue) is at a maximum. (See illustration: "Profit Maximization for a Pure Monopolist" in this concepts book).

B. Misconceptions concerning monopoly pricing
   1. Highest price -- the monopolist chooses to maximize overall profits not charge the highest price.
   2. Max unit profits -- the monopolist chooses to maximize total profits not unit profits.
   3. Economic profits -- it is possible for the monopolist to incur a loss (not guaranteed economic profits).

IV. Economic Effects of Monopolies

A. The existence of a pure monopoly has significant effects on the economy as a whole.
   1. A monopolist keeps prices high by restricting output; as a result, there is a misallocation of resource (as compared to a competitive market).
   2. The justification for a monopoly is that consumers benefit because of lower per unit costs due to economies of scale -- is that true?
      a. If there are economies of scale present in the production process than the monopolist can produce the good or service at a lower long-run average total cost than smaller firms under pure competition.
      b. However, a monopolist is more susceptible to X-inefficiency than are competitive producers because the monopolist is shelter from competitive forces, which put pressure on a firm to be internally efficient to survive.
      c. Looking at dynamic efficiency (focuses on the question of whether monopolists are more likely to develop more efficient production techniques overtime than are competitive firms), competitive firms have the motivation to employ efficient production techniques -- their survival depends upon it! Under the monopoly model presents two schools of thought -- the first being that with the absence of competition the monopolist has every reason to be satisfied with the status quo and "file" any new advances. In addition, any cost reductions will add to the monopolist's profit, only a small amount, if

any, will be passed along to the consumer. The second idea is that technological advance will increase profits. In addition, research and technological advance can be used as a barrier to entry.

d. Since corporate stock ownership is in the hands of upper income groups, monopolistic profits contribute to income inequality (distribution) in the economy.

3. Assessment and Policy Options – patents expire and barriers to entry may not be completely successful. Therefore, the government looks at monopoly on a case-by-case basis.

V. Price Discrimination

A. Definition -- price discrimination occurs when a firm sells a product to two different buyers at different prices without justification by differences in cost.

B. Conditions required for price discrimination to be profitable
1. The seller must have control over price and quantity. (Monopoly power)
2. The seller must classify (segment) customers into groups according to their elasticity of price.
3. Resale of the product must be nonexistent

C. Consequences of price discrimination
1. A monopolist can increase profits by practicing price discrimination (knowing how far you can "push" your customers).
2. A discriminatory monopolist will produce a larger output because for example, when the price is lowered it only applies to the additional units sold - not the prior units.

D. Examples of Price Discrimination
1. Different electric rates to residential and industrial users.
2. Higher adult movie ticket prices as compared to children's movie ticket prices.
3. Different rates for airline passengers who are business or vacation travelers.

VI. Pricing Policies for a Monopolist

A. Monopolist's price (or profit maximizing price) - <u>Unregulated</u>
1. Use MR = MC Rule
2. Since MC is less than price, there is a misallocation of resources (See Graph 3).

B. Socially optimum price (or Marginal cost price) - <u>Regulated</u>
1. Where P = MC (the standard of perfect competition).
2. At the intersection of P = MC a ceiling price is established which resolves the underallocation issue.
3. Price may be so low that ATC is not always covered (loss for firm). (See Graph 3).

C. Fair return price (or Full-cost price) - <u>Regulated</u>
1. Where P = ATC.
2. Covers all costs and includes a normal profit but may underallocate resources. (See Graph 2).
3. Price which the government is likely to impose.

Graph 2

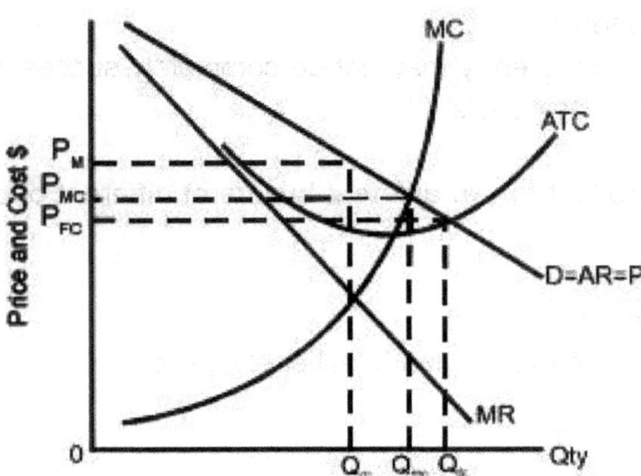

Graph 3

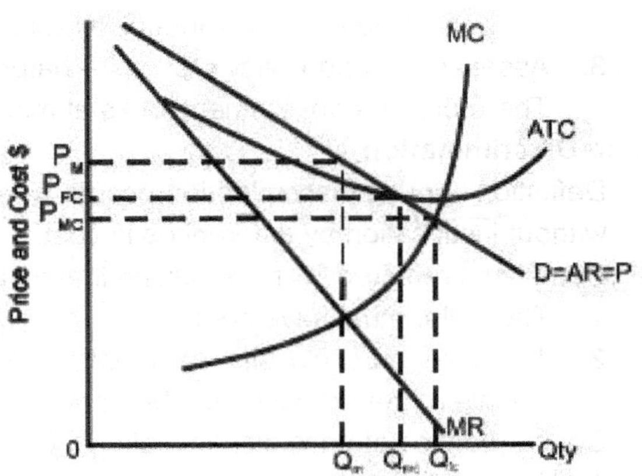

VII.Dilemma of Regulation

A. Tradeoffs of pricing policies

1. The dilemma of regulation is that the socially optimum price may cause losses for the monopolist; a fair-return price results in underallocation of resources.
2. Price regulation can offset the tendency of monopolists to earn economic profits by underallocating resources.

VIII.Long-run for a Monopolist

A. Economic profits depend on

1. Barriers to entry
2. Demand for the product
3. Government regulation

B. A monopolist produces higher long-run profits, as compared to the other market models.

IX. Last Word: "Monopoly Power in the Internet Age"

X. Web-based question (see your Instructor)

Key Terms

pure monopoly	misallocation of resources
barrier to entry	X-inefficiency
price-maker	dynamic efficiency
natural monopoly	price discrimination
tying agreement	monopolist's price
unfair competition	socially optimum price
economies of being established	fair-return price
monopoly demand	dilemma of regulation

"Pure Monopoly"

PROBLEMS

1. The following is a table for a monopolist:

   A. Complete the table below.

   B. Prepare three graphs:
   Graph #1 - Graph TR and TC
   #2 - Graph MC, MR, and ATC
   #3 - Graph NR

   C. What is the profit-maximizing or loss-minimizing quantity? 3 Label on graph.

   D. What is TFC? $20

Quantity Per day	AR = P	TR	TC	ATC	MC	MR	NR
0	$12	0	$20	-			$-20
1	11	11	24	24	4	11	-13
2	10	20	27	13.5	3	9	-7
3	9	27	32	10.67	5	7	-5
4	8	32	39	9.75	7	5	-7
5	7	35	49	9.8	10	3	-14
6	6	36	63	10.5	14	1	-27
7	5	35	83	11.86	20	-1	-48

PROBLEMS

2. The following is a table for a monopolist:

   A. Complete the table below.

   B. Prepare three graphs:
   Graph #1 - Graph TR and TC
   #2 - Graph MC, MR, and ATC
   #3 - Graph NR

   C. What is the profit-maximizing or loss-minimizing quantity? 7-8 Label on graph.

   D. What is TFC? $22

Quantity Per day	AR = P	TR	TC	ATC	MC	MR	NR
0	$21	0	$22	–			$-22
1	20	20	37	37	13	20	-17
2	19	38	42	21	5	18	-4
3	18	54	45	13	3	16	9
4	17	68	47	11.75	2	14	21
5	16	80	50	10	3	12	30
6	15	90	54	9	4	10	36
7	14	98	59	8.43	5	8	39
8	13	104	65	8.13	6	6	39
9	12	108	72	8	7	4	36
10	11	110	80	8	8	2	30
11	10	110	89	8.09	9	0	21
12	9	108	99	8.25	10	-2	9

PROBLEMS

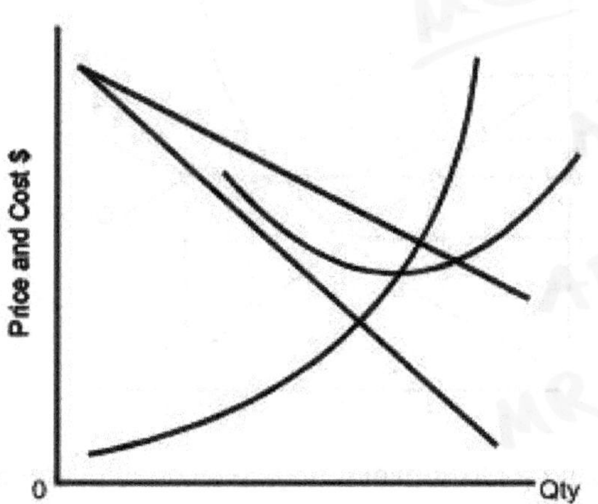

3. The accompanying diagram refers to a monopolist.
   a. Label all of the curves.

   b. Show the level of output that the unregulated monopolist will sell and label it (Qe).
   Show the price at which the unregulated monopolist will sell and label it (Pe).

   c. Shade in the area that shows the monopolist's profit or loss.

   d. Show the level of output that the regulated monopolist would produce if it followed the marginal cost pricing (socially optimum pricing) and label it (Qmc) and also the price level and label it (Pmc).

   e. Show the level of output and pricing if the regulated monopolist followed the full-cost or fair-return pricing approach and label it (Qfc) and (Pfc).

   f. Compare the three levels of pricing.

   g. Does the profit-maximizing monopolist produce at a level of output which optimally uses its plant? Explain.

"Pure Monopoly"

Self-Test

Exhibit II

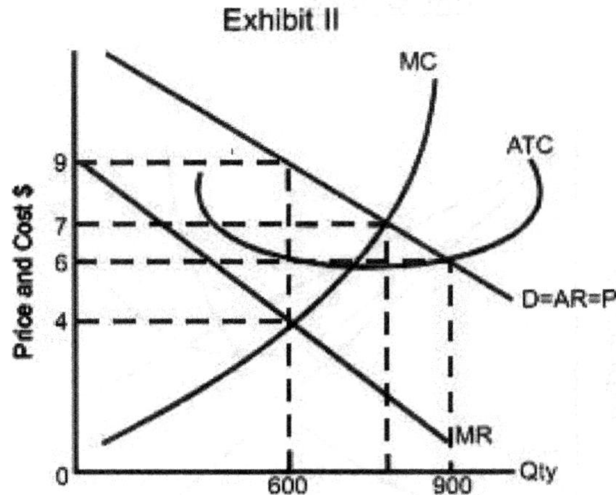

1. In Exhibit II, the profit-maximizing (or loss-minimizing) level of output for this pure monopolist is:
   a. 400 units per day c. 850 units per day
   b. 600 units per day d. 900 units per day
2. In Exhibit II, the maximum total economic profit that this pure monopolist can earn is approximately:
   a. $6,900 b. $3,600 c. $1,800 d. -$1,800
3. In Exhibit II, what is the profit-maximizing price?
   a. $9.00 b. $7.00 c. $6.00 d. $4.00
4. In Exhibit II, the full-cost or fair-return price allowed by the government is:
   a. $6.00 b. $7.00 c. $8.00 d. $4.00
5. In Exhibit II, following the socially optimum pricing policy, the price would be set at approximately:
   a. $6.00 b. $7.00 c. $8.00 d. $4.00
6. A monopolist normally makes output decisions:
   a. in the inelastic range of the demand curve
   b. at the point of unit elasticity on the demand curve
   c. in the elastic range of the demand curve
   d. without reference to the price elasticity of demand
7. The demand curve for a firm in a monopolistic industry is:
   a. always a straight line c. perfectly elastic
   b. slightly less than the industry curve d. the same as the industry demand curve
8. If a firm is enjoying economic profits over the long-run, it is safe to say that:
   a. it is too big c. it is efficiently allocating resources
   b. it is being efficiently managed d. it is not a perfectly competitive market
9. Which of the following describes the relationship of the marginal revenue curve to the demand (average revenue) curve in a monopoly situation?
   a. The marginal revenue curve is above and has a steeper slope than the average revenue curve.
   b. The marginal revenue curve falls below and has a steeper slope than the average revenue curve.
   c. The average revenue curve is above and has a steeper slope than the marginal revenue curve.
   d. The average revenue curve falls below and has steeper slope than the marginal revenue curve.
10. Which of the following is <u>not</u> a condition necessary for successful price discrimination?
    a. The seller must have control over price and quantity.
    b. The buyer must be relatively inelastic to price changes.
    c. The seller must segment customers.
    d. Resale of the product is nonexistent.

"Monopolistic Competition and Oligopoly"

Chapter Orientation

In the previous two concepts, you learned about the characteristics of a purely competitive market and a monopoly market. The last concept focuses on the last two models: monopolistic competition and oligopoly. Seeing "monopoly" and "competition" together may seem self-contradictory or a paradox, however, we will see that this market lies between the two extremes. For example, there are lots of Mexican restaurants in your area (competition) but you have one that is your favorite (monopoly). As a result, your favorite restaurant has a "partial monopoly" depending upon your elasticity of price.

An oligopolistic market structure characterizes much of American industry. For example, the airline, automobile, cigarette, soft drink, and cereal industries all operate under oligopolistic market conditions. Oligopoly displays less competition and more strategic behavior.

The concept opens with a definition of monopolistic competition and covers its characteristics, as compared to the other two markets in which you should have learned. In addition, how a monopolistically competitive firm determines price and output using the MC = MR rule, the profit picture in both the short-run and the long-run; and the "wastes" of monopolistic competition will be examined. Also, non-price competition, such as product developments and advertising will be evaluated.

In addition, you will learn the distinctive features of an oligopolistic market and be able to distinguish oligopoly from the other market structures -- pure competition, pure monopoly, and monopolistic competition. The chapter opens with a definition of an oligopoly market, and then presents the underlying feature: mutual interdependence. This condition leads to behavior which is different from all the other models and therefore is difficult for economists to stereotype into a specific market structure (so four models to explain oligopoly behavior are presented — Kinked Demand Curve, Collusive, Price Leadership, and Cost-plus pricing).

How the profit maximizing (or loss minimizing) price and output are determined; the role of non-price competition; and the economic impact of oligopoly market will be examined. Lastly, a real world oligopoly market (the beer industry with a reference to microbreweries) will be illustrated.

Learning Objectives

After reading this chapter in the text, and completing the following exercises in this concepts book, you will be able to:

1. Define monopolistic competition.
2. List and explain the characteristics of monopolistic competition.
3. Determine the price and output for a monopolistically competitive firm wishing to maximize profits (minimize loss) in the short-run, when given the necessary information.
4. Explain why a monopolistically competitive firm usually earns a normal profit in the long-run.
5. Explain and identify the "wastes" of monopolistic competition. (inefficiency)
6. Explain why product differentiation may offset these "wastes".
7. List the types of non-price competition.
8. Present the pros and cons of advertising.
9. Compare monopolistic competition with the other two markets (pure competition and pure monopoly).
10. Discuss the elasticity of demand as compared to the other markets.
11. Define oligopoly.

12. List and explain the characteristics of an oligopoly market.
13. Distinguish between homogeneous and differentiated oligopolies.
14. Define concentration ratio and give an example of a highly concentrated industry.
15. State the underlying causes of an oligopoly market.
16. Explain why mutual interdependence complicates the prediction of price and output by an oligopolist.
17. Compare and contrast the four models used to explain oligopoly behavior.
18. Discuss why oligopolists may choose to emphasize nonprice competition.
19. Explain the three forms of non-price competition.
20. Compare the Schumpeter-Galbraith view with the traditional view of oligopoly and discuss the empirical evidence.
21. Compare the beer industry to the characteristics of an oligopoly market.

<u>Chapter Highlights</u>

I. Monopolistic Competition

A. Market model
   1. Definition of monopolistic competition—a market characterized by many sellers in a market where the product of each seller is similar in nature, but differentiated in other ways. Because there are so many sellers, no one seller has much influence over price and, therefore, must differentiate its product in order to gather a large share of the market.
   2. Characteristics
      a. Large number of sellers—each with a small percentage of the market. As a result, no collusion, no mutual interdependence among firms.
      b. Product differentiation—a product is similar to other products, but not identical. Therefore, consumers have preference for certain products which give specific sellers, within limits, higher prices.
      c. Non-price competition—rivalry on product quality, advertising, etc. Since products are differentiated, it is natural to advertise their attributes or location and service might be factors.
      d. Entry into the market is relatively easy due to the fact that sellers are typically small-sized firms.
      e. Examples—most clothing items, such as shoes, dresses, and various food products, etc.

II. Price and Output Determination in Monopolistic Competition

A. The firm's demand curve
   1. Highly (but not perfectly) elastic due to the fact that there are substitutes available (perhaps not your favorite brand).
   2. The demand curve of a monopolistically competitive firm is less elastic than that of a purely competitive firm (product differentiation); but more elastic than that of a pure monopoly firm (substitutes available).

B. Short-run profits (or losses)
   1. In the short-run, a firm will maximize profits (or minimize losses), by producing the output designated by the intersection of MC and MR.
   2. A firm under monopolistic competition can incur economic profits in the short-run (as well as normal profits or losses).

C. Long-run profits or losses
   1. The tendency in the long-run is to earn a normal profit (or break even).
   2. The entry and exit of firms will tend to change the profit (or loss) picture.
   3. Whenever firms enjoy short-run economic profits, other firms see this market as lucrative and the entry of these new firms causes economic profits to be competed away. The demand curve will fall and become more elastic (because each firm has a smaller share of total demand and faces more close-substitutes). This causes the disappearance of economic profits because eventually price is equal to ATC.

4. Whenever firms are realizing a loss, this will cause firms to exit or leave the industry until normal profits are restored in the long-run.

III. Monopolistic Competition and Efficiency

A. Neither Productive nor Allocative Efficiency
   1. Under Monopolistic competition, neither productive nor allocative efficiency occurs.

B. Excess capacity
   1. With the existence of too many sellers, there is an under-allocation of resources (under pure competition, fewer firms would produce the same total output at a lower price).
   2. Since there are so many sellers, products are differentiated (due to competition), which gives consumers a variety from which to choose (to maximize satisfaction).

IV. Product Variety

A. Benefit of product variety
   1. Consumers are offered a wide range of types, styles, brands, quality, etc. of products from which to choose.

B. Further complexity
   1. Spurs rivals to copy or improve on a technological advantage.
   2. Profits realized from successful product development can be applied to further research.
   3. Critics argue that many product alterations are superficial (example: a flashier container). Also, development may have "planned obsolescence".

C. Product differentiation and product development may offset the "wastes" of monopolistic competition.

V. Oligopoly

A. Market model
   1. Definition -- an oligopoly market consists of relatively few sellers of a standardized or differentiated product. Because there are only a small number of firms in the market, the actions of each firm affect the other firms which cause them to be "mutually interdependent". High barriers to entry help to prevent new firms from entering the market.
   2. Characteristics of an oligopoly
      a. Fewness -- a market situation where there are very few sellers -- several firms dominating the entire industry so that these firms are in a position to set price.
      b. Type of product
         1. Homogeneous oligopolies produce a standardized product.
         2. Differentiated oligopolies produce a differentiated product.
      c. Control over price, but Mutual Interdependence
         1. Each firm is a "price maker"
         2. Strategic/Behavior — self-interested behavior
      d. Measure of Industry Concentration
         1. Definition — the percentage of all sales contributed by the leading four firms in an industry (measures "fewness"). Generally, when it is greater than 40 percent or more the industry is oligopolistic.
         2. Shortcomings of concentration ratios:
            (a) Localized markets— Pertains to the entire nation (regional measurement might be more applicable).
            (b) Inter-industry competition is ignored (competition between two products of different industries).
            (c) World trade — Data is for American producers only (does not include import competition).
            (d) Herfindahl Index is a formula, which gives greater weight to large firms and therefore addresses the extent to which one or two firms dominate the industry.

"Monopolistic Competition and Oligopoly"

VI. Oligopoly Behavior: A Game Theory Overview

A. Definition of Game Theory — the study of how people behave in strategic situations

B. Mutual interdependence

1. Oligopoly is a market situation where there are few sellers. As a result, each seller knows that the other sellers will react to its changes in price and quantity.
2. Sellers will quickly follow a price cut (touch off a price war), but are reluctant to raise price (lose market share).

C. Collusive tendencies

1. Oligopoly often leads to collusion (a formal or informal arrangement to "fit prices").

D. Incentives to cheat

1. An oligopolist is tempted to cheat. By lowering its price (secretly) it will increase sales (and profits!)

VII. Three Oligopoly Models: There is no one model for oligopoly because of "diversity" and "mutual interdependence."

A. The Kinked demand curve: Non-collusive Oligopoly

1. Oligopoly behavior is illustrated by a demand curve with a "bend" and a corresponding marginal revenue curve with a "step".
2. These two curves are based upon elasticity of price, mutual interdependence, and non-collusion. (See Figure 1 and Figure 2).

The Kinked Demand Curve

Figure 1

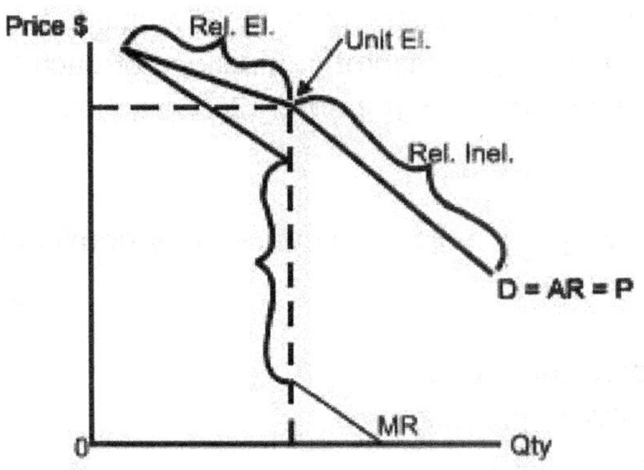

Price $
Rel. El.
Unit El.
Rel. Inel.
D = AR = P
MR
0
Qty

Figure 2

Price $
P
MR
AR = D = P
0
Q
MR
Qty

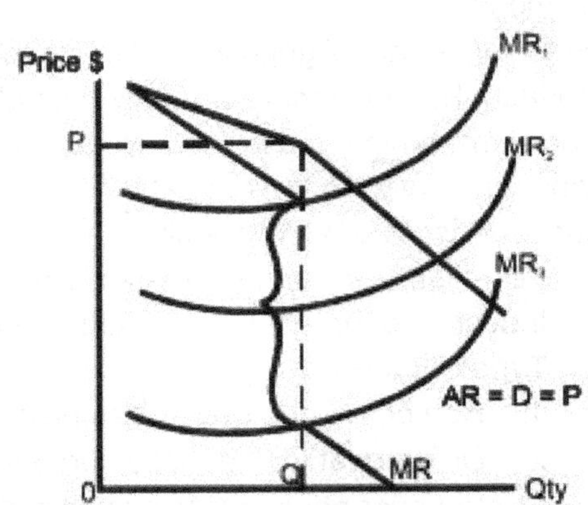

3. To maximize profits (or minimize loss) the oligopolist will produce where MC = MR.
4. The equilibrium price and quantity are relatively stable, as compared to the other markets, because once the price and output have been established, the individual firm is reluctant to raise price (in the elastic range of the demand curve; TR decreases) or lower price (in the inelastic range of the demand curve; TR decreases). Hence, for any marginal cost in the "step" area of the MR curve (see MC1 to MC3 in Figure 2) the selling price and quantity will remain stable.
5. When MC falls outside the "step" of the MR curve, selling price and quantity will have to change, however, profits will not be as high (as at the "kink").
6. It is possible for an oligopolist to earn an economic profit in the long-run because of high barriers to entry.

7. Criticisms of the kinked-demand model:
   a. Price rigidity may not fit every oligopolistic industry.
   b. Does not explain the entry/exit idea.
   c. No insight into how the equilibrium price was established.
   d. Does not explain how prices change.

B. Cartels and other Collusion
   1. Firms in an oligopoly coordinate activities for profit maximization (also called a "shared monopoly"). An agreement, usually secret, among competitors to engage in anticompetitive practices is in violation of the Sherman Act -- which declares any contract, combination, or conspiracy in restraint of trade, illegal.
   2. Given similar cost and demand conditions the oligopolistic firms will collude and strive for the same price and output as a monopoly (MC = MR).
   3. Identical price policies are not themselves evidence of collusion. More revealing are the measures taken to ensure compliance with price and output decisions. A "cartel" typically involves a formal written agreement with respect to both price and production. This tight-knit agreement involves pressuring member firms to comply (Overt collusion: OPEC).
   4. A "gentlemen's agreement" is an informal verbal agreement (perhaps made at a cocktail party or on the golf course) on price, leaving market shares to the individual seller to determine. (Covert Collusion)
   5. Obstacles to collusion
      a. Demand and cost differences -- make it difficult to agree on price.
      b. Number of firms -- the larger the number, the more difficult to collude.
      c. Cheating -- price concessions can be used by buyers as a leverage for a better deal.
      d. Recession -- a down turn in the economy, causes markets to slump and therefore the temptation to cut price is great.
      e. Potential entry attracts new entrants (foreign firms).
      f. Legal obstacles: antitrust -- as mentioned earlier, collusion, and price-fixing are illegal in the United States.
   6. Overt collusion: the OPEC Cartel comprises 12 oil-producing nations who supply 43% of the world's oil.
   7. Covert collusion: bid rigging, car parts or refrigerator compressors, etc.

C. Price Leadership: Model
   1. An informal situation in which the dominant or largest firm in an industry acts as a leader in setting a price that other firms in the industry will follow. (Example: cigarette pricing)
   2. Tactics used by a price leader:
      a. Infrequent price adjustments (afraid of price war).
      b. Communication (ex.: speeches).
      c. Price does not necessarily reflect short-run profits for the industry (to avoid new entrants).

VIII. Oligopoly and Advertising

A. Both monopolistic competition and oligopoly rely on advertising.

B. Positive effects of advertising:
   1. Provides information
   2. Finances national communications
   3. Stimulates product development
   4. Expands production resulting in economies of scale (lower per unit costs even including the cost of advertising)
   5. Promotes competition
   6. Promotes full-employment

C. Potential negative effects of advertising:
   1. Objective of advertising is to persuade (not much relevant information is given).
   2. Advertising expenditures are relatively unproductive, therefore, it represents inefficient use of scarce resources
   3. Significant external costs are entailed by advertising.
   4. Much advertising is self-canceling (advertising war).
   5. Advertising leads to less competition
   6. Most economists are reluctant to accept advertising as an important determinant of the levels of output and employment.

IX. Oligopoly and Efficiency

A. Allocative and Productive Efficiencies - To compare the efficiency of an oligopolist with that of a pure competitor is difficult, barrier two distinct views have evolved:
   1. The competitive view contends that since an oligopoly is a "shared monopoly" it reacts in the same way as a monopoly, without government regulation.
   2. Large oligopolistic firms are needed for technological progress (dynamic efficiency).

B. Qualifications
   1. Increased foreign competition.
   2. Limit pricing.
   3. Technological Advance.

X. Last Word: Internet Oligopolies

XI. Web-based Question/Problem (see your Instructor)

Key Terms

monopolistic competition
partial monopoly
noncollusion
product differentiation
nonprice competition
wastes of monopolistic competition
oligopoly
fewness
homogeneous oligopoly
differentiated oligopoly
concentration ratio
interindustry competition
horizontal merger
kinked demand curve
product development
external costs
self-canceling
price war
mutual interdependence
collusive oligopoly
shared monopoly
price leadership
cartel
gentlemen's agreement
tacit collusion
cost-plus pricing

PROBLEMS

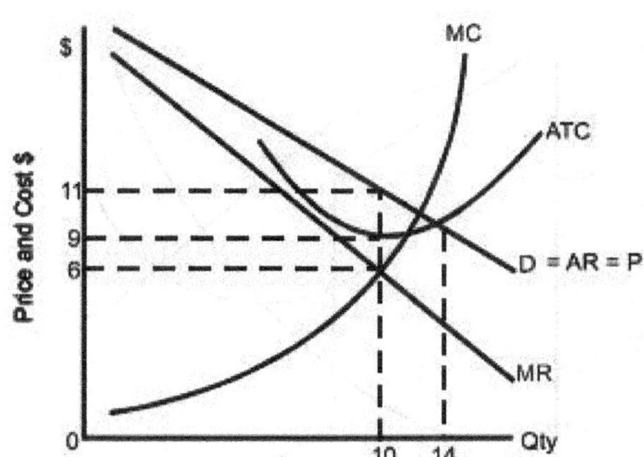

1. Shown above are the cost and revenue curves for a monopolistically competitive firm.
   a. The firm will produce approximately _________ units of output and charge approximately $_________ per unit.
   b. The firm's net revenue is approximately $_______. The firm is thus earning (normal profit, economic profit, or a loss) _________________________.
   c. In the long run, new firms (will tend to/will not tend to) ________________________ enter the industry.
   d. In the long run, each firm (will/will not) _________________ tend to earn a normal profit.

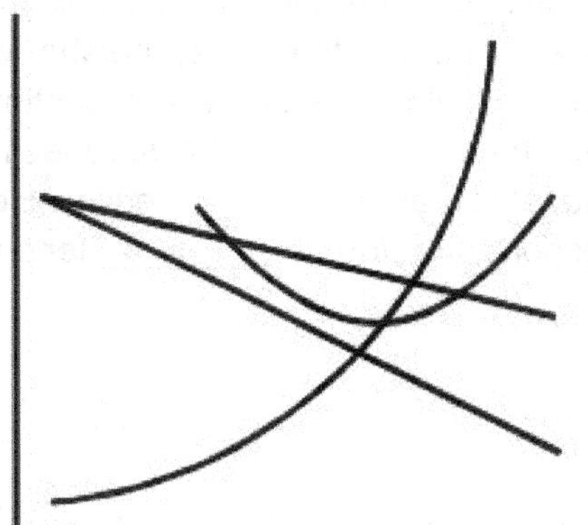
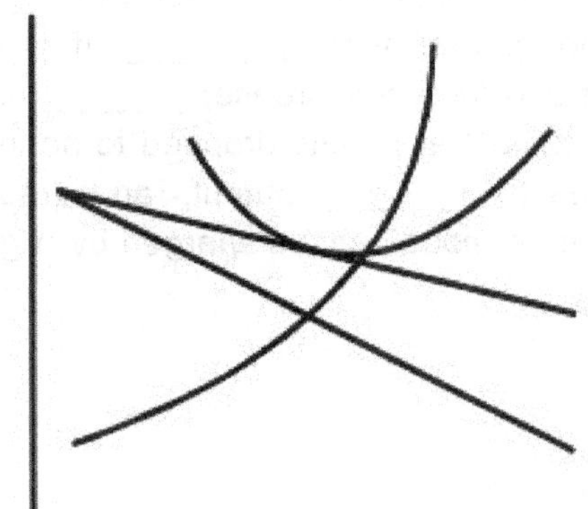
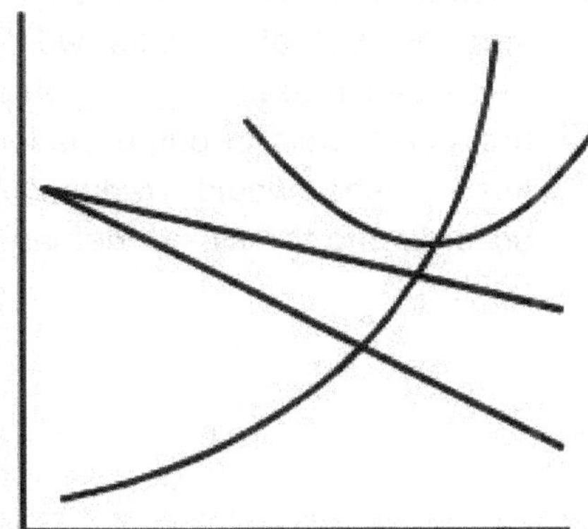

2. Shown above are the profit/loss positions for a firm under monopolistic competition.
   a. Label all the curves and the X and Y axis.
   b. Label the profit maximizing (or loss minimizing) price (Pe), output (Qe) and cost price (CP).
   c. Indicate whether an economic profit, a normal profit, or a loss has occurred.
   d. Shade in the area of profit or loss.

PROBLEMS

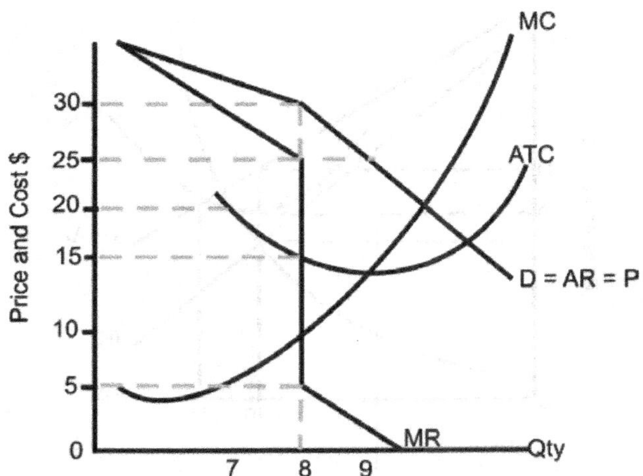

3. Shown above are the cost and revenue curves for an oligopolistically competitive firm.

   a. To maximize profit, the oligopolist will produce approximately _______ units of output and charge approximately $_______ per unit. The net revenue per unit will be approximately $_______, and the total profit/loss will be approximately $_______.

   b. Assume that the oligopolist's MC curve shifts upward. He/she would continue to produce 8 units of output as long as MC at 8 units were no greater than $_______. If it were greater than this, he/she would (reduce/increase) _______ output and (reduce/increase) _______ price. Similarly, he/she would continue to produce 8 units of output as long as MC at 8 units dropped to no less than $________. If it were less than this, he/she would (reduce/increase) _______ output, and (reduce/increase) _______ price. Hence, according to the kinked demand curve model, prices charged by oligopolists (do/do not) _______ tend to be rigid.

"Monopolistic Competition and Oligopoly"

PROBLEMS

4. What are the types of collusion? What role does collusion play in an oligopoly market? Is collusion legal in the United States? Why or why not? Do you think that American businesses collude? Why or why not?

5. Why is there so much advertising in monopolistic competition and oligopoly? What are the pros and cons of advertising – list at least three from each category.

6. What is a concentration ratio? What does it tell us? Give an example of a highly concentrated industry. What are the shortcomings of concentration ratios?

7. Define mutual interdependence. Cite an industry that is currently involved with a "price war" or where all the firms are currently raising prices. What is the impact on the consumer?

Self-Test

EXHIBIT III

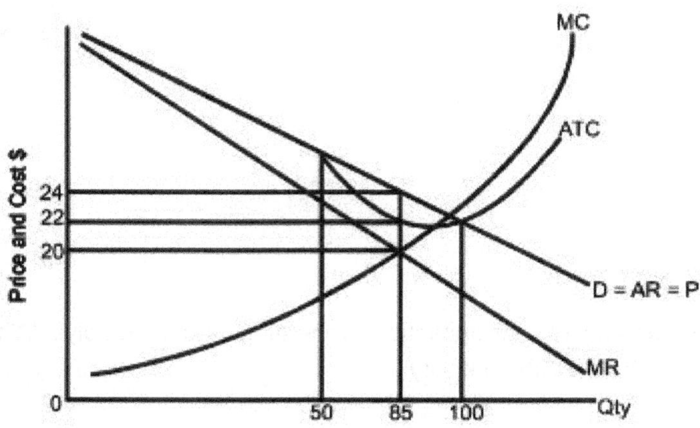

1. The monopolistically competitive firm views its demand curve as being:
   a. Unimportant in relation to other firms
   b. Highly inelastic as compared to Monopoly
   c. Of unitary elasticity
   d. Highly elastic as compared to Monopoly

2. In Exhibit III, the firm's profit-maximizing or equilibrium price is:
   a. $20
   b. $22
   c. $23
   d. $24

3. In Exhibit III, the firm's profit-maximizing or equilibrium quantity is:
   a. 50
   b. 85
   c. 100
   d. 115

4. This firm will realize an economic:
   a. profit of $340
   b. profit of $0
   c. profit of $170
   d. loss of $340

5. In Exhibit III, in the long run, firms will:
   a. enter the market causing a normal profit.
   b. enter the market causing economic profits.
   c. leave the industry due to loss.
   d. no way to tell from this graph.

Self-Test (continued)

6. Purely competitive markets and monopolistically competitive markets are similar in that there are:
   a. identical products sold by all firms in each market
   b. a large number of small producers in each market
   c. a small number of large producers in each market
   d. none of the above

7. Entry of the new firms into the industry in response to short-run economic profits will cause:
   a. demand to increase for the firm
   b. demand to shift downward and to the left and become more elastic for the firm
   c. demand to remain constant for the firm
   d. none of the above

8. Which of the following is the correct ranking, from highest to lowest, of the relative price equilibrium for a given industry under monopolistic, purely competitive, and monopolistically competitive market situations, assuming the same cost structures?
   a. monopolistic; monopolistically competitive; and purely competitive
   b. purely competitive; monopolistically competitive; monopolistic
   c. monopolistically competitive; monopolistic; purely competitive
   d. purely competitive; monopolistic; monopolistically competitive

9. Short-run equilibrium in a monopolistically competitive industry requires a firm to produce at that point where:
   a. any difference between average revenue and average cost is computed away
   b. marginal revenue equals marginal cost
   c. no cost exists in the short-run
   d. the demand curve is perfectly elastic

10. The three basic forms of monopolistic competition are:
    a. price competition, product variation, and the costs of production
    b. price competition, product differentiation, and product promotion (advertising)
    c. advertising, consumer satisfaction, and product variation
    d. none of the above

Exhibit IV

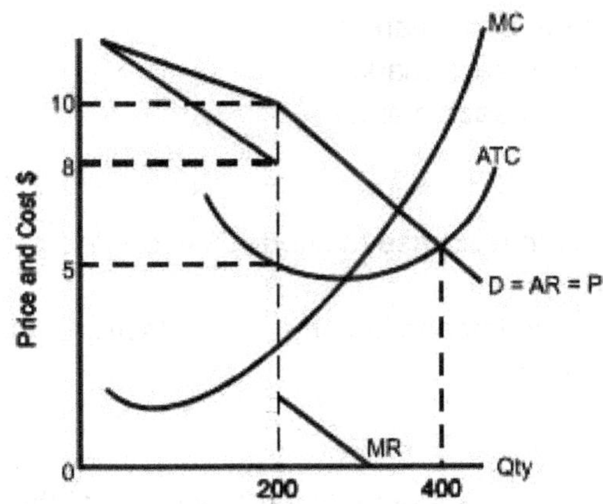

11. In Exhibit IV, the equilibrium price and output is:
    a. $8; 200
    b. $5; 200
    c. $10; 200
    d. $5; 400

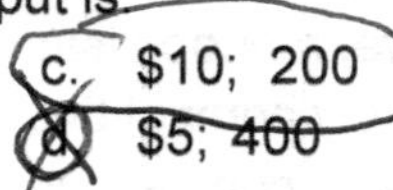

12. In Exhibit IV, the economic profit realized at the equilibrium output is:
    a. $1,000
    b. $600
    c. $2,000
    d. $1,600

13. In Exhibit IV, the firm's total revenue at its most profitable output is:
    a. $200
    b. $1,000
    c. $2,000
    d. $1,600

14. Which of the following industries is an illustration of a homogeneous oligopoly?
    a. soaps and detergents
    b. typewriters
    c. aluminum
    d. cigarettes

15. The kinked demand curve of an oligopolist is based on the assumption that:
    a. other firms will determine their pricing and output policies in collusion with the given.
    b. competitors will ignore a price cut but follow a price increase.
    c. competitors will match both price cuts and price increases.
    d. competitors will follow a price cut but are reluctant to follow a price increase.

Self-Test (continued)

16. When an oligopolist considers raising the price of his/her product, and expects the other firms in the industry to follow suit, the oligopolist is a(n):
    a. shared monopolist
    b. collusive cartel
    c. noncollusive oligopolist
    d. price leader

17. Which of the following is not a model for an oligopoly market?
    a. mutual interdependence
    b. kinked demand curve
    c. price leadership
    d. cost-plus pricing

18. An oligopoly market model is characterized by:
    a. many firms with differentiated product
    b. many firms with standardized products
    c. few firms with differentiated products
    d. few firms with standardized or differentiated products

19. Concentration ratios:
    a. measures the percentage of all sales contributed by the leading four or eight firms
    b. measures "fewness"
    c. are limited because inter-industry competition is ignored
    d. all of the above

20. Dynamic Efficiency means that:
    a. oligopolists act as a "shared monopoly"
    b. oligopoly is less desirable than monopoly because it is not subject to government regulation
    c. the oligopoly market gives only an outward appearance of competition
    d. large oligopolistic firms are needed for technological progress

REVIEW SHEET: UNIT II MICROECONOMICS

ECON 106 – UNIT II REVIEW

Be sure to bring a #2 pencil, graph paper and calculator!

PART I: 40 Multiple Choice questions (2 points each or a total of 80 points)

1. Know the definitions of "economic cost" and how to calculate it.
2. Know the difference between accounting profit and economic profit.
3. Know what is meant when economic profit is positive, negative or equal to 0. Slide 7
4. Know the difference between the short-run and the long-run.
5. Know all the cost curves in the short-run: Total (TFC, TVC, TC): Average (AFC, AVC, ATC): Marginal (MC) — be able to calculate, graph and recognize. Be able to calculate TFC from a qty. of 0 and the TC column.
6. Know where to find the "most efficient level of production". Slide 25
7. Know the relationship between MC and AVC, ATC.
8. Know all the production curves: Total Product (TP); Average Product (AP); Marginal Product (MP) and the relationships between TP and MP; AP and MP.
9. Know where to find "diminishing returns" (MP column).
10. Know the definition of the LRATC, economies, and diseconomies of scale.
11. Know the characteristics of each of the four market models, how they are similar and different from each other and be able to give examples for each.
12. Know why a perfectly competitive firm faces a perfectly elastic demand curve.
13. Know where the short-run supply curve is under pure competition and why a firm will still stay open even though it is earning a loss in the short run.
14. Locate the shut-down point under pure competition.
15. Know the three techniques to maximize profit, or minimize loss, in the SR.
16. Distinguish between the "most efficient level" and the "most profitable level" and know why a firm might be efficient and earn a loss or why a firm might be inefficient and earn an economic profit, etc.
17. Know about Increasing-Costs, Decreasing-Costs and Constant-Cost industries.
18. For each market, be able to calculate the selling price (Pe), cost price (CP) and the profit or loss per unit, as well as the total profit or loss.
19. For each market, know what is possible to earn (economic, normal or loss) in both the short-run and long-run.
20. Know the pricing policies for a Monopolist (under regulated and unregulated conditions).
21. Know the definition of "price discrimination" and the conditions required.
22. Describe how a firm creates "barriers to entry."
23. Know why a Monopolistically Competitive firm is less elastic than a Competitive firm, but more elastic than a Monopolist.
24. Know what is meant by "economic inefficiency (wastes of monopolistic competition")".
25. Know what is meant by "mutual interdependence".
26. Know about cartels and collusion and why there are incentives to "cheat."
27. Know what is meant by "concentration ratios" and why they are important.
28. Know why the "Kinked-Demand Curve" can be used to describe oligopoly behavior.
29. ~~List the major issues in favor of advertising and against advertising.~~
30. Define "price leader" and how it is used in oligopoly behavior.

REVIEW SHEET: UNIT II MICROECONOMICS

PART II: Problems (10 points each or a total of 20 points)

Answer only TWO of the THREE problems, listed on the exam.

Problem #1: The Production Function (Example: Workbook page 182, #1)
Problem #2: Table and three techniques (Example: Workbook page 195, #2)
Problem #3: Draw three different market models, illustrate economic profit, normal profit or a loss, as indicated. Label Pe, Qe, CP (cost price) and shade where appropriate.

FORMULA SHEET: WORKBOOK PAGE 223
PROFIT/LOSS POSITIONS FOR ALL MODELS: WORKBOOK PAGE 223

REVIEW TEXTBOOK, CLASS NOTES, (ON WORKSHEET), WORKBOOK, CANVAS (QUIZZES AND PP SLIDES)

Any questions please contact your Instructor or visit our new "Learning Commons" located in the Bankier Library.

GOOD LUCK!!

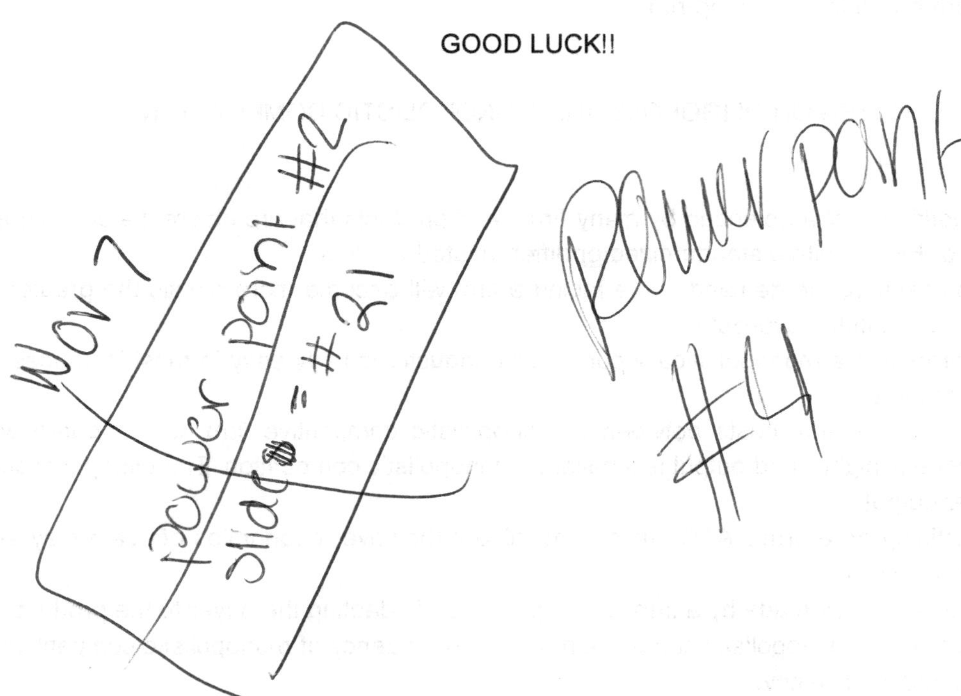

REVIEW SHEET: UNIT II MICROECONOMICS

NOTES ON MONOPOLY

1. The demand curve facing a monopolist is the same as the industry demand curve.
2. Monopoly may not be highly profitable (not guaranteed economic profits).
3. Price is not determined by supply and demand as in perfect competition.
4. By adhering to MC=MR Rule, a monopolist will guarantee either maximum profits or minimum losses.
5. A monopolist must lower price to increase sales, therefore MR<P(=AR).
6. Pricing policies for a monopolist include: (1) monopolist's price (MC = MR Rule) (2) marginal cost price (MC = P) (3) full-cost price (ATC = P).
7. A monopoly produces less quantity than under perfect competition; therefore, it is considered a misallocation of resources (MC < P).
8. A necessary condition for effective price discrimination is that products for sale must be separable among buyers or markets, according to their elasticity.
9. A necessary condition for effective price discrimination is that resale is nonexistent.
10. Economic profits are possible in the long-run.

NOTES ON OLIGOPOLY AND MONOPOLISTIC COMPETITION

1. Monopolistic competition is characterized by many firms and products that are differentiated. Oligopoly has a few large firms ("Big 4 or Big 8") with a standardized or differentiated product.
2. In monopolistic competition, the demand curve facing a firm will become more elastic the greater the number of sellers (greater # of substitutes available).
3. The entry of new firms into a monopolistically competitive industry is fairly easy in most instances. It is difficult to enter an oligopoly market.
4. Comparing long-run equilibrium costs between a monopolistic competitive firm as compared with a perfectly competitive firm, price is higher and output is smaller in monopolistic competition. The oligopolist charges a higher price with a smaller output.
5. The effect of advertising on a firm's ATC curve is to raise it (however economies of scale may actually lower a firm's costs on the average).
6. Selling costs are expenditures made by a firm for the purpose of adapting the buyer to the product.
7. The expression "wastes of monopolistic competition" refers to tendency of monopolistic competitive firms to suffer from overcrowding and inefficiency.
8. Those firms that survive in monopolistic competition tend to earn normal profits in the long run; oligopolists may earn economic profits in the long run.
9. Monopolistic competition leads to underutilization of firms, due to the large number of firms.

REVIEW SHEET: UNIT II MICROECONOMICS

Four Market Models: Profit/Loss Positions

Market Model	Short-run	Long-run
1. Pure Competition	Economic Profit Normal Profit Loss	 Normal Profit Loss
2. Pure Monopoly	Economic Profit Normal Profit Loss	Economic Profit Normal Profit Loss
3. Monopolistic Competition	Economic Profit Normal Profit Loss	 Normal Profit Loss
4. Oligopoly	Economic Profit Normal Profit Loss	Economic Profit Normal Profit Loss

Formula Sheet

$$MP = \frac{\blacktriangle TP}{\blacktriangle \text{Units of Labor}} \qquad AP = \frac{TP}{\text{Units of Labor}}$$

$$TC = TFC + TVC \qquad MC = \frac{\blacktriangle TC}{\blacktriangle Q}$$

$$AFC = \frac{TFC}{Q} \qquad AVC = \frac{TVC}{Q}$$

$$ATC = \frac{TC}{Q} = AFC + AVC$$

$$TR = \text{Price x Quantity Demanded}$$

$$MR = \frac{\blacktriangle TR}{\blacktriangle Q} \qquad AR = \frac{TR}{Q}$$

Total profit (or loss) = TR - TC = Net Revenue

ATC x Q = TC

REVIEW SHEET: UNIT II MICROECONOMICS

1. For each market model shown,
   a. Label all of the revenue and costs curves.
   b. Label the profit maximizing (or loss minimizing) selling price—Pe, quantity—Qe and cost price (CP).
   c. State whether an "economic profit", a "normal profit", or a "loss" has occurred.
   d. Shade the profit/loss area.

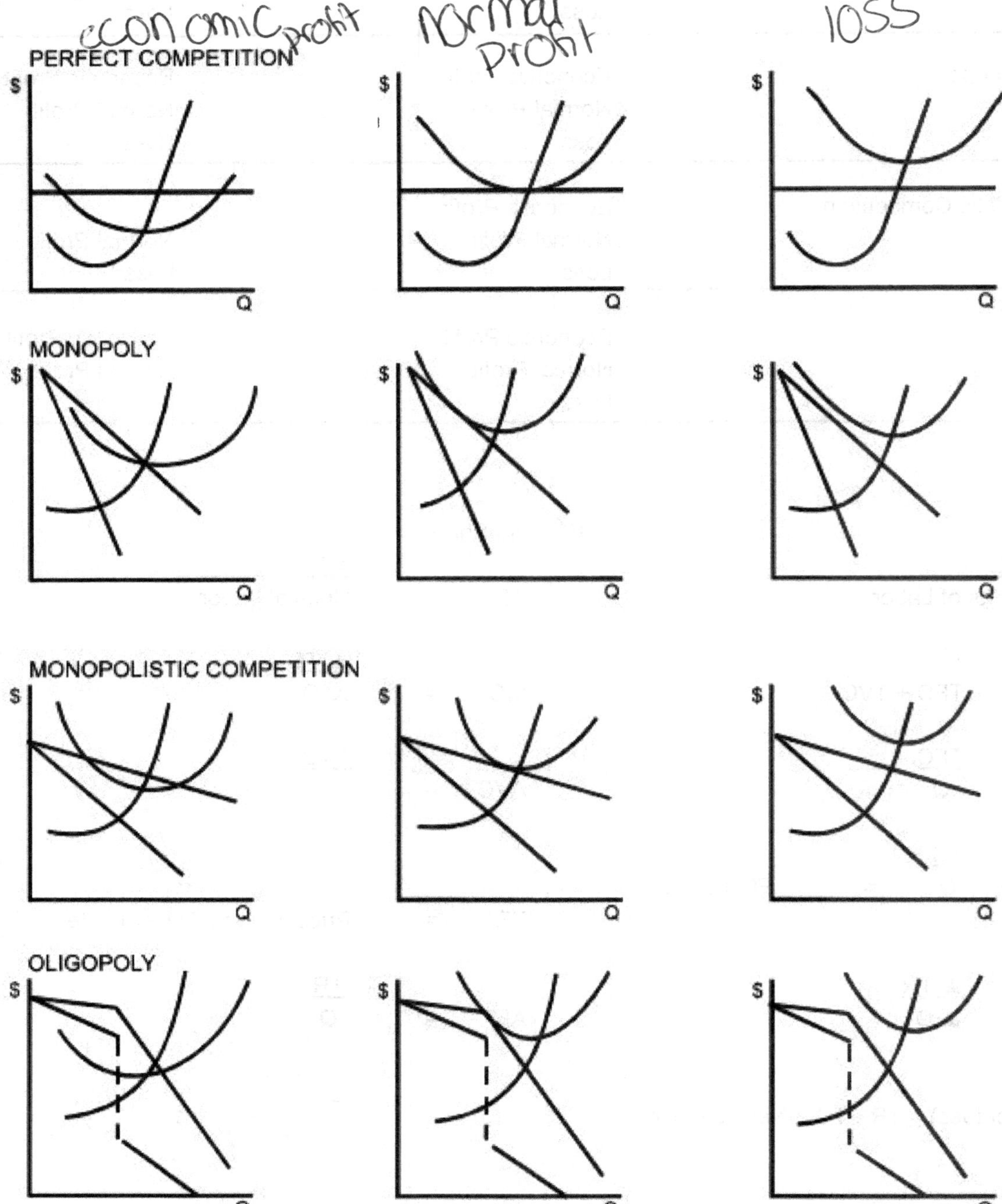

2. Fill in the following table based upon the information, which you have learned.

TABLE I
"Comparing Market Structure"

Market Model:	Pure Competition	Monopolistic Competition	Oligopoly	Pure Monopoly
Number of Firms:				
Type of product				
Control over price				
Conditions of entry				
Nonprice Competition				
Economic Profits in Long-run?				
Examples:				

MICROECONOMICS

Unit III

"The Demand for Resources"

Chapter Orientation

Up to this point, you have studied the supply and demand for final goods and services. Now we will complete the circular flow and examine the supply and demand for the factors of production -- land, labor, capital and entrepreneurial ability -- that are needed to create the final product.

In the resource markets, businesses now determine the demand curve for resources (there is an inverse relationship between wage and units of a resource). Households now determine the supply curve for resources (there is a direct relationship between wage and units of a resource).

Labor receives wages; owners of land receive rent; the price paid for capital is interest, and entrepreneurs receive profit. How is the price paid to these factors determined?

In a purely competitive market the price paid is determined by the forces of supply and demand. It gets a bit more complicated when big unions or big business try to manipulate the competitive price to their own advantage (imperfect market). These issues will be discussed in the next two concepts.

You will find that many of the concepts and analytical tools which you used in determining the profit maximizing (or loss minimizing) price and quantity in the output markets can also apply to the resource markets -- factor demand and supply. Also, many of the terms will remain the same except that a word might be added to denote the resource markets rather than the output markets.

Learning Objectives

After reading this chapter in the text and completing the following exercises in this concepts book, you will be able to:

1. List the major reasons for studying resource pricing.
2. Define the marginal productivity theory.
3. Explain the factor markets using a simple circular flow diagram.
4. State the ways a firm determines the "worth" of an employee.
5. Explain in the resource markets who "demands" and who "supplies".
6. Define marginal product (MP) and explain how this concept illustrates the law of diminishing returns.
7. Define marginal revenue product (MRP) and calculate MRP when given data from a purely competitive market.
8. Define and calculate average revenue product (ARP) when given the necessary information.
9. Explain why the demand for resources is derived demand.
10. Define and calculate the marginal resources cost (MRC) when given the necessary data.
11. State the technique used by a profit-maximizing firm to determine how much of a resource it will employ and apply it when you are given the necessary data.
12. Explain what curve represents the demand curve in a competitive market.
13. List three reasons which would cause a change in factor demand (shift the curve), and explain their impact.
14. State what effect the elasticity of resources and causes a "change in quantity demanded" for the factor.
15. State the rule employed by a firm to determine the least-cost combination of resources and apply this rule when given the necessary data to determine the quantities to purchase.
16. State the pros and cons of marginal productivity theory.

"The Demand for Resources"

Chapter Highlights

I. Introduction of the Input Markets

A. Background

1. You will recall from the simple circular flow model that the flow of money and goods/services between households and businesses are carried out in the two markets: resource and product. In the Product market, we determined the product price and quantity (output). In the resource market, we will determine the factors price and quantity (input). This will complete our understanding of the simple circular flow model. (See Figure below).

Figure 1
Simple Circular Flow Model

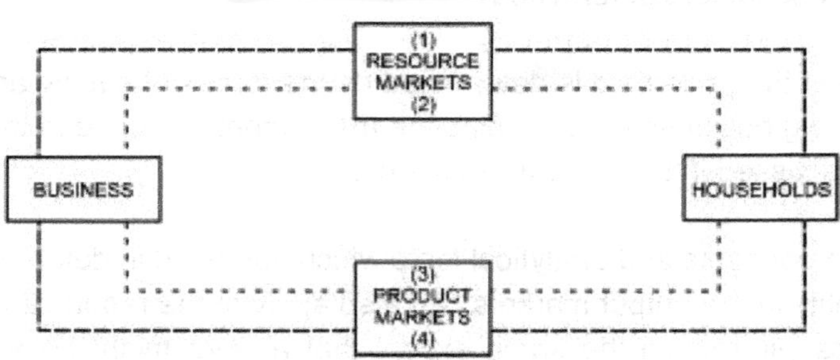

II. Significance of Resource Pricing

1. Money incomes determination -- resource prices influence the size of individual incomes.
2. Cost minimization -- resources represent a cost to the firm (takes away from profits), therefore to maximize profit the most efficient (least cost) combination should be purchased.
3. Resource allocation -- resource prices allocate scarce resources among businesses.
4. Policy issues -- resource prices bring up the question of equity between profits and wages. What degree of income inequality is acceptable? Should the government tax the "excess"?

III. Marginal Productivity Theory of Resource Demand

A. Terms and Formulas

1. Resource Demand as a Derived Demand -- factor demand is taken from the demand for the final good or service, which resources help produce.
   a. A firm determines the demand for a resources based upon productivity, the going-market rate, and the value of the final product produced.
2. Marginal Productivity Theory – in a purely competitive market, a worker is paid a wage (money payment) that is equal to his/her marginal output (marginal revenue product) or "worth".
3. How does an employee determine his/her worth? (Going market rate, education, training, etc.)
4. Marginal product (MP) -- the change in output resulting from an additional unit of a resource (the amount each resource demands).

$$MP^* = \frac{\blacktriangle \text{ Total Product}}{\blacktriangle \text{ Units of Resource}}$$

   a. MP declines because of the law of diminishing returns.
   b. *MP is graphed at the midpoints.

3. Marginal revenue product (MRP) -- the change in total revenue resulting from an additional unit of a resource (value each resource adds).

   $$MRP^* = MP \times \text{Product's price} = \frac{\Delta \text{ Total Revenue}}{\Delta \text{ Units of Resource}}$$

   a. Combines the MP (production added) and the price of the product (value added) to determine the "worth" of a resource. In a competitive market a resources is paid what it's worth (MRP = resource price).
   b. Since the MRP curve determines a resources' worth to a business, the MRP curve is the <u>demand curve</u> for a firm (it indicates the number of units a business will hire at alternative prices or wages).
   c. *MRP is graphed at the midpoints.
4. Average revenue product (ARP) -- is the "per unit" revenue received by a firm.

   $$ARP = \frac{\Delta \text{Total Revenue}}{\Delta \text{Units of Resource}}$$

5. Marginal resource cost (MRC) -- the change in total resource cost resulting from an additional unit of a resource (cost each resource adds).

   $$MRC^* = \frac{\Delta \text{ Total Resource Cost}}{\Delta \text{ Units of Resource}}$$

   a. *MRC is graphed at the midpoints.
6. Summary of terms and formulas. See Table 1 below.

Table 1
Resource Terms

Production	Revenue	Cost
TP (Total Product)	TR (Total Revenue)	TRC (Total Resource Cost)
MP (Marginal Product)	ARP (Average Revenue Product)	MRC (Marginal Resource Cost)
	MRP (Marginal Revenue Product) ↳ resource demand curve	

Formulas

Production	Revenue	Cost
TP (given)	TR = TP x Product's Price	TRC = # Workers x Wage Rate
$MP = \frac{\Delta \text{ TP}}{\Delta \text{ Units of Resource}}$	$ARP = \frac{\text{TR}}{\text{Units of Resource}}$	$MRC = \frac{\Delta \text{ TRC}}{\Delta \text{ Units of Resource}}$
	$MRP = \frac{\Delta \text{ TR}}{\Delta \text{ Units of Resource}}$ = MP x Product's Price = Demand Curve	

B. Profit maximization (or loss minimization) techniques:
   1. Use the MRP = MRC Rule (similar to the MR = MC rule in the output markets).

2. It will be profitable for a firm to hire additional units of a resource up to the point where MRP equals MRC. Another technique which will give the same results in the TR - TRC Rule where the difference between TR and TC is the greatest (profit max) or the smallest (loss min).
3. Summary: (See Table 2 below).

Table 2

Profit max (or loss min) in short run:

1. MRP = MRC Rule
2. TR - TRC Rule

Table 3

In the Resource Market:

A.	Who Demands?	Business
B.	Who Supplies?	Households

VI. Market Demand for a Resource

A. Purely competitive markets

1. The MRP curve is the resource demand curve for a purely competitive seller. Because of diminishing returns (MP decreases) the resource demand curve is downward sloping (product price is constant).

B. Imperfect competition

1. The MRP curve is also the resource demand curve under imperfect competition. The resource demand curve is downward sloping because of diminishing returns and because the product price is falling as output increases.

C. Market demand

1. The market demand curve can be found by summing together all of the individual resource demand (or MRP) curves. (See Figure 2 below).

Figure 2
Market Demand for Labor

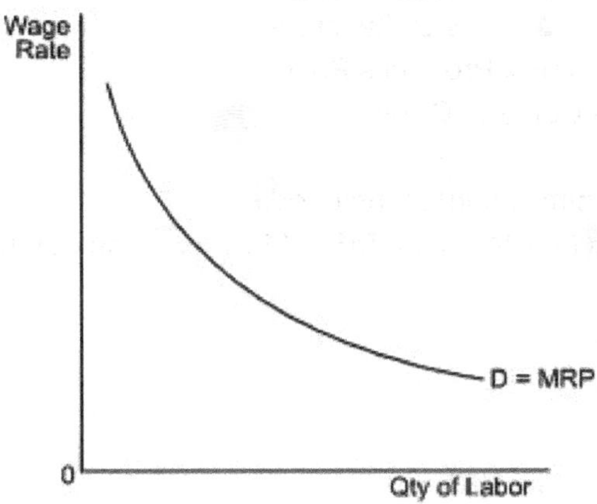

V. Determinant of Resource Demand

A. A change in resource demand (new demand curve — See Figure 3 below).

1. The resource demand curve will shift due to:
    a. Changes in product demand -- (shifts the curve in the same direction).
    b. Productivity changes -- (shifts curve in the same direction).
        1. Quantities of other resources
        2. Technological Progress
        3. Quantity of the variable resource
    c. Change in the price of a substitute factor -- (the substitution and output effects work in opposite directions). If the substitution effect outweighs the output effect, the demand for labor will move in the same direction. It will move in the opposite direction, if the output effect outweighs the substitution effect.
    d. Change in the price of a complementary factor -- (shifts in the opposite direction).

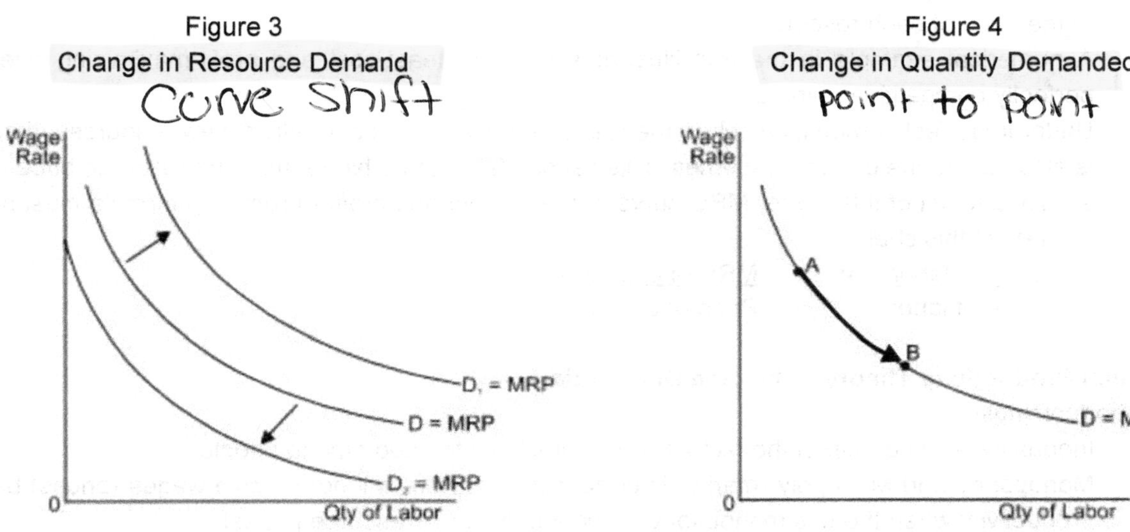

2. Occupational Employment Trends
    a. The demand for service workers is rapidly outpacing the demand for manufacturing, construction and mining.
    b. Of the top ten fastest-growing occupations, in percentage terms (2010-2020), service occupations dominate the list.
    c. Three of the top occupations are directly related to healthcare due to the aging of U.S. population (baby boomers) and the presence of private and public insurance.
    d. The greatest job losses relate to "labor saving" technology, textiles, and apparel.

VI. Elasticity of Resource Demand

A. A change in the "quantity" of resource demand

1. Movement along the resource demand curve due to changes in the price (wage) of a factor — (See Figure 4 above).
2. Elasticity of resource demand measures the extent producers will change the quantity of a resource (labor) when price (wage) changes.

3. Factors that influence the elasticity of resource demands:
   a. Difficulty in finding substitutes
   b. The elasticity for the output (final product).
   c. The labor cost - total cost ratio.

VII. Optimum Combination of Resources

A. The Least-Cost Rule

1. Since in the long-run all resources are variable, we need to calculate the least-cost combination of resources of a firm will select to maximize profits. This approach is similar to the idea of consumer equilibrium measured in "utils" of satisfaction per dollar.
2. $$\frac{\text{MP of labor}}{\text{Price of labor}} = \frac{\text{MP of capital}}{\text{Price of capital}} = 1$$
   The cost of any output is minimized when the ratio of the MP of a resource to its price is the same for all the resources the firm employs.
3. To maximize profits, a firm in a competitive market would hire where the MRP of each resource is equal to the price of each resource.
4. A numerical example in the text illustrates how the least-cost and profit-maximizing rules apply in a perfectly competitive market.
5. Under imperfect competition, when the resource price is raised to attract new resources, that higher price is also paid to the current resources. This causes MRC to be higher than the resource price.
   a. As a result of this higher MRC curve our least-cost and profit-maximizing formula must be adjusted to reflect this change.
   $$\frac{\text{MRP of labor}}{\text{Price of labor}} = \frac{\text{MRP of capital}}{\text{Price of capital}} = 1$$

VIII. Marginal Productivity Theory of Income Distribution

A. Shortcomings

1. Inequality -- ownership of the factors are not justly distributed among people.
2. Monopsony and Monopoly (market imperfections), factors will not receive wages (prices) based on their productivity when there is monopsony or monopoly in the resource markets.

IX. Last Word: Input Substitution — The Case of ATMs

X. Web-based Question (see your Instructor)

Key Terms

marginal productivity theory
circular flow model
factors of production
derived demand
marginal product (MP)
law of diminishing returns
marginal revenue product (MRP)
average revenue product (ARP)
marginal resource cost (MRC)
MRP = MRC Rule
substitution effect
output effect
least-cost rule
profit-maximizing rule
monopsony
elasticity of resource demand

PROBLEMS

1a. Complete the following table:

Units of Resource	TP	MP	Price	Product TR	ARP	MRP
1	17		$20			
2	31					
3	43					
4	53					
5	60					
6	65					

b. Assume the cost of labor is $100 per person per day. Calculate the TRC and MRC per day. (Use chart below).

c. Assume the cost of labor is $200 per person per day. Calculate the TRC' and MRC' per day. (Use chart below).

Units of Resource	Wage Rate	TRC	MRC	Wage Rate	TRC'	MRC'
1	$100			$200		
2						
3						
4						
5						
6						

d. Prepare two (2) separate graphs.
Graph #1 - Graph TR and TRC, TRC' Graph #2 - Graph MRP and MRC, MRC'

e. How many persons would you hire at $100 per day? How many at $200 per day?

MP* = $\frac{\blacktriangle TP}{\blacktriangle \text{Units of Resource}}$

ARP = $\frac{TR}{\text{Units of Resource}}$

TR = TP x Product Price

TRC = Units of Labor x Wage Rate

MRP* = $\frac{\blacktriangle TR}{\blacktriangle \text{Units of Resource}}$

MRC* = $\frac{\blacktriangle TRC}{\blacktriangle \text{Units of Resource}}$

= MP x Product's price

= Demand Curve

*graph at midpoints

"The Demand for Resources"

Self-Test

1. Which of the following statements best explains why we can say that demand for a factor input is a "derived" demand?
   a. The demand for factor inputs is based on the demand for the final product.
   b. The demand for factor inputs is based on the productivity of the factor inputs.
   c. The demand for factor inputs is developed from the relative availability of the factor inputs.
   d. The demand for factor inputs is based on changes in demand resulting from advanced technology.

2. Which of the following statements best describes the relationship between "marginal product" and "diminishing returns"?
   a. Increasing marginal product is indicative of diminishing returns from increasing the units of resource.
   b. Decreasing marginal product reflects diminishing returns from increasing the units of resources.
   c. Decreasing marginal product is the result of diminishing returns from decreasing the units of resource.
   d. Decreasing marginal product reflects diminishing returns from the units of resource, which are always constant.

3. Which of the following best accounts for the shape of the resource demand curve in imperfect competition?
   a. A factor demand curve will have an initial positive slope due to the increase in demand for a product.
   b. A factor demand curve will have a downward slope due to the slope of the demand curve for the final product.
   c. A factor demand curve will be downward sloping due to the diminishing returns associated with factor productivity and the downward slope of the demand curve for the final product.
   d. A factor demand curve has a shape, which depends solely on the shape of the demand curve for the final product.

4. Which of the following statements best defines marginal revenue product of a resource?
   a. The additional value to final product contributed by the average of all factor inputs.
   b. The value obtained by multiplying MP by total revenue.
   c. The additional value to total revenue contributed by an additional unit of resource.
   d. The additional output contributed by an additional unit of a resource.

5. Select from the alternatives below the one that correctly completes the following sentence: "Since the demand for butter is ______ because of the availability of alternatives, the demand for resource factors that produce butter tends to be ______.
   a. elastic; inelastic
   b. elastic; available
   c. elastic; elastic
   d. inelastic; inelastic

"The Demand for Resources"

Self-Test – (continued)

6. Which of the following is not a justification for studying resource pricing:
   a. Resource prices influence the size of individual incomes.
   b. Resource prices allocate scarce resources.
   c. Resources represent a cost to the firm.
   d. Resources bring about equality in a competitive market.

7. The circular flow model helps to explain
   a. The price and quantity of goods and services
   b. The price and quantity of the factors of production.
   c. The interaction of households and businesses in the product and resource markets.
   d. All of the above.

8. The MRP curve is the:
   a. demand curve for the competitive seller.
   b. demand curve for the imperfectly competitive seller.
   c. demand curve for the market.
   d. all of the above.

9. Which of the following will cause a quantity change in resource demand?
   a. the rate of decline of MP.
   b. a change in the wage rate.
   c. productivity changes.
   d. the percentage of total production costs.

10. The least-cost approach states that:
    a. when given a specific output, the least-cost approach will also be the profit-maximizing combination.
    b. the profit-maximizing combination will also be the least-cost approach
    c. the least-cost approach is a separate formula and therefore, independent of the profit-maximizing combination.
    d. to maximize profits, a firm must minimize costs.

"Wage Determination"

Chapter Orientation

Since the last concept laid the foundation for the "Resource (Input) Market", we can now build on these concepts and apply them to the price (wage) and quantity of labor in six different kinds of labor (situation) markets.

It is interesting to compare the salary of a top actor or athlete with a top teacher. Why is there such a difference?

The concept opens with the definition of wages and explains why advanced industrial nations have high real wages. It then details specific labor markets and how the wage rate and quantity of labor are determined. You should have an understanding of each of the markets and be able to distinguish one market from another. The first market will be a competitive market based upon supply and demand. The remaining markets will be based upon who has the economic power (clout)? Having this "edge" tilts the direction of the wage rate, rather than wages being based upon supply and demand in the marketplace.

In addition, the concept discusses minimum-wage laws; wage differentials that exist among occupational groups; and human capital investment -- any action that improves the productivity of workers. Lastly, we will explore the "principle agent problem" and discuss the ways to remedy this dilemma.

Learning Objectives

After reading this chapter in the text and completing the following exercises in this concepts book, you will be able to:

1. Define wages (or wage rate); distinguish between nominal wages and real wages.
2. List the factors that have contributed to the high level of real wages in advanced industrial countries.
3. Explain how the wage rate and quantity of labor are determined in a competitive and in monopsonistic labor market (use graphs for each).
4. Explain how the unions seek to raise wage rates and the impact of these actions on the employment of labor.
5. Compare the wage rate and the level of employment in a competitive labor market with what happens when the industrial workers become unionized (use one graph).
6. Use a graph to explain the wage rate and level of employment under a bilateral monopoly.
7. Discuss the controversy over minimum-wage (pros and cons) and present the empirical evidence.
8. Define wage differential and explain the three major factors that influence this inequity.
9. Define investment in human capital.
10. Discuss the cause-effect chain in the theory of human capital.
11. Present the criticisms of the human capital theory.

Chapter Highlights

I. Labor, Wages and Earnings

A. Economists use the term "labor" to apply to
   1. All blue and white-collar workers
   2. Professional people
   3. Owners of small businesses.

B. Definition of wages (or the wage rates) -- are the prices paid to secure labor. Nominal wages (or money wages) represent the amount of money a worker receives per hour, per week, etc. Real wages represents the purchasing power of wages.

C. Definition of earnings -- the wage rate multiplied by the amount of time worked are equal to earnings.

"Wage Determination"

II. General Level of Real Wages

A. High real wages in the U.S. and other industrially advanced countries is because the demand for labor has been strong compared to the supply of labor.

B. Role of productivity
1. Plentiful capital -- workers have access to large amounts of capital goods.
2. Abundant natural resources -- the countries are richly endowed with natural resources.
3. Advanced technology -- workers use capital equipment and their technology is superior.
4. Labor quality -- workers have the health, vigor, education and training and are more efficient.
5. Other factors such as the efficiency and flexibility of management; the social, business, and political environment; the vast size of our domestic market; and increased specialization of production enabled by free-trade agreements.

C. Real Wages and Productivity - The real income per worker can increase only at about the same rate as output per worker.

D. Secular Growth and Stagnation - Although the American population and the labor force have grown significantly over the decades, those increases have been more than offset by the demand for labor as a result of increased productivity. The result has been a long-run (secular) increase in wage rates.

III. Real Wages & Productivity

A. Types of market models
1. We will be examining <u>six</u> different labor market models:
   a. Purely Competitive Model
   b. Monopsony Model
   c. Demand-Enhancement Model or called "Ideal" (Increasing the demand for labor) attempt by union
   d. Exclusive or Craft Unionism (union restricts the supply of labor)
   e. Inclusive or Industrial Unionism (union threatens a strike to secure a wage rate above the competitive equilibrium)
   f. Bilateral monopoly market
2. Economic Power - See Table 1 below.

<u>Table 1</u>

Economic Power	Market Model
1. No One	1. Purely Competitive (S=D) Model
2. Business	2. Monopsony (Co. Town)
{ 3. Union	{ 3. Demand Enhancement Model (or "Ideal")
{ 4. Union	{ 4. Exclusive for Craft Unionism
{ 5. Union	{ 5. Inclusive or Industrial
6. Indeterminate	6. Bilateral Monopoly

3. The wage rate and the level of employment depends upon the supply and the demand for labor and the competitiveness of the market.

IV. Purely Competitive Model

A. The wage rate and level of employment is determined by the intersection of the labor demand and labor supply curves in the market.
1. Market demand is found by summing the individual MRP curves in the market.
2. The <u>market</u> supply curve is upward sloping, because the wage must rise to attract more workers.
   a. Once the going-rate has been established, the individual <u>firm</u> faces a perfectly elastic supply curve.
   b. An <u>individual</u> worker's supply curve is "backward bending", due to the tradeoffs between work and leisure hours. The "substitution effect" says that in the beginning you will replace leisure hours with

more work hours. The income effect says that at a certain point, a worker will tradeoff work hours for more leisure hours. (See Figure 1).

Figure 1
A Competitive Model of Wage Determination

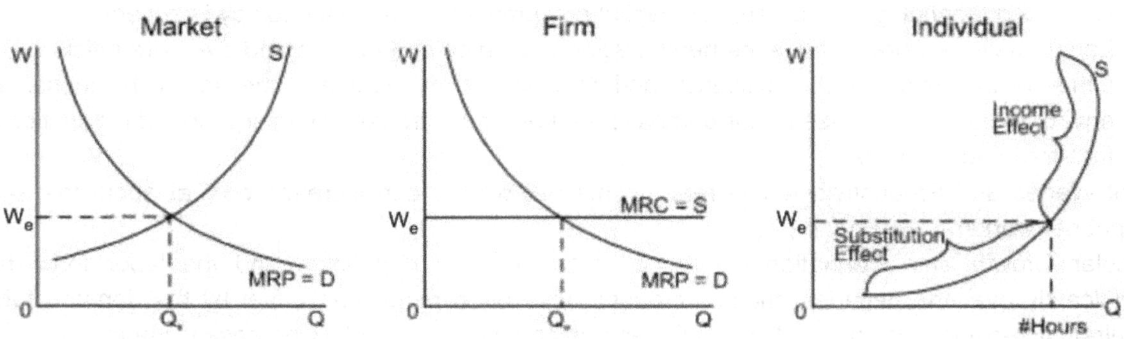

V. Monopsony (from the Greek word meaning "single buyer")

A. Definition -- one buyer (employer) in a populated nonunionized area.

B. Examples of monopsony markets: a "company town", such as a paper or textile mill or a silver mine.

C. A monopsonist must increase wages to attract new workers and should also increase the wages of the present employees (or else suffer low morale). Therefore the MRC is higher than the supply curve (MRC > supply curve) because the cost of hiring a new employee is his/her rate plus the extra amount for the present workers). (See Figure 2).

Figure 2
Monopsony

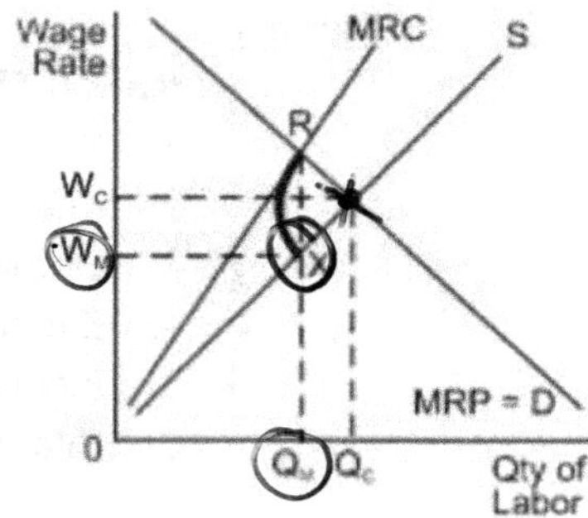

D. The relationship of a monopsonist is similar to a monopolist's demand and marginal revenue curves.

E. The monopsonist will hire until MRC = MRP. In Figure 2, MRC crosses MRP at point "R" (our reference point). From point "R" go to the quantity of labor (X-axis) to determine the number of workers (Qm). How much will a monopsonist pay these workers? Go up to the height of the supply curve (point X) for the wage rate (Wm), on the y-axis.

F. Compare the monopsonists wage rate and quantity of labor with that of a purely competitive market where the wage rate is Wc (higher) and the quantity of labor hired is Qc (higher).

G. The difference between the reference point (R) and the wage rate (x) is called "monopsonistic exploitation" (shown by the bracket).

know the graphs + match models

VI. Union models

A. **Demand-Enhancement Model (Increasing the Demand for Labor or "Ideal Model")** - unions seek to raise wage rates by increasing the demand for labor. (See Figure 3 below).

Figure 3 Demand-Enhancement Model (Increasing Labor Demand or "Ideal Model")

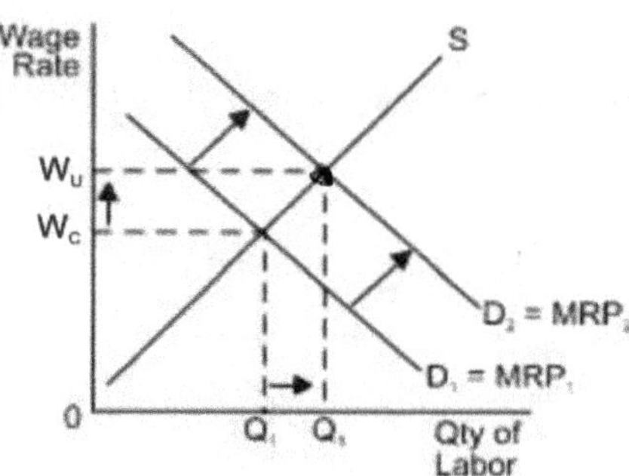

1. A union will attempt to increase labor demand by:
   a. Increasing the demand for the product or service (derived demand) by advertising or by political lobbying.
   b. Enhancing labor productivity -- more union involvement in establishing joint labor-management committees to increase labor productivity.
   c. Alter the prices of other related goods -- increase the price of substitute resources (example: increase the minimum wage) or reduce the price of a complementary resource.
2. In reality, unions are actually trying to protect declines (rather than increases) in the demand for labor.

B. **Exclusive or craft unionism** -- by limiting the supply of labor, unions may increase wage rates, "also called labor monopoly". (See Figure 4).

Figure 4 Craft Unionism

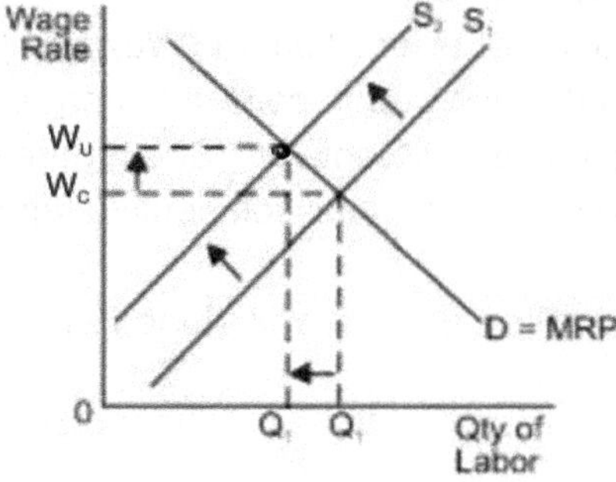

1. A union will restrict the labor supply by:
   a. Supporting legislation which restricts the supply of labor
   b. Adopting techniques to limit membership (exclusive unionism) or lobbying for licensing of trades (occupational licensing).

C. **Inclusive or industrial unionism** -- most unions week to organize <u>all</u> potential workers (a characteristic of industrial unions such as automobile workers). A "strike threat" by <u>all</u> the workers will deprive the firm of its labor supply. If no workers will work for a wage less than that demanded by the union (for example $12) the labor supply curve with a "strike threat" will have a "kink" in it (point "K"). To attract additional workers after point "K", a firm must increase the wage rate. Hence, the shape of the labor supply curve will be WuKS. (See Figure 5).

Figure 5 Inclusive or Industrial Unionism

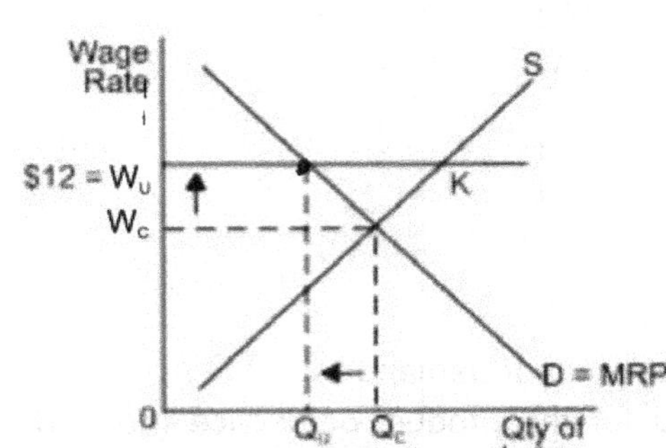

1. The result of this "strike threat" will be fewer workers demanded (hired) by business.

D. Wage Increases and Unemployment - Empirical evidence has shown that union members receive a wage advantage over nonunion members (on the average of 15 percent). However, the actions of exclusive (restricts labor supply) and inclusive ("strike threat") unionism causes unemployment within the ranks because the union seeks such a high wage rate, as compared to the competitive rate. Two ways the unemployment impact can be offset are:
   1. Growth of the economy spurs demand for labor over time.
   2. Elasticity - The size of the unemployment impact is based upon the elasticity of demand for labor.

VII. Bilateral monopoly -- "a monopsonist buys from a monopolist". For example: "Big labor clashes with big business". A bilateral monopoly is a market in which there is only one seller of a resource (labor monopoly) and only one buyer (monopsonistic or a powerful company).

A. The union will seek a wage rate above the equilibrium (Wu) and the monopsonist will seek a wage rate of (Wm). The outcome is indeterminant (based upon collective bargaining), but will fall somewhere between Wu and Wm depending on which side has the advantage. (See Figure 6, below). The two monopoly powers tend to offset each other resulting in competitive or near-competitive results (no exploitation).

Figure 6 Bilateral Monopoly

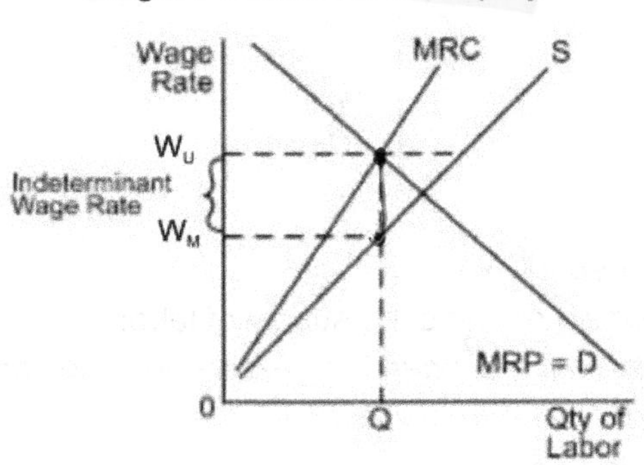

VIII. The Minimum-Wage Controversy

A. The U.S. has had a Federal minimum wage (currently $7.25 per hour) since 1938. In New Jersey the minimum wage rate is $8.38 per hour.

B. Case against -- minimum-wage causes firms higher costs, which results in the hiring of fewer workers or closing down the business. In addition, many workers receiving minimum wage do not live in impoverished households

C. Case for -- in certain markets wages can increase without causing unemployment; also it increases worker productivity.

D. Empirical evidence suggest that the overall effect of minimum-wage is uncertain. However, it has strong political support.

IX. Wage Differentials

A. Definition of wage differentials -- differences in wage rates among occupations.

B. Reasons for wage differentials

1. Marginal Revenue Productivity
    a. Occupations differ in the amount of revenue they contribute to their employer. Example: top athletes generate billions of dollars over a course of a season, so the "Marginal Revenue Productivity" is very high.
2. Noncompeting groups
    a. Ability — workers have different abilities and their wages and salaries are based upon supply and demand.
    b. Education and Training: Investing in Human Capital
    Noncompeting groups (causing wage differentials) exist to a large extent because of differing amounts of investment in human capital. A human capital investment is any action that improves the productivity of workers; the expenditures on education, improving health and the mobility of workers.
3. Compensating differences -- wage differentials are paid to compensate for the nonmoney differences among jobs. (For example: risk, danger, night shift, etc.).
4. Market imperfections -- because workers are not perfectly mobile (reluctant to leave their home; lose their union card or license by moving to another state) or because they are in a minority group (discrimination, unions/and Government restraints and lack of job information) wage differentials persist.

X. Pay and Performance

A. Principal Agent Problem

1. Definition — a conflict of interest arises when agents (workers) pursue their own objectives to the detriment of the principal (employer's goals).
2. Ways to Remedy
    a Monitor workers
    b Incentive Pay Plan
        (1) Piece Rates
        (2) Commissions and Royalties
        (3) Bonuses, Profit Sharing and Stock Options
        (4) Efficiency Wages
3. Addenda: Negative-side Effects
    a Ways to remedy may cause poor quality, fraudulent sales, etc.

XI. Last Word: Are Chief Executive Officers (CEOs) overpaid?

XII. Web-based Question (see your Instructor)

"Wage Determination"

Key Terms

wage (rate)
earnings
nominal wage
real wages
marginal resource cost (MRC)
competitive labor market
"backward bending supply curve"
substitution effect
income effect
monopsony
principal agent problem
monopsonistic exploitation
exclusive unionism
cost-benefit analysis
craft union
occupational licensing
labor monopoly
inclusive unionism
strike threat
industrial union
bilateral monopoly
indeterminant wage
minimum-wage
wage differentials
noncompeting groups
compensating differences
theory of human capital
cause-effect chain in human capital

PROBLEMS

1. Table 1 below shows the cost of a revenue schedule for a Monopsonist.

Table 1

Units of Labor	Wage Rate	TRC	MRC	MRP
0	$50	____		
			____	$240
1	$60	____		
			____	$200
2	$70	____		
			____	$160
3	$80	____		
			____	$120
4	$90	____		
			____	$80
5	$100	____		
			____	$40
6	$110	____		

Formulas:

TRC = Wage Rate x Quantity of Labor

MRC* = $\frac{\blacktriangle \text{ TRC}}{\blacktriangle \text{ Units of Resource}}$ *graphed at the midpoint

a. Fill in the table above.

b. On one graph, plot MRC, the supply curve and MRP.

c. What will be the wage rate and quantity of labor for this monopsonist?

PROBLEMS

2. Answer the following questions based on Figure 7 below.

Figure 7

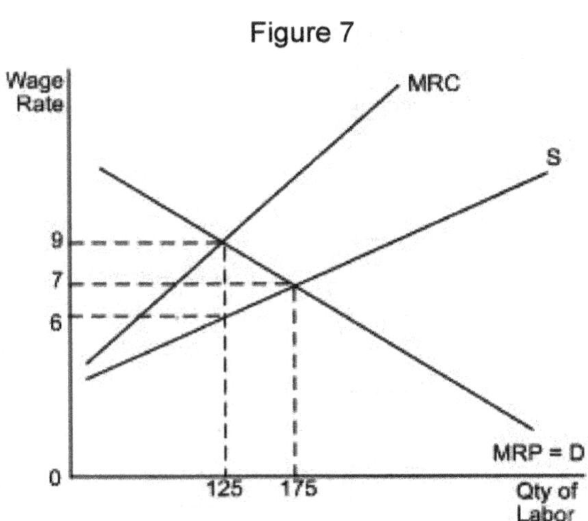

1. In equilibrium, the perfectly competitive employer will pay a wage rate of:

   a. $4 b. $6 c. $7 d. $9

2. In equilibrium, the perfectly competitive employer will hire how many workers?

   a. 100 b. 150 c. 200 d. 175

3. In equilibrium, the monopsonistic employer will pay a wage rate of:

   a. $4 b. $6 c. $7 d. $9

4. In equilibrium, the monopsonistic employer will hire how many workers?

   a. 100 b. 150 c. 200 d. 125

5. The amount of "monopsonistic exploitation" in the wage rate is:

   a. $1 b. $2 c. $3 d. $4

6. Under a bilateral monopoly, the wage rate will be:

   a. $2 b. $4 c. $6 d. Indeterminant Range Between $6-$9

PROBLEMS

3. Answer the following questions based on Figure 8 below.

Figure 8

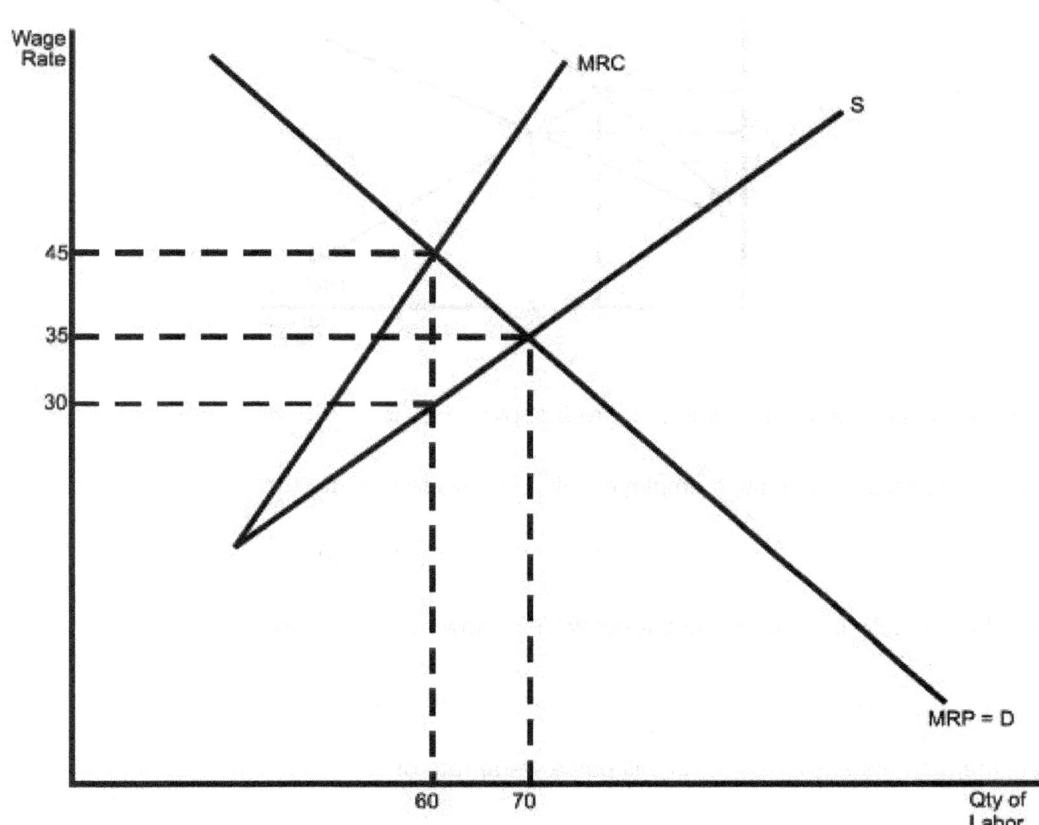

1. Under perfect competition, an employer would hire ___7___ persons and pay ___38___ per hour.

2. Under monopsony, an employer would hire _______ persons and pay ________ per hour.

3. Under a bilateral monopoly, the wage will be between _______ and _______.

4. The amount of "monopsonistic exploitation" in the wage rate is:

   a. $10   b. $13   c. $15   d. $18

"Wage Determination"

Self-Test

Figure 9

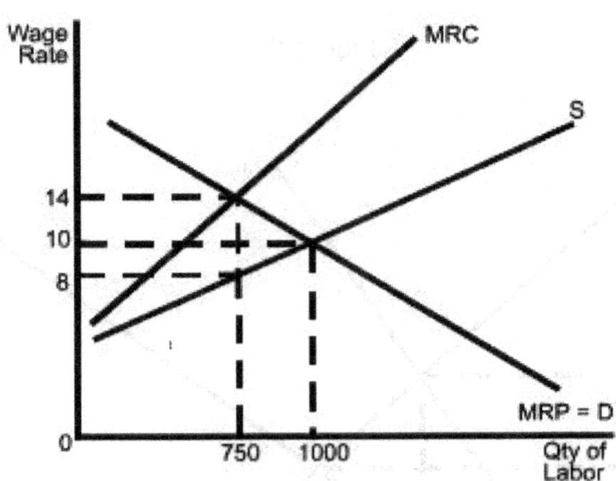

Answer the following six questions based upon Figure 9 above.

1. In equilibrium, the perfectly competitive employer will pay a wage rate of:

   a. $5 b. $8 c. $10 d. $12.50

2. In equilibrium, the perfectly competitive employer will hire how many workers:

   a. 500 b. 600 c. 1,000 d. 750

3. In equilibrium, the monopsonistic employer will pay a wage rate of:

   a. $8 b. $14 c. $10 d. $12.50

4. In equilibrium, the monopsonistic employer will hire how many workers:

   a. 500 b. 600 c. 1,000 d. 750

5. Under monopsony, with no union, the equilibrium wage rate in this market would be:

   a. $8 b. $10 c. $12.50 d. $14

6. If a labor union successfully bargained for a wage of $10 per hour, what would happen to total employment? (based upon question #5)
   a. it would increase by 250 workers
   b. it would not change
   c. it would decrease by 250 workers
   d. no way to tell from the diagram

"Wage Determination"

Self-Test (continued)

Figure 1

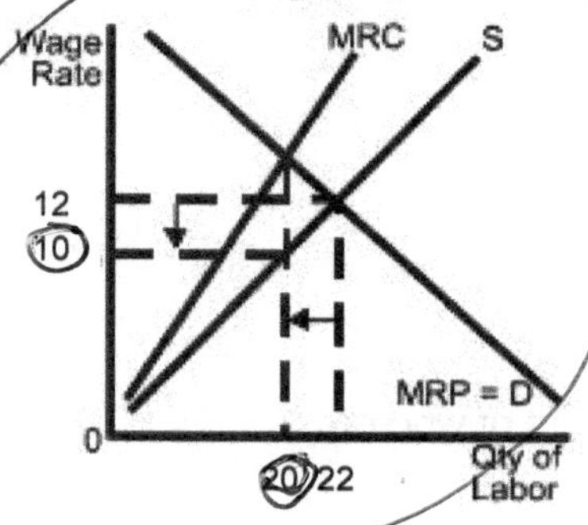

Figure 2

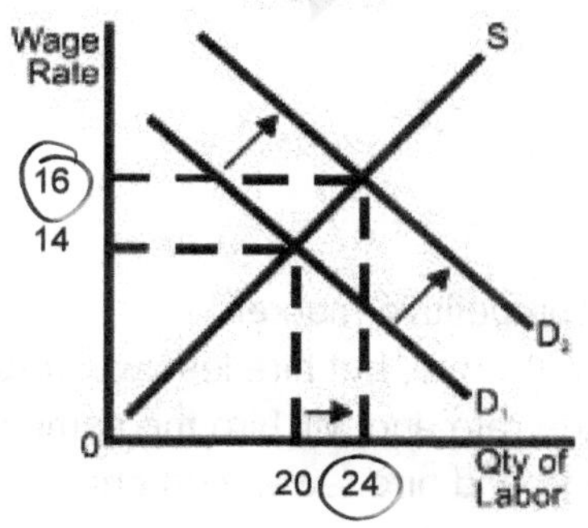

Figure 3

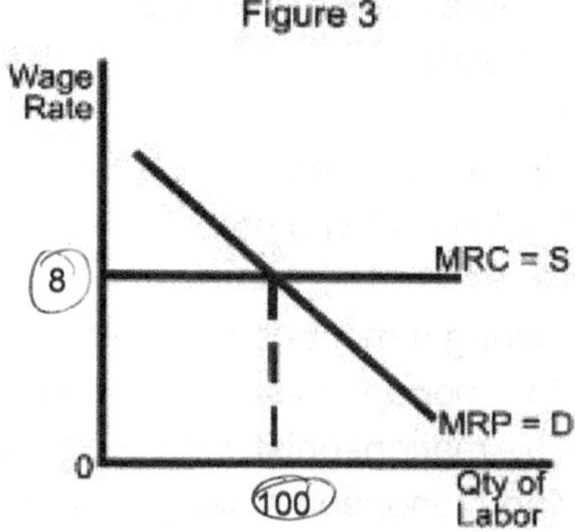

Answer the following questions based on Model Name _________, Wage _________ and Qty. __________ in (new) equilibrium.

Figure 4

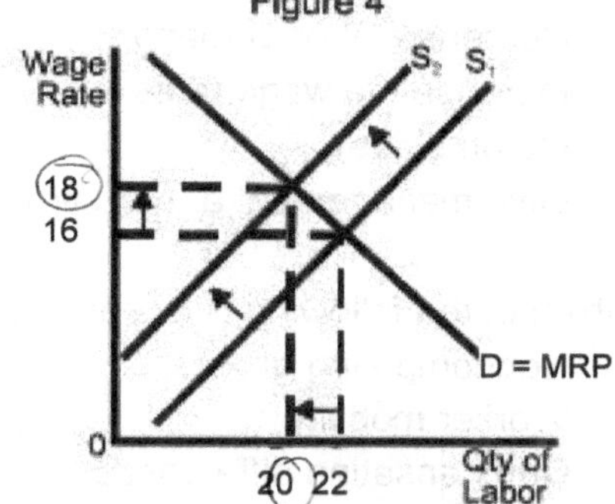

Figure 5

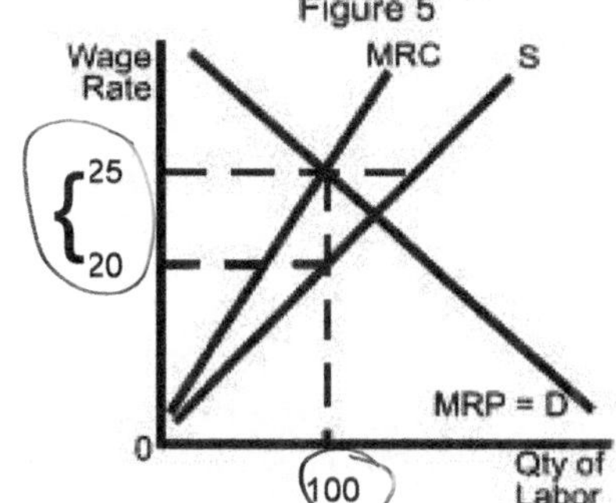

Figure 6

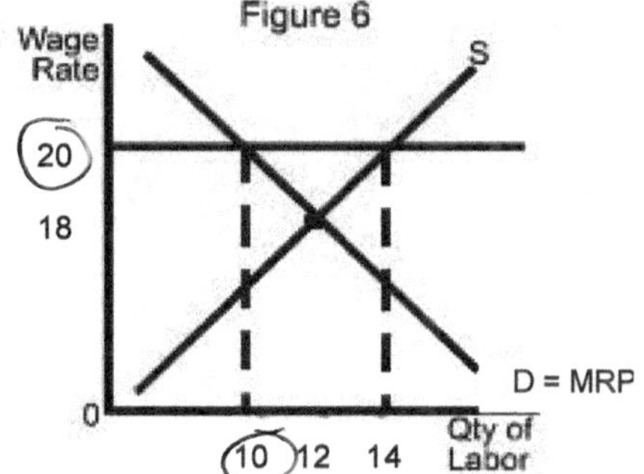

7. What model does Figure 1 represent?
   a. Bilateral monopoly; $12; 22
   b. Monopsony; $10; 20
   c. Inclusive unionism; $12; 22
   d. Craft unionism; $10; 20
8. What model does Figure 2 represent?
   a. Pure competition; $14; 20
   b. Inclusive unionism; $16; 24
   c. Craft unionism; $14; 20
   d. Increasing demand for labor (or Ideal); $16; 24
9. What model does Figure 3 represent?
   a. Inclusive unionism; $8; 100
   b. Increasing labor demand; $8; 100
   c. Pure competition; $8; 100
   d. Bilateral monopoly; $8; 100
10. What model does Figure 4 represent?
    a. Craft unionism; $18; 20
    b. Increasing demand unionism; $16; 22
    c. Pure competition; $16; 22
    d. Monopsony; $18; 20
11. What model does Figure 5 represent?
    a. "Strike threat"; $25; 100
    b. Craft unionism; $20; 100
    c. Bilateral monopoly; $20-25; 100
    d. Monopsony; $20; 100
12. What model does Figure 6 represent?
    a. Craft unionism; $18; 12
    b. Bilateral monopoly; $18-20; 10
    c. Pure competition; $18; 12
    d. Inclusive unionism; $20; 10

Self-Test (continued)

13. Under pure competition, a single firm faces a supply curve that is:
    a. Inelastic
    b. Elastic
    c. Upward sloping
    d. Backward bending

14. Comparing a monopsonist with a purely competitive market:
    a. The monopsonist will pay the same wage rate, but hire less workers.
    b. The monopsonist will pay a lower wage rate and will hire the same amount of workers.
    c. The monopsonist will pay a lower wage and hire fewer workers.
    d. The monopsonist will hire more workers at a lower wage.

15. Unions seek many goals, but their main objective is to:
    a. Decrease labor demand
    b. Increase the wage rates
    c. Go on strike
    d. Give management a "hard time".

16. Which of the following is a reason for wage differentials?
    a. Noncompeting groups
    b. Worker mobility
    c. Compensating differences
    d. All of the above

"Rent, Interest and Profits"

Chapter Orientation

Up to this point, we have studied the four factors of production -- land, labor, capital, and entrepreneurial ability. However, we have really only focused on the demand and supply of labor to determine the wage rate and quantity of their respective payments -- rent, interest, and profits will now be examined in this concept.

Rental payments for land, interest payments for capital, and profits received by entrepreneurs, are similar to wage payments made to labor. Land, as a productive factor, includes all natural resources. Land is in fixed supply or perfectly inelastic because it will be there regardless of whether it has a building, a house, or is left idle. Therefore, the owner earns (pure) economic rent because no income was necessary to "create" the land.

The interest rate is the price paid for the use of money (to buy capital goods). The theory of interest is that the interest rate is determined by the supply (the Federal Reserve System) and demand (consumers, businesses, the government) for money.

Profits are "rewards" or surpluses over and above all costs. The justification for earning a profit is because of bearing risk or because of creating new products. Why would anyone be motivated to take a risk or try something new if there wasn't a potential for profits? Profits are signals for entry into (or exit from) a market.

Learning Objectives

After reading this chapter in the text, and completing the following exercises in your concepts book, you will be able to:

1. Distinguish between economic rent and pure economic rent.
2. Explain what determines the amount of economic rent paid.
3. Discuss why economic rent is a surplus and the plans that Henry George had in mind.
4. Explain why the owners of land do not all receive the same economic rent.
5. Discuss if economic rent is a surplus, why a firm must pay rent.
6. Define the interest rate and discuss why interest rates vary.
7. Identify the two demands for money and state the role that each plays in determining the interest rate.
8. Distinguish between real and nominal interest rates.
9. Explain how the real interest rate effects investment decisions; the equilibrium level of NNP; and the allocation of capital goods.
10. Distinguish between economic profit, normal profit and business (accounting) profit.
11. State the reasons economists give to explain why economic profits occur.
12. Discuss the general function of profits in the American economy.
13. State the current relative size of labor's and of the capitalists' share of national income.
14. Describe the historical trend of wages and salaries.

"Rent, Interest and Profits"

Chapter Highlights

I. Economic Rent

A. Definition -- the price paid for use of land and other natural resources which are completely fixed in supply (perfectly inelastic). Therefore, demand is the only active determinant of land rent. The intersection of supply and demand determine the equilibrium land rent (See Figure 1).

Figure 1
Economic Rent
Perfectly Inelastic Supply

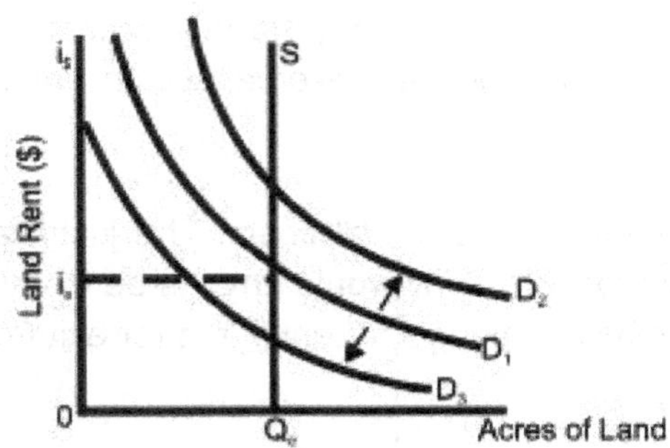

B. Perfectly Inelastic Supply
   1. The supply of land is perfectly inelastic (a free and nonreproducible gift of nature").
C. Land Rent: A Surplus Payment
   1. Other resource that are not fixed in supply offer entrepreneurs an incentive to produce more (Example: apartment buildings, warehouses, etc.) if the price goes up.
D. Application: A single-tax on land
   1. Henry George (1839-1897) in his book Progress and Poverty (1879), stated that a single-tax on land, which is equal to the surplus that landowners receive from their land, should be placed on the land, to finance government expenditures. He felt that increases in land rent belonged to the society as a whole and should be taxed away (up to 100%) and spent for public uses.
   2. George's book gained support in the United State, during the late nineteenth century, causing a single-tax movement.
   3. Criticisms of the single-tax on land
      a. A single-tax on land would not bring in enough revenue to finance all government expenditures.
      b. Most income payments fall into the interest, rent, wages, and profits categories. Capital improvements made on the land, cannot be separated from economic rent.
      c. Unearned income is not limited to just land.
   4. Those in favor of a tax on land argue that:
      a. Landowners typically are a high-income minority who receive high incomes with little or no expenditure of effort or money.
      b. A tax on land does not contribute to a misallocation of resources – it does not have the same effect as high property taxes.
E. Equilibrium Rent and Changes in Demand
   1. The demand for land can shift up or down due to such factors as the productivity of the land, the price of the product produced, etc.

F. Productivity Differences and Rent Differences
   1. Differing productivities of land causes varying economic rent. This is due to soil, fertility, climatic factors, location, etc.
G. Alternative Uses of Land
   1. From society's standpoint, land is to be used by society (no alternative), therefore rents are a surplus; however, land does have alternative uses and therefore payments must be made by business to attract that land from alternative uses, as a result, rental payments are a cost.

II. Interest

A. Definition of interest -- the price paid for the use of money usually stated as a percentage. Because the use takes place over time, interest must be expressed as a rate per unit ($1) over time (usually one year). In 1968, Congress passed the Truth in Lending Act, which requires full disclosure of the rates on finance charges and other consumer credit transactions.
   1. Money is not an economic resource; it does not produce goods and services; however, money "buys" capital goods.
   2. There exists a wide range of interest rates based upon risk, maturity, loan size, taxability, and market imperfections, such as a small country bank monopolizing the local economy.
   3. The "pure" rate of interest is the rate of interest paid on virtually riskless bonds (Example: Long-term U.S. government securities).
B. Loanable Funds Theory of Interest (Determining the equilibrium interest rate) – See Figure 2
   1. The intersection of the demand curve for money and the supply curve for money determines the equilibrium rate of interest.
      a. The supply of loanable funds is represented by an upward sloping supply curve because households will make available larger quantities of funds at high interest notes.
      b. Total demand for loanable funds is inverse: businesses will borrow more (for capital goods) at lower interest rates.
   2. Extending the Model
      a. Financial Institutions – banks attract households to save (intermediary)
      b. The Federal Reserve also controls the supply of loanable funds
   3. Time Value of Money
      a. Money is more valuable to a person the sooner it is obtained
      b. Compound interest – total interest that cumulates over time
      c. Present value of money – an amount of money to be received in the future
      d. Future value of money – the amount some current value of money will grow in future

Figure 2 Supply and Demand for $

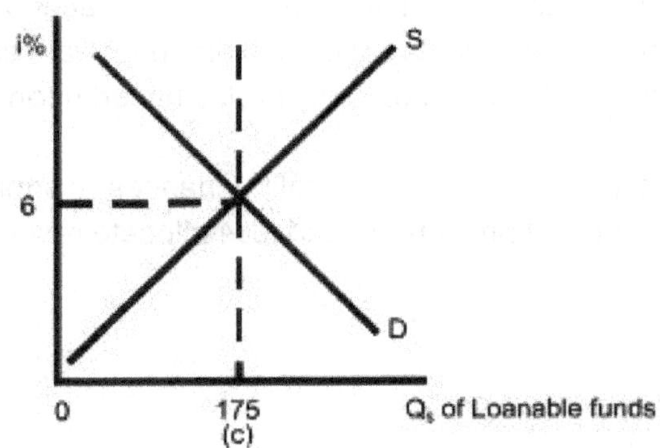

4. The nominal interest rate is the interest rate expressed in current dollars; the real interest rate is adjusted for inflation and is expressed in real dollars (or the nominal rate minus the rate of inflation). Investment decision-making is based upon the real rate of interest.

Nominal Interest Rate - Inflation = Real Interest Rate

5. The interest rate effects investment, which in turn affects the level of output, employment, and prices.
6. The interest rate allocates money (which buys capital goods) to those industries which are the most productive and profitable (they can afford it) and therefore impacts on society as a whole. However, large oligopolistic borrowers are in a better position than a small purely competitive firms so the interest rate's allocation of capital is not without some faults.
7. Application: Usury Laws
   a. Nonmarket Rationing - in the market, loans will be made to the most credit-worthy borrowers (which defeats the goal of usury laws).
   b. Gainers and Losers - credit-worthy borrowers will gain (lenders will lose) because of below-market interest rates.
   c. Inefficiency - Legal maximum interest rates may ration funds to less - productive uses.

III. Economic Profits

A. Economic profits vs. business (accounting) profits
   1. Recall from the "cost chapter", that accountants take revenues minus expenses (or explicit costs) to calculate business (accounting) profit. Economists go one step further and subtract implicit costs (such as a normal profit, opportunity cost, etc.) to get economic profits which are excess or pure profits.

B. Role of the Entrepreneur - Profit is the reward or payment to the entrepreneur for operating in a dynamic economy (signal for entry/exit).

C. Insurable and Uninsurable Risks
   1. Insurable risks are those risks for which you can buy insurance.
   2. Uninsured risks are the result of unpredictable and uncontrollable changes in demand and supply. They fall into four categories.
      a. Changes to general environment
      b. Changes to the structure of the economy
      c. Changes in government policy
      d. New products or production methods by rivals

D. Sources of Economic Profit:
   1. Risk and profit
   2. Innovation and profit new products or new methods of production.
   3. Monopoly and profit -- an innovative firm can enjoy economic profits, minimize risk, and become a monopoly. However, bearing risk in a dynamic and uncertain economy and the undertaking of innovations and more socially desirable than monopoly profits based upon the cutting output to drive prices up.

E. Functions of Profits
   1. Profit and Total Output — the pursuit of profit enhances economic growth.
   2. Profit and Resource Allocation — profit and loss allocate resources among alternative uses.

"Rent, Interest and Profits"

IV. Income Shares

A. Current Shares

1. Trends

a. Wages and salaries comprise 70% of national income; using a broader definition, they comprise 80% of national income.

b. The capitalist share (corporate profits, plus interest, plus rent) is only 20% of national income.

V. Last Word: Determining the Price of Credit

VI. Web-based Question (see your Instructor)

<u>Key Terms</u>

economic rent
incentive function
single-tax movement
interest
Truth in Lending Act
"pure" interest rate
theory of interest
transactions demand for money
asset demand for money
nominal (money) interest rate
Loanable funds theory
real interest rate
economic (pure) profit
implicit cost
explicit cost
normal profit
business (accounting) profit
static economy
dynamic economy
uninsurable risk
capitalist's share

PROBLEMS

1. Henry George felt that a single-tax on land would be appropriate because land rent is considered pure economic rent. Discuss the pros and cons of this theory.

2. What is interest and what is the economic function of interest rates?

3. What is the economic function of profits? How do economists differ from accountants in their view of profits?

Table 1

Rent per acre	Quantity Demanded
$500	2,000
400	4,000
300	6,000
200	8,000
100	10,000

4. Assume that the number of acres of land available in a particular area is 8,000 and the demand schedule is illustrated in Table 1.

   a. What is the total amount of pure economic rent (per acre)? ________

   b. How many acres will be rented based upon Table 1? ________

   c. Graph the supply and demand curves for this land and label the equilibrium rent/acre (Re) and number of acres (Qe).

   d. If the landowners were taxed (Henry George's idea), $200/acre, the number of acres rented would be ________.

5. Describe the current and historical trends of wages and salaries. How have benefits impacted "take home pay?"

6. What structural changes have impacted on labor's and the capitalist share of national income? Discuss.

7. Currently, our interest rates are extremely low, what impact does that have on the economy?

PROBLEMS (continued)

Figure 3

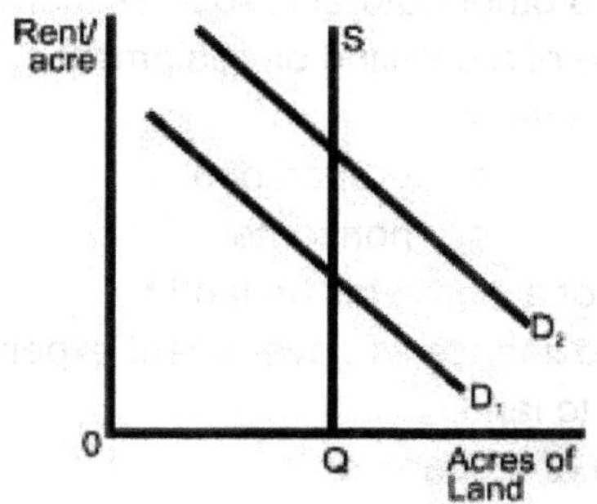

8. In Figure 3, at Demand (D1):

   a. Shade in the area of economic rent.

   b. Label the graph economic rent or pure economic rent.

   c. Label the rent/acre (Re) and the number of acres rented (Qe).

9. Discuss the two functions of profits.

"Rent, Interest and Profits"

<u>Self-Test</u>

1. Which of the following best defines the term "economic rent"?
   a. the returns on any factor of production which is elastic in supply.
   b. payments made for the use of capital borrowed to increase production.
   c. the price paid for the use of land and other natural resources in fixed supply.
   d. Payments made to an owner for use of a dwelling or equipment.
2. Under pure economic rent, the supply curve is:
   a. perfectly elastic.
   b. perfectly inelastic.
   c. proportional
   d. horizontal.
3. Which of the following is <u>not</u> a criticism of a single-tax on land?
   a. does not bring in enough revenue to finance all government expenditures.
   b. unearned income is not just limited to land.
   c. does not contribute to misallocation of resources.
   d. capital improvements cannot be separated from rent.
4. The "pure interest" rate is the rate:
   a. banks lend to their best customers.
   b. banks lend to each other.
   c. the Federal Reserve lends to its member banks.
   d. paid on U.S. government securities.
5. Which of the following describes "profit"?
   a. reward or payment to an entrepreneur.
   b. signals to enter/exit an industry.
   c. the prime energizer of the capitalist economy.
   d. all of the above.
6. Which of the following is <u>not</u> a justification for economic profits?
   a. innovation.
   b. risk.
   c. monopoly power.
   d. static economy.
7. Economic profits differ from business accounting profits because:
   a. they measure revenues minus expenses.
   b. they include explicit cost.
   c. they include implicit cost.
   d. they exclude opportunity cost.
8. Using the broades definition, Wage and Salaries comprise what percentage of National Income?
   a. 75%
   b. 55%
   c. 80%
   d. 20%
9. Wages and salaries are a share of GDP received for:
   a. all labor services.
   b. blue-collar labor services.
   c. administrative labor services.
   d. entrepreneurial labor services.
10. Profits are defined by economists as:
    a. a residual from sales revenue after costs of production have been met.
    b. the money return on capital.
    c. the return to management.
    d. none of the above.

"Labor Market Institutions and Issues: Unionism, Discrimination, and Immigration"

Chapter Orientation

In the "Wage Determination Concept", you studied how labor unions attempt to raise wage rates. Organized labor is involved with more than just wages -- it has an impact on its rank-and-file, the business, and the economy. About 14.6 million U.S. workers (11.1 percent) in 2014, belong to unions. Most belong to the AFL-CIO (Teamsters, United Auto Workers), Communication Workers, and Carpenters. The rest belong to the National Education Association, the Nurses' Union and the United Mine Workers. Unionism in the United States is largely an urban phenomenon, six heavily urbanized states (NY, CA, PA, IL, OH and MI) account for approximately half of all union members. This appendix focuses on American unionism, by opening with a brief history. It is interesting to see how legislation has swung from pro-management to pro-union and back again. When one side was/seemed too powerful, laws were passed to protect the other side. After this brief history, the chapter discusses labor-management relations and the process of collective bargaining, followed by a discussion of present and future membership, and closes with the economic effects of unions.

The second topic is "discrimination". How is discrimination defined? What are the types of discrimination? What is the "Crowding Model"? "Taste for Discrimination Model"? With discrimination costing billions of dollars, why do we discriminate? What is "statistical discrimination"? Other than discrimination, what other reasons are there for differences in male-female earnings? These questions will be explored in this chapter.

Lastly, the third topic is "immigration". After a brief overview of the history of immigration in the U.S. and current immigration laws, the chapter focuses on the economics of immigration. How many people enter the U.S. legally or illegally each year? What are the economic ramifications of this flow?

Learning Objectives

After reading this chapter in the text, and completing the following exercises in this concepts book, you will be able to:

1. Discuss the earliest beginnings of American unionism.
2. Describe the attitude and behavior of the courts and business toward labor unions throughout history.
3. Define the three fundamental ideas of Samuel Gompers.
4. Explain the Norris-LaGuardia Act (1932).
5. Explain the Wagner Act (1935) or the National Labor Relations Act.
6. Define the role of the National Labor Relations Board (NLRB).
7. Contrast Samuel Gompers and the AFL with John E. Lewis and the CIO.
8. Discuss the provisions of the Taft-Hartley Act of 1947.
9. Define the objectives of the Landrum-Griffin Act of 1959.
10. State what the trend has been in regard to union memberships over the past thirty years, and present three hypotheses to explain this occurrence.
11. Define the collective bargaining process and explain the four basic areas usually covered.
12. Discuss the impact unions have on the wage rates for their members, on the wages of nonunion workers and on the average level of real wages in the American economy.
13. Describe and evaluate the pros and cons concerning the impact of unions on efficiency and productivity and give the empirical evidence.
14. Discuss discrimination and its economic effect on the American economy.
15. Define the "Crowding Model" and the "Taste for Discrimination Model"?
16. What is "statistical discrimination"?
17. Assume discrimination disappears, what is the economic effect on men, women and society as a whole.
18. Discuss the pros and cons of immigration and explain what the U.S.'s position should be on immigration.

"Labor Market Institutions and Issues: Unionism, Discrimination, and Immigration"

<u>Chapter Highlights</u>

I. Unionism In America

A. Introduction -- The Industrial Revolution, in the late 1700s, changed the nature of our work force. Prior to the Industrial Revolution, the labor force was composed of mostly farmers, since our economy was largely agricultural. Growth of mass production and factories lured workers into the cities, where they found themselves highly exploited, because of poor working conditions ("sweat shops").

B. *Repression phase: 1790 to 1930*

1. Although these conditions were horrible for all workers, including children, progress, was very slow in forming unions to protect the workers.
2. Local craft unions (shoemakers, printers, carpenters, etc.) were the only labor unions that were able to survive. Skilled workers were few in number and they were able to control their own numbers by requiring union membership as a necessary condition for admission to apprenticeship in the trade.
3. By contrast, the supply of unskilled labor was much more plentiful and was continually fed by immigrants. As a result, any union of unskilled labor was quickly undercut by unskilled nonunionized workers.
4. In addition, the hostility of the courts toward labor unions and the reluctance of American businesses to recognize and bargain with unions contributed to the slow progress in organizing the labor force.
5. Some of the obstacles to unionization were: the criminal conspiracy doctrine (unions were guilty of criminal conspiracy and hence illegal), injunctions (a restraining order which stipulated that an action -- such as a strike -- not be carried out), discriminatory discharge and black listing (effected present and future employment), lockout (management closes up shop for a while), yellow-dog contracts (workers agreed not to join a union as a condition of employment), and company unions or paternalism (a labor union dominated or controlled by management).
6. From 1869 up until 1911, the Knights of Labor was the first national union for all workers.
7. In 1886, the American Federation of Labor (AFL) was founded by Samuel Gompers -- "the father of the American Labor movement". His fundamental ideas were:
   a. Business unionism (higher wages and better working conditions)
   b. Political neutrality (not tied to one party)
   c. Trade autonomy (organized by craft)
8. Business Unionism — Unionism concerned with short-run economic objectives of higher pay, better benefits, shorter hours, and improved working conditions.

C. *Union Growth: 1930 to 1947*

1. With the onset of the Great Depression, the public's attitude toward big business fell. The federal government passed two prolabor acts:
   (a) Norris-LaGuardia Act of 1932 -- declared yellow-dog contracts illegal and made it more difficult to obtain an injunction.
   (b) Wagner Act of 1935 (officially called the National Labor Relations Act) -- guaranteed labor the right of self-organization and the right to bargain collectively with employers. The act listed several "unfair labor practices on the part of management and set up the National Labor Relations Board (NLRB) or "Labor Board" which investigates unfair labor practices and conducts elections among employees to determine if they want to become unionized and which union they want to represent them. The Wagner Act was "labor's Magna Charta".
2. As a result of these two acts, union membership grew at a rapid pace. In addition, the Wagner Act made it easier to organize unskilled, as well as skilled labor.
   (a) John L. Lewis contended that unions should shift from craft unions to industrial unions, which would include skilled and unskilled labor in a particular industry or a group of related industries.
   (b) Congress of Industrial Organization (CIO) was formed in 1936. It was a highly successful union especially in the auto and steel industries.

D. *Curbing Union Power: 1947 to date*

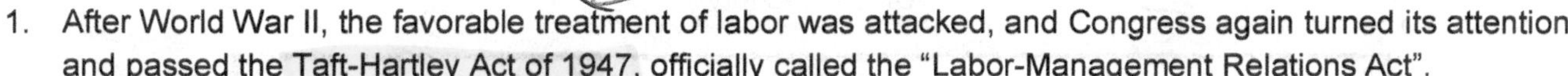

1. After World War II, the favorable treatment of labor was attacked, and Congress again turned its attention and passed the Taft-Hartley Act of 1947, officially called the "Labor-Management Relations Act".
   (a) Outlined and prohibited certain "unfair union practices".
   (b) Regulated the internal administration of unions.
   (c) Specified the collective bargaining process; abolished the closed shop and made state right-to-work laws legal.
   (d) Set up a procedure for health and safety strikes.
2. In the 1950s the progress of the labor movement slowed down; membership grew slowly. Congress again turned its attention on organized labor and didn't like what it saw: corrupt unions, links with organized crime, and the unions did not seem to be benefitting their rank-and-file.
   (a) In 1959, Congress passed the Landrum-Griffin Act, or officially called, the "Labor-Management Reporting and Disclosure Act". Financial practices, elections, officers, constitutions, member rights, etc. came under this law, and the unions were required to be more responsive to the membership.

II. The Decline of Unionism

A. Merger of the AFL-CIO

1. In 1955, the AFL and CIO merged to improve its political influence and because a unified effort was needed to organize nonunion firms and industries.
2. The marriage of the AFL-CIO has not brought about a resurgence of organized labor currently, about 14.6 million workers or 11.1% of the labor in 2014 were organized. In 1980 that figure was 22 million workers or 25% of the labor force.

B. Reasons for the decline of union membership

1. Structural-changes in the economy -- a variety of structural changes have taken place such as the shift from manufacturing to services; import competition; and the composition of the labor force -- women, youths, and part-time workers are difficult to organize.
2. Business opposition -- management's opposition to unions has become more aggressive lately, as a result of the increased union wage advantage, which causes union firms to be less profitable than nonunion firms. Legal and illegal tactics, by management, have helped reduce union membership.
3. Move to "sunbelt" – businesses have moved from northeast and midwest (unionism is a "way of life") to the south of southwest (hard to organize).

III. Collective Bargaining

A. The Work Agreement

1. Definition -- collective bargaining is a process by which decisions regarding wages, hours, and conditions of employment are determined by the interaction of workers (acting through their unions) and employers usually brought about by compromise rather than by strikes or violence.

B. The Bargaining Process

1. Collective bargaining agreements usually cover four basic areas:
   (a) Degree of recognition and status accorded the union. (See Figure 1 next page).
   (b) Wages and hours
   (c) Seniority and job protection.
   (d) Procedure for settling grievances.

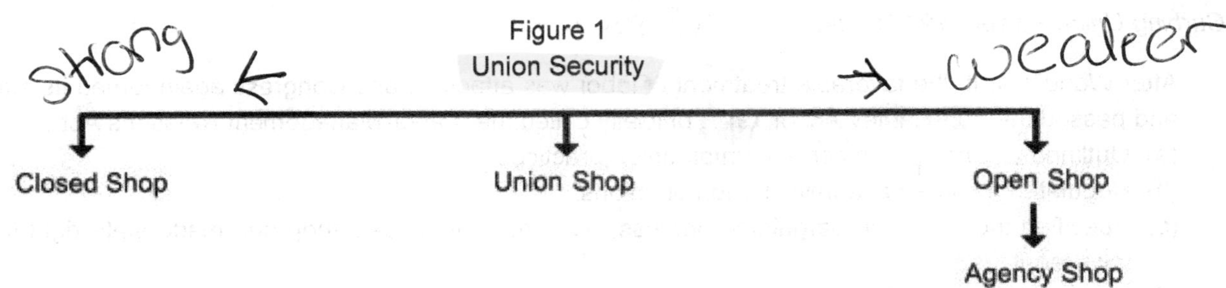

Closed Shop -- strongest union protection -- makes union membership a precondition to employment. The Taft-Hartley Act (1947) outlawed closed shops and permitted its prohibition by individual states in "right-to-work" laws (currently 25 states have "right-to-work laws).

Union Shop -- stipulates that all workers must belong to the union that represents their bargaining unit upon employment (after a grace period, usually 30 days).

Open Shop -- a situation in which the employer is free to hire without considering an applicant's union status and the worker's under no obligation to join a union. The open shop does not give the union any security -- they must seek out the workers and recruit them on a voluntary basis.

Agency Shop -- exists when workers in a bargaining unit are not required to join the union, but must make a payment equal to the dues. This shop eliminates the "free rider" problem in which nonunion workers benefit from the union representation. Agency shops are particularly important to the union in states with right-to-work laws.

C. The Bargaining Process:
   1. Collective bargaining is a continuous process (but usually starts 60 days before the end of a contract).
   2. Labor and management eventually compromise and reach an agreement and sign a new contract.
   3. Sometimes strikes and lockouts can occur within the framework of the Landrun-Griffin Act of 1959 (National Labor Relations Act).

IV. The Economic Effects of Unions

A. The unions wage advantage -- empirical evidence suggests that union workers do receive a higher wage and better fringe benefits (15% on the average) than do nonunion workers. (Today, the focus is on higher pay, better benefits, shorter hours and improved working conditions.)
   1. Unions have had little impact on the average level of real wages received by the total labor force because union gains have been at the expense of nonunion workers. (Fewer union workers are hired at the higher wage -- those unemployed may seek employment in nonunion labor markets).

B. Efficiency and productivity
   1. Unions exert a negative impact upon efficiency by:
      (a) Featherbedding and work rules – engaging in "make work" or by resisting more efficient technology.
      (b) Output losses from strikes
      (c) Efficiency losses from labor misallocation – union workers have higher wage rates
   2. Unions exert a positive impact upon efficiency by:
      (a) Reduced worker turnover – more experienced workforce
      (b) Voice mechanism – speak with a collective voice, no individual retaliation.
      (c) Employer receives a greater return on training due to worker longevity thereby increasing willingness to upgrade skills of workforce.

3. Mixed Research Findings - empirical evidence is not clear on a conclusion regarding the effect of unionization on efficiency and productivity -- some industries have increased, while others have decreased.

V. Labor Market Discrimination

A. Definition of labor market discrimination-occurs when individuals or groups, who have the same abilities, education, training, and experience as other workers, are accorded inferior treatment with respect to hiring, occupational access, promotion, or wage rate.

B. Costs of Discrimination
1. One estimate of economic and social policies were successful the U.S. economy would gain $325 billion per year by ending gender discrimination.

C. Economic Analysis of Discrimination
1. Taste-for-Discrimination Model
   a. Def. – when applied to employer discrimination, employers discriminate against non-preferred workers.
   b. Discrimination coefficient – by employing non-preferred workers there is a cost associated with it.
   c. Prejudice and the Market (African American-White Wage Ratio) – decreases the demand for Africa Americans will cause the equilibrium wage rate down.
   d. Competition and Discrimination – will reduce discrimination in the long run.
2. Statistical Discrimination – people judged on the average characteristics of a group they belong to

D. Occupational Segregation: The Crowding Model
1. Definition of occupation segregation – the practice of crowding women and minorities into lower-paying, less desirable occupations.
2. The "Crowding Model" illustrates that society gains from a more efficient allocation of resources when discrimination is abandoned.
3. Discrimination redistributes national income and by creating inefficiencies, diminishes its size
4. Discrimination blocks certain individuals from providing their maximum contribution to society

VI. Immigration

A. Number of Immigrants
1. History of immigration in the U.S. (currently immigrations have averaged 1 million/year in U.S. This figure doesn't include illegal immigrants, which number approximately 250,000/year.)

B. Economics of Immigration
1. Supply and Demand analysis suggests that the movement of migrants from a poor to a rich country will:
   a. increase the national income
   b. reduce the average level of wages
   c. increase business incomes in the receiving country
2. The opposite effects will occur in the sending country, but the world as a whole can expect to realize a larger total output.

C. Complications and Modifications
1. Costs of Migration
   a. Explicit and implicit costs vs. (expected) benefits – now that the wage rate in U.S. is six times Mexico's rate, there is greater benefit to migrate to the U.S.
2. Remittances and backflows
   a. Causes an altering of gains and losses through time (money sent back home)
3. Full employment vs. unemployment (many immigrants hope to find work in another country)
   a. When a country has unemployed workers collecting unemployment compensation, it might benefit from migration.

4. Fiscal impacts: The major overhaul of the U.S. welfare system in 1996 denied welfare benefits (for five years) to new legal immigrants.
   a. Evidence suggests that immigrants are net contributors to the fiscal system of the host country.
   b. Direct social welfare costs of illegals are low because of fear of detection and most illegals are working.
5. Research Findings
   a. Immigration reduces the wages of native-born workers with low education
   b. The overall effect of immigration on the average American wages is less clear. Scholarly estimates range from -3% to +2%.

D. The Illegal Immigration Debate
   1. The issues involved in determining the economic aspects of immigration are complex. There are two viewpoints: the traditional perception and the counterview. Much depends upon the character of the immigrants themselves and the economic conditions of the host country.
   2. Most economists conclude that illegal immigrants reduce wage rates in low-wage labor markets, take jobs some Americans don't want and expand total employment in low-wage occupations.
   3. The deportation of illegal immigrants would cause the wage rate to increase in low-skilled labor markets (U.S. workers want more money) but not increase employment on a one-to-one basis with number deported.
   4. Illegal immigration imposes a high net fiscal burden on state and local governments (local schools, local medical care, local criminal justice, etc.).
   5. "Braindrain" – countries are concerned about the emigration of highly educated workers, particularly if they received subsidized education.

VII. Last Word: Immigration Reform: The Startling Slowdown in Illegal Immigration
VIII.Web-Based Question (See your Instructor)

<u>Key Terms</u>

criminal-conspiracy doctrine
injunction
lockout yellow-dog contract
company union
business unionism
AFL
Norris-La Guardia Act
Wagner Act
NLRB
CIO
Taft-Hartley Act
Landrum-Griffin Act
structural change hypothesis
managerial-opposition hypothesis
jurisdictional strike
discriminatory discharge
blacklisting
sympathy strike
occupational segregation
legal and illegal immigrants

secondary boycott
feather bedding
closed shop
open shop
agency shop
nonunion shop
right-to-work law
managerial prerogative
COLA
grievance procedure
seniority
fringe benefit
collective voice
exit mechanism
voice mechanism
craft union
industrial union
wage, employment, occupational, and human-capital discrimination

"Labor Market Institutions and Issues: Unionism, Discrimination, and Immigration"

PROBLEMS

1. Define the four shops in union security.

2. What impact did the Taft-Hartley Act have on the shops listed above?

3. Explain what brought about unionism in the United States.

4. Discuss the three phases of unionism: repression phase, union growth, and the curbing union power phase.

5. What is the current status of union membership in the United States? What do you predict for the future? Why?

6. What is collective bargaining? What are the four basic areas usually covered in collective bargaining?

7. From a wage standpoint, is a worker better off belonging to a union? Discuss.

8. Briefly define the Norris-LaGuardia Act, the Wagner Act, and the Landrum-Griffin Act.

9. What are the three theories to help explain the trend in union membership? Define each theory and state which one(s) you agree with.

10. Define "economic discrimination" and explain the four areas of discrimination. What does the "crowding out model" tell us about discrimination?

11. Other than discrimination, list other reasons for the differences in male-female earnings?

12. Discuss the pros and cons of immigration (both legal and illegal). In your opinion, what should be the U.S.'s immigration policy?

13. What do most economists conclude regarding illegal immigration?

14. What is "braindrain" as it relates to international migration?

"Labor Market Institutions and Issues: Unionism, Discrimination, and Immigration"

Self-Test

1. Which is the best description of the rationalization for lockouts?
   a. to reduce output in response to decreased demand for the product.
   b. to minimize property damage during periods of unrest.
   c. to disrupt production and weaken management's bargaining position.
   d. to discontinue workers' income and weaken labor's bargaining position.
2. A company union is:
   a. the duly elected representative of labor in any firm.
   b. the bargaining agent for management in labor disputes.
   c. a labor union dominated or controlled by management.
   d. an organization of companies designed to give management strength in conflicts with labor unions.
3. The rationalization for the formation of company unions is:
   a. to provide labor with a bargaining agent in its endeavors to get favorable wage contracts.
   b. to protect workers from outside agitators who may make unreasonable demands on management.
   c. to weaken the strength of other labor unions which may obtain wage contracts favorable to labor.
   d. to provide labor a legitimate channel of communications.
4. Which of the following is NOT a theory of discrimination:
   a. Statistical
   b. Lorenz Curve
   c. The Crowding Model
   d. Occupational segregation
5. Which of the following is not a complication of immigration?
   a. explicit and implicit costs
   b. "cheap" labor
   c. remittances
   d. backflows
6. Which of the following pieces of legislation declared yellow-dog contracts illegal and made it more difficult to obtain an injunction?
   a. Wagner Act.
   b. Norris-LaGuardia Act.
   c. Taft-Hartley Act
   d. Landrum-Griffin Act.
7. Which of the following pieces of legislation declared that financial practices, elections, constitutions, member rights, etc. came under the law?
   a. Wagner Act.
   b. Norris-LaGuardia Act.
   c. Taft-Hartley Act
   d. Landrum-Griffin Act.
8. Which of the following pieces of legislation guaranteed labor the right of self-organization and the right to bargain collectively?
   a. Wagner Act.
   b. Norris-LaGuardia Act.
   c. Taft-Hartley Act
   d. Landrum-Griffin Act.
9. Which of the following pieces of legislation outlined and prohibited certain "unfair union practices"; specified the collective bargaining process and abolished the closed shop, etc.?
   a. Wagner Act.
   b. Norris-LaGuardia Act.
   c. Taft-Hartley Act
   d. Landrum-Griffin Act.
10. The National Labor Relations Board was established by:
   a. Wagner Act.
   b. Norris-LaGuardia Act.
   c. Taft-Hartley Act
   d. Landrum-Griffin Act.

REVIEW SHEET: UNIT III MICROECONOMICS

ECON 106 – UNIT III REVIEW

Be sure to bring a #2 pencil, graph paper and calculator!

PART I: 40 Multiple Choice questions (2 points each or a total of 80 points)

1. Know why we study "resource pricing".
2. Know what is meant by "derived demand".
3. Know what is meant when MRC>MRP; MRC<MRP; MRC=MRP and how to adjust the quantity (Qe) of labor.
4. Know how the "Simple Circular Flow Model" helps to explain both the output and input markets. (Units II and III)
5. Know the definition and how to calculate: TP, MP, TR, ARP, MRP, TRC & MRC.
6. Know the two rules to maximize profit (or minimize loss) in the resource market.
7. Know the difference between a movement along the Demand Curve (=MRP), shifting of the Demand Curve (=MRP) and the reasons for these changes.
8. Know that the MRP Curve is always the Demand Curve for every labor market model.
9. As the Production Manager know how to find the "Law of Diminishing Returns".
10. Know the labor supply curve (shape) for competitive and noncompetitive firms.
11. Know examples of every resource market model.
12. Know every resource market model and how to determine We and Qe.
13. Know which curves to look at to determine how many workers are hired and how many workers are available: know how to calculate unemployment.
14. Know how labor unions attempt to increase wages for its members.
15. Know how wages and number of workers (employment) differ for a competitive labor market versus a monopsonistic labor market.
16. Know the pros and cons of raising the minimum wage rate.
17. Know about wage differentials (noncompeting groups – ability and investment in human capital, compensating differences and market imperfections).
18. Know about the "Marginal Productivity Theory of Income Distribution".
19. Know about the % distribution of National Income (NI).
20. Know the definition of "economic rent".
21. Know the name of the economist who advocated a single tax on land.
22. Know how to calculate the real rate of interest.
23. Know what is meant by the "pure rate of interest".
24. Know what happens to the interest rate when D$>S$ and D$<S$.
25. Know how to calculate economic profits.
26. Know about the four types of shops and give examples.
27. Know about the Norris-LaGuardia Act, the Landrum-Griffin Act, the Taft-Hartley Act and the Wagner Act.
28. Know what percentage union membership is of the labor force.
29. Define "collective bargaining" and when it is utilized.
30. Know about the function and trend of American unionism.
31. Define "labor market discrimination".
32. ~~How much is the complications and modifications (federal and state) of discrimination?~~
33. ~~What are the complications and modifications of migration?~~
34. ~~What effects do immigrants have on tax revenue and government spending in U.S. (both federal and state)?~~
35. ~~Why do many people oppose immigration?~~

REVIEW SHEET: UNIT III MICROECONOMICS

<u>PART II:</u> *Problems (10 points each or a total of 20 points)*

Answer only <u>TWO</u> of the FOUR problems, listed on the exam.

Problem #1: Pure Competition problem — End of Micro Unit III Worksheet

Problem #2: Monopsony problem — End of Micro Unit III Worksheet

Problem #3: Resource Demand Problem — Workbook pg. 235

Problem #4: For five Resource Markets (graphs shown) — list the model name, and the wage and quantity in equilibrium – Workbook pg. 249

FORMULA SHEET: WORKBOOK PAGE 269

<u>REVIEW TEXTBOOK, CLASS NOTES (ON WORKSHEET), WORKBOOK, CANVAS (QUIZZES AND PP SLIDES)</u>

Any questions please contact your Instructor or visit our new “Learning Commons” located in the Bankier Library.

GOOD LUCK!!

REVIEW SHEET: UNIT III MICROECONOMICS

Formula Sheet

Marginal Product (MP)* = $\frac{\blacktriangle \text{TP}}{\blacktriangle \text{Units of Resource}}$

Marginal Revenue Product (MRP)* = MP x Product's Price = $\frac{\blacktriangle \text{TR}}{\blacktriangle \text{Units of Resource}}$ = Demand

Total Revenue (TR) = TP x Product's price

Average Revenue Product (ARP) = $\frac{\text{TR}}{\text{Units of Resource}}$

Total Resource Cost (TRC) = Units of Resource x wage rate

Marginal Resource Cost (MRC)* = $\frac{\blacktriangle \text{TRC}}{\blacktriangle \text{Units of Resource}}$

*graphed at the midpoints

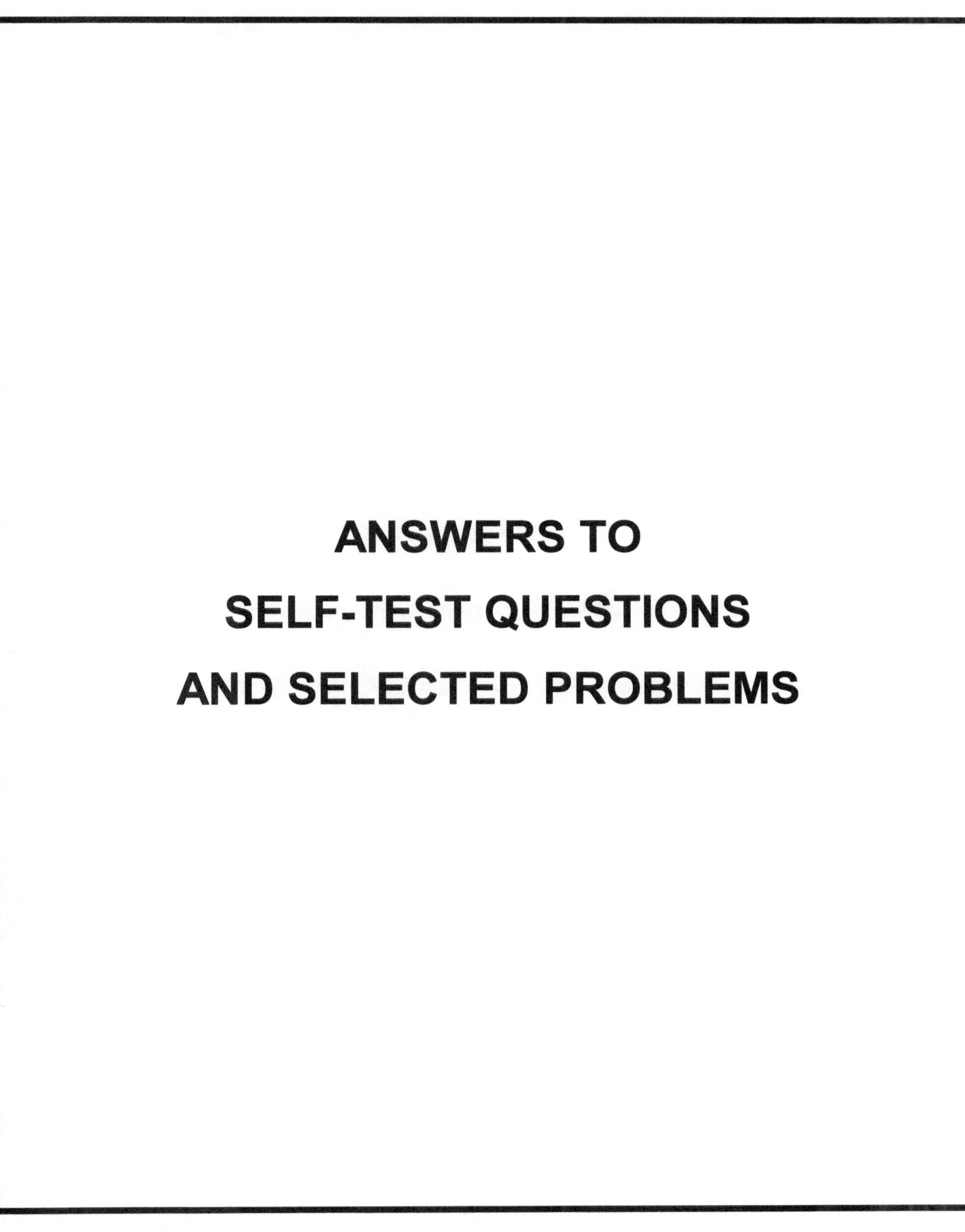

ANSWERS TO SELF-TEST QUESTIONS AND SELECTED PROBLEMS

MACRO GRAPHS

1.1 GRAPH OF X VERSUS Y

Slope = 1

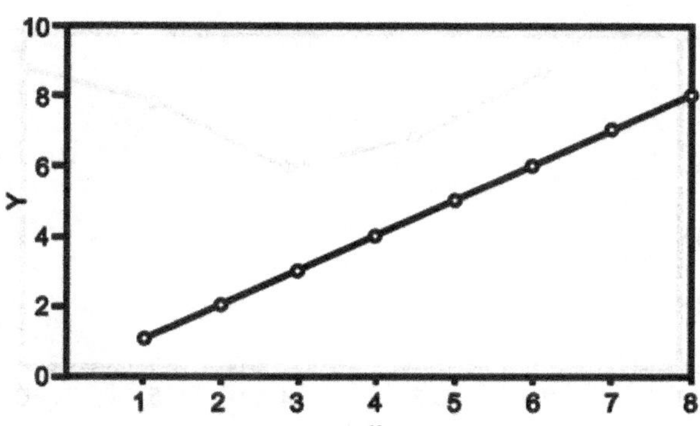

1.2 GRAPH OF X VERSUS Y

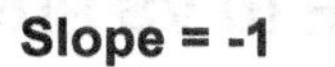

Slope = -1

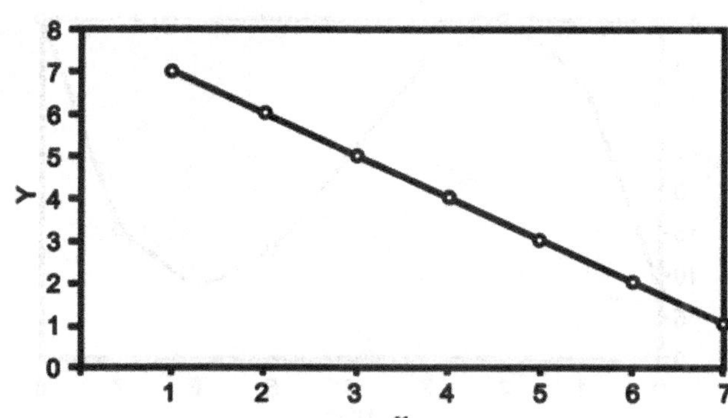

1.3 GRAPH OF X VERSUS Y

Slope = 2

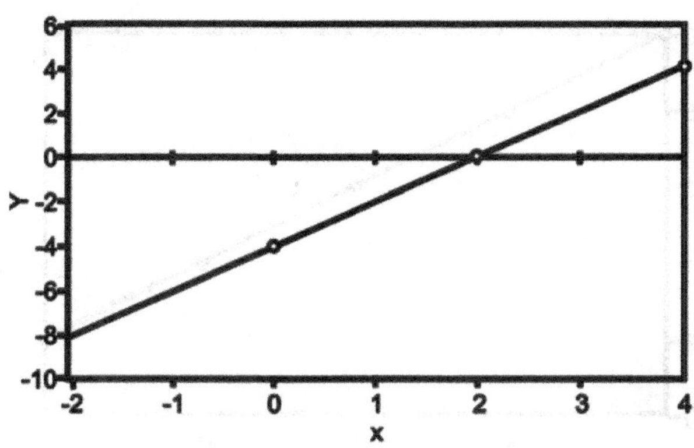

1.4 GRAPH OF X VERSUS Y

Slope of D = -1 Slope of S = 1

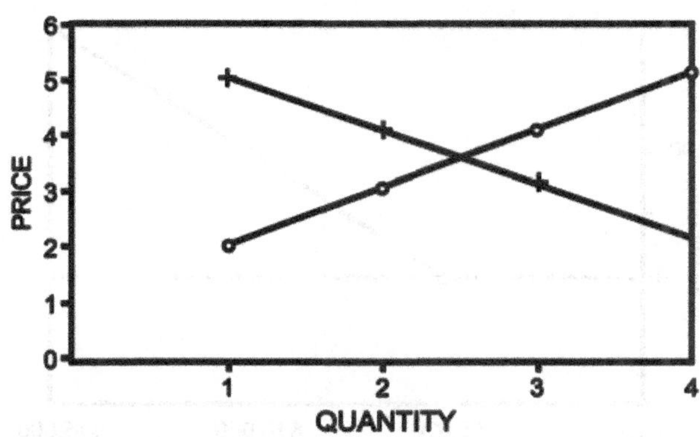

Point of Intersection (2.5, 3.5)

1.5 GRAPH
TIME (t) VS PRICES (P)

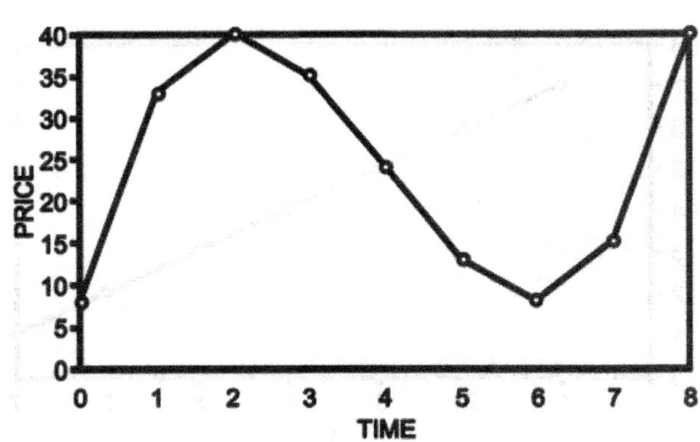

1.6 GRAPH OF A VERSUS B

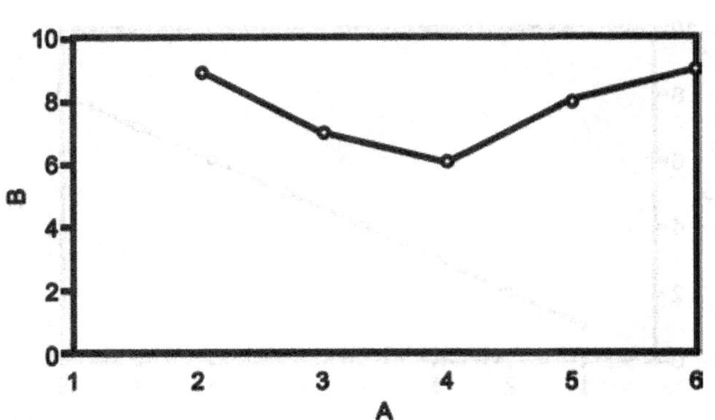

1.7 GRAPH OF INCOME VS. SAVINGS

Slope = .2

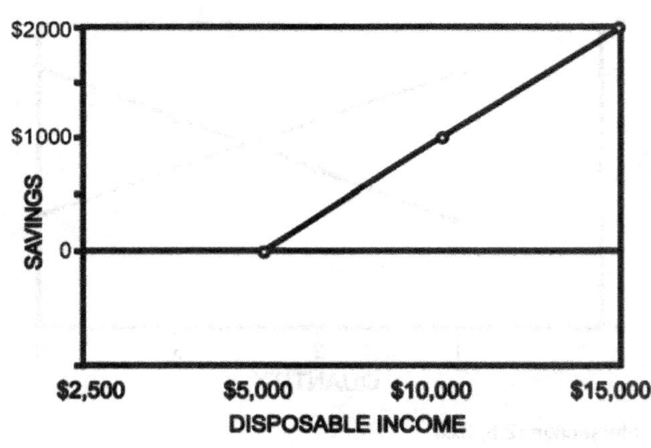

(c) direct relationship

1.8 GRAPH % RATE VS. BILLIONS $

Slope = -.4
Inverse relationship

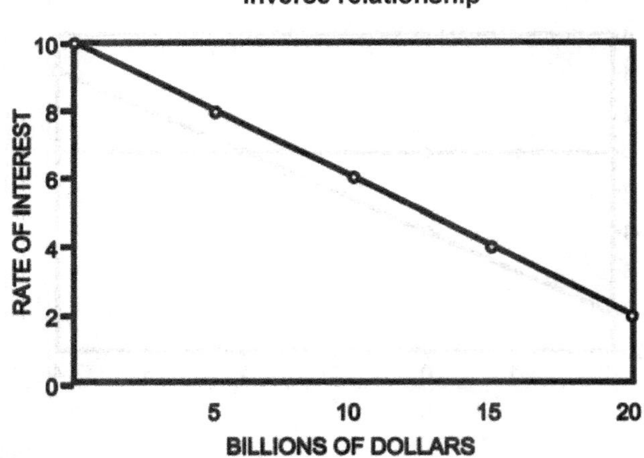

MICRO GRAPHS

1.1 GRAPH PROBLEM #1

Slope = -.1
Inverse Relationship

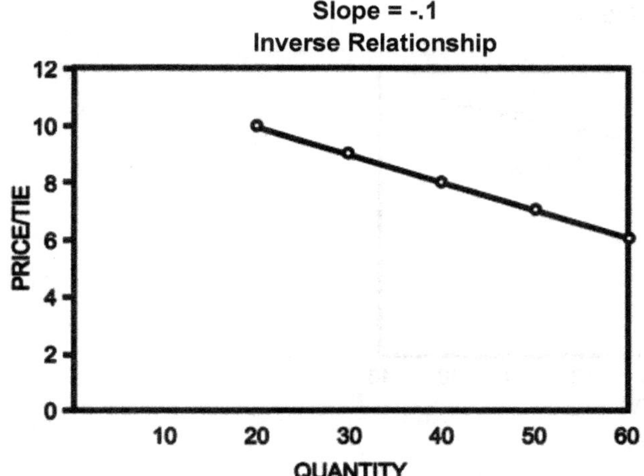

1.2 GRAPH PROBLEM #2

Slope = .4
Direct Relationship

PRICE/WALLET
120
110
80
60
40
20
0
100 150 200 250 300
QUANTITY

1.3 GRAPH PROBLEM #3

Slope = 1
Direct Relationship

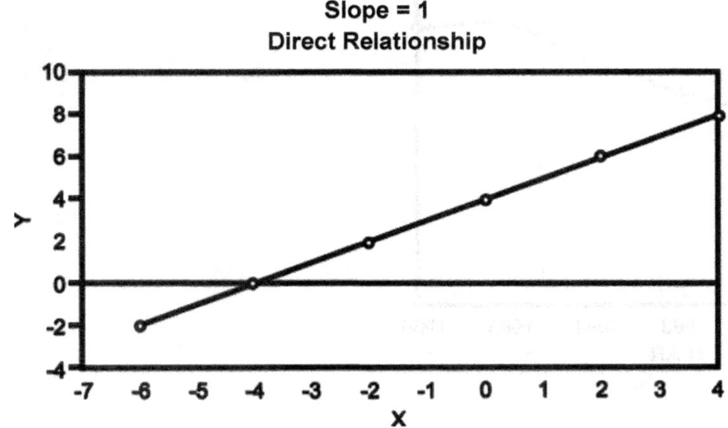

1.4 GRAPH PROBLEM #4

Slope of A1 = -.25 Slope of A2 = .25
Point of Intersection (10, 7.5)

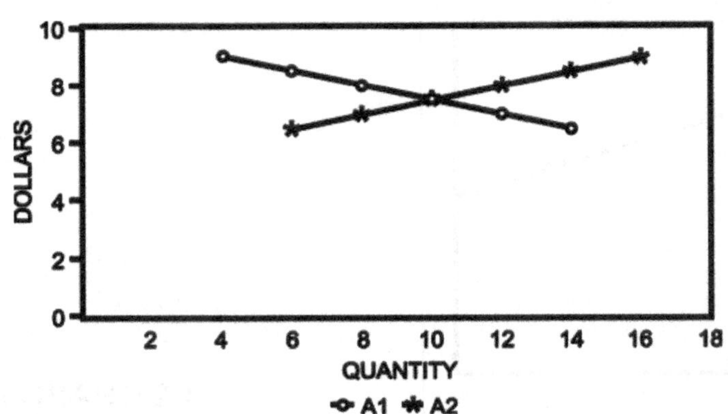

1.5 GRAPH PROBLEM #5

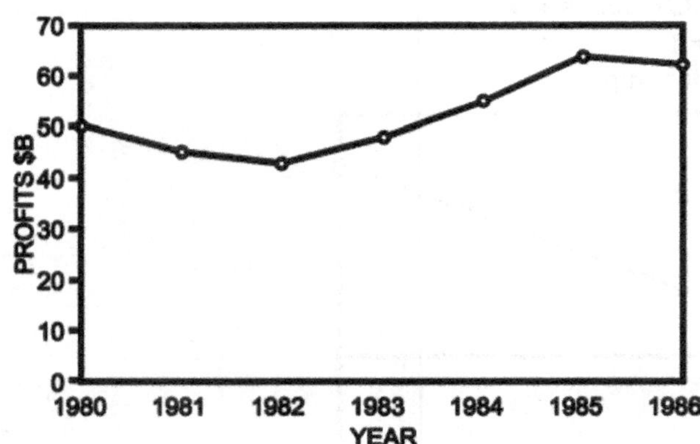

Production – Possibility Problem

Self-test Questions – PPC (Workbook pgs. 11-15)

1. C; 2. B; 3. C; 4. D; 5. C; 6. B; 7. A; 8. B; 9. D

Self-test Questions – Terms (Workbook pg. 16)

1. B; 2. B; 3. B; 4. D; 5. D; 6. B; 7. B; 8. C; 9. A; 10. C

Problem 1

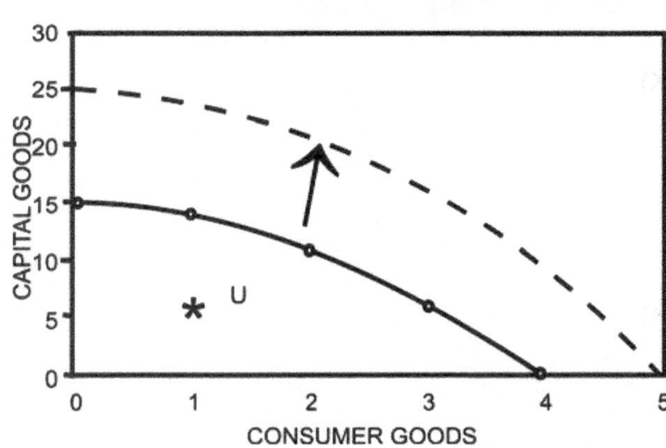

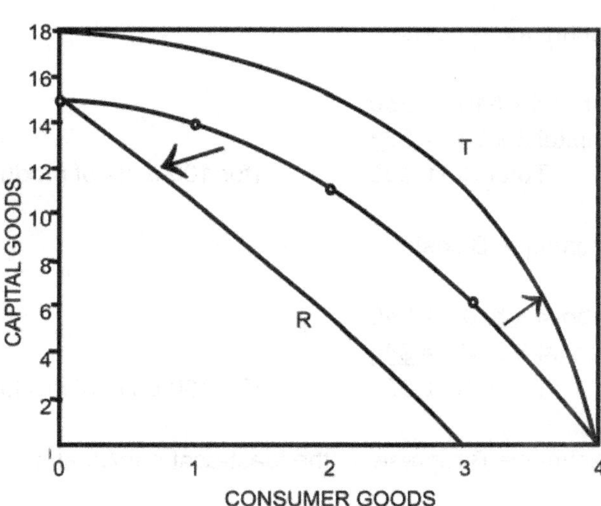

a. Sacrifice of Capital
<u>goods for Consumer goods</u>

-1
-3
-5
-6

b. See graph
c. See graph
d. See graph

e. The Law of Increasing Costs:
As you trade-off resources from one good to another, the sacrifice becomes greater and greater because resources are not perfectly shifted. This is illustrated by the "bow" shaped PPC Curve.

Problem 2: C; Problem 3: D; Problem 4: D; Problem 5: A

"The Market System and the Circular Flow"

Self-test Questions

1. C; 2. B; 3. D; 4. B; 5. C; 6. D; 7. D; 8. D; 9. C; 10. B

Problem 1: Least-cost Problem (Table 1)

a. Technique A costs:

Labor 5 x $10 = $50
Capital 8 x $4 = $32
Total Cost $82 (for 100 units of product X)

Technique B costs:

Labor 4 x $10 = $40
Capital 5 x $4 = $40
Total Cost $80 (for 100 units of product X)

Technique B represents the least-cost combination.

b. Firms will want to use the least-cost technique because it yields the greatest profit.

c. If product X sells for $85/each, total profit will be (using Technique B):

Selling Price $85/each
Cost Price $80/each
$5/profit each

or 100 units X $5/each = $500 profit

Problem 6.

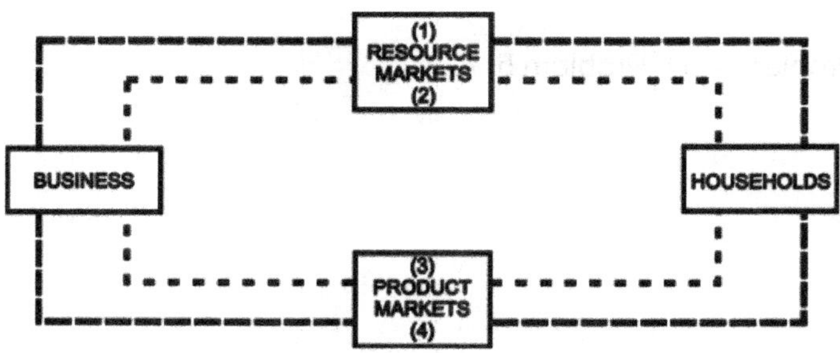

Counterclockwise flow of resources and goods and services; clockwise flow of money income and consumption expenditures. Households are the resources owners (supply-side) and Businesses are the buyers of resources (demand-side). Households purchase the finished goods and services (demand-side) and businesses are the suppliers (supply-side).

"Individual Markets: Demand and Supply"

MACRO Self-test Questions

1. A; 2. C; 3. C; 4. B; 5. B; 6. B; 7. $10, 75; 8. SURPLUS, 50; 9. Shortage, 50; 10. $6; 11. $6; 12. C; 13. A; 14. Ceiling; 15. C

Problem 1

a. Amount of Surplus or Shortage

10,000
6,000
Equilibrium
-7,000
-15,000

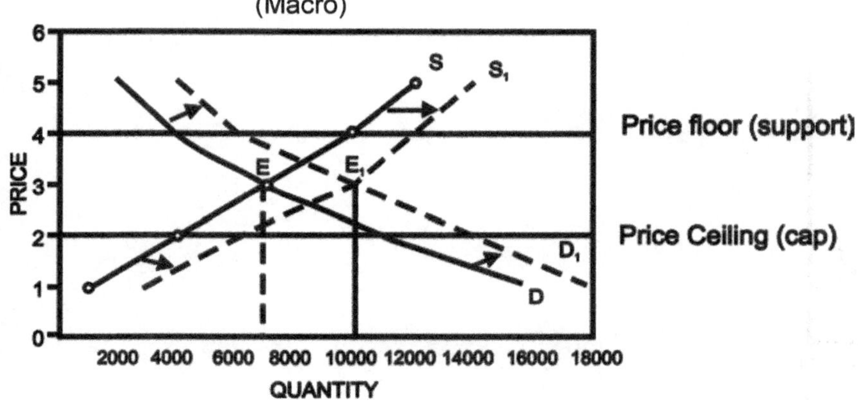

b. 3; 7,000 bushels
c. Surplus occurs at any price above $3
   Shortage occurs at any price below $3
d. See graph above
e. See graph above
   Change in income shifts the demand curve
   Change in resource cost shifts the supply curve
f. See graph above
   The government establishes a ceiling price to:
   1. protect the consumer
   2. control inflation
g. See graph above
   The government establishes a floor price to:
   1. protect the seller
   2. insure an ample supply and competition

Problem 2

a. Total Market Demand

2
5
9
13
20

b. See graph

c. Increase in demand (demand curve shifts to the right), see graph.

3.2 MARKET DEMAND CURVE

(Macro)

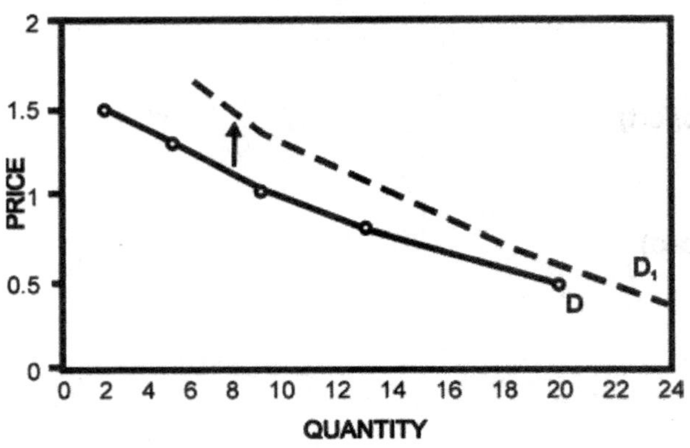

Problem 3

See answer on next page (same as micro)

"Individual Markets: Demand and Supply"

MICRO Self-test Questions

1. A; 2. C; 3. C; 4. D; 5. A; 6. C; 7. $15,100; 8. Shortage, 50; 9. Surplus, 50; 10. $20; 11. $20; 12. C; 13. A; 14. Floor; 15. C

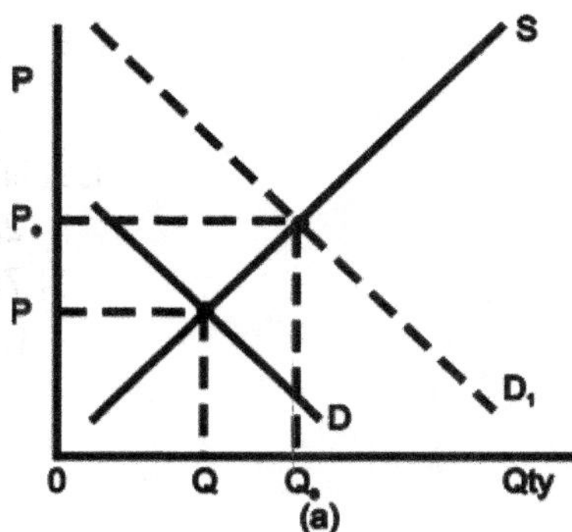

(a)

Increase in demand
Increase in qty. supplied

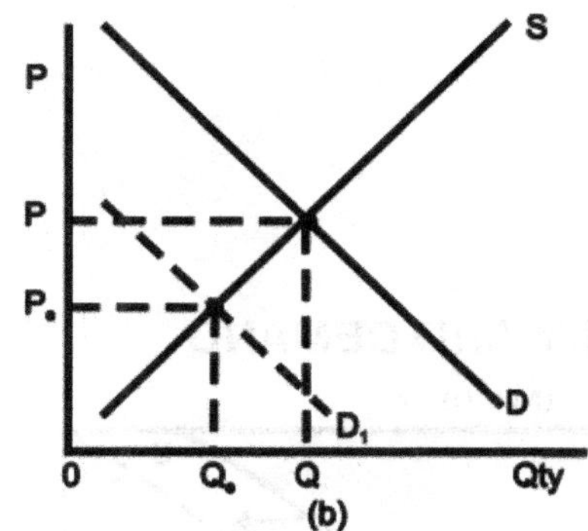

(b)

Decrease in demand
Decrease in qty. supplied

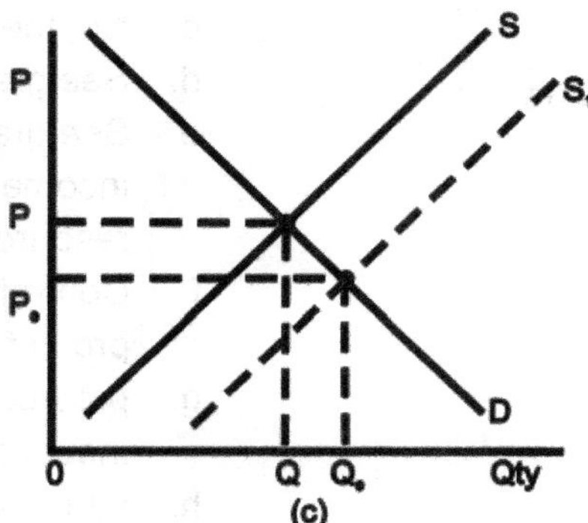

(c)

Increase in qty. demanded
Increase in supply

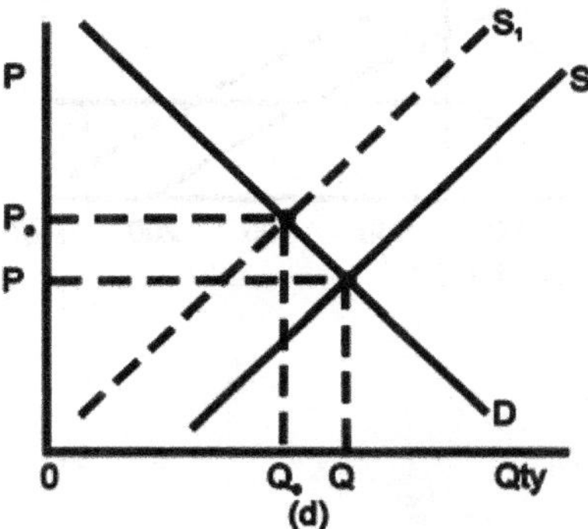

(d)

Decrease in qty. demanded
Decrease in supply

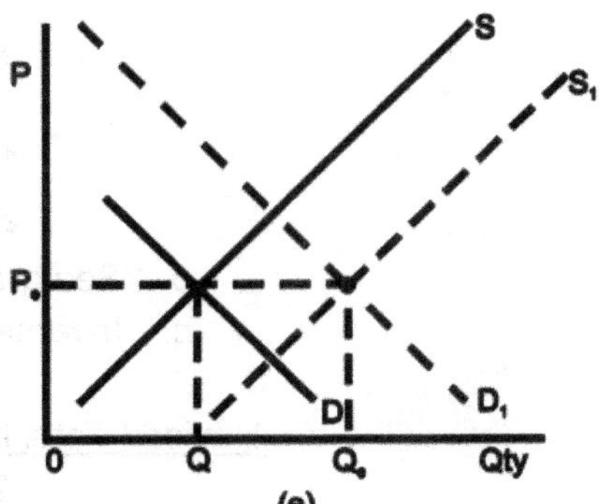

(e)

Increase in demand
Increase in supply

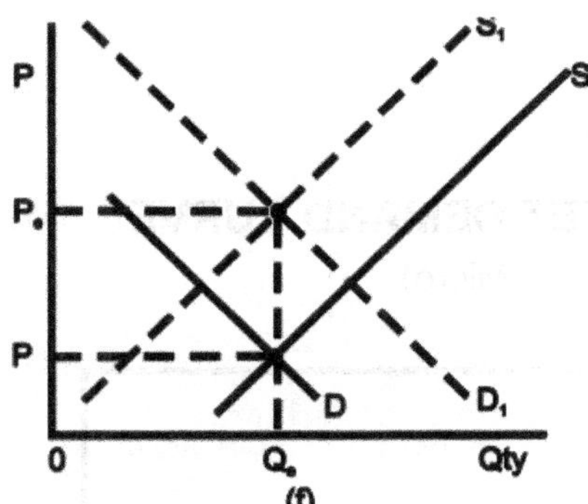

(f)

Increase in demand
Decrease in supply

Problem 1

Amount of Surplus
or Shortage

- 100
- 50
Equilibrium
25
75
125

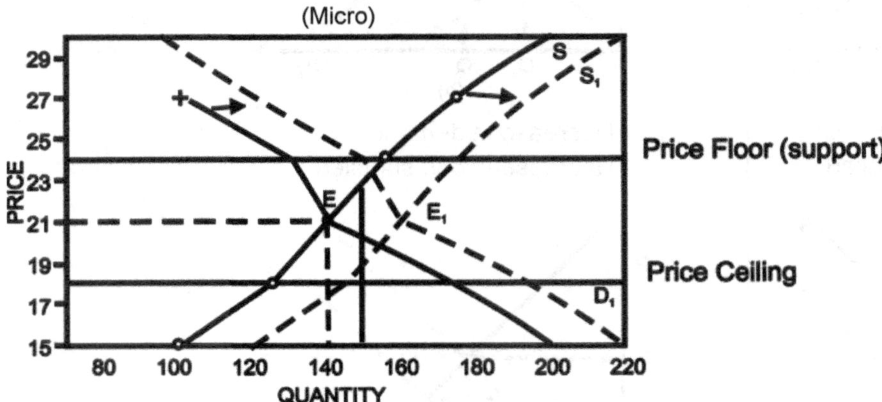

a. $21; 140 DVDs
b. Surplus above $21
   Shortage below $21
c. No, the opposite
d. See graph
e. See graph
   income; taste; technology
   resource cost
f. Control inflation
   protect consumer
g. protect seller
   insure an ample supply
h. surplus of 75
i. $18; 175 videos

Problem 2

Total Market Demand

2
5
11
17
23

b. See graph
c. Inverse relationship

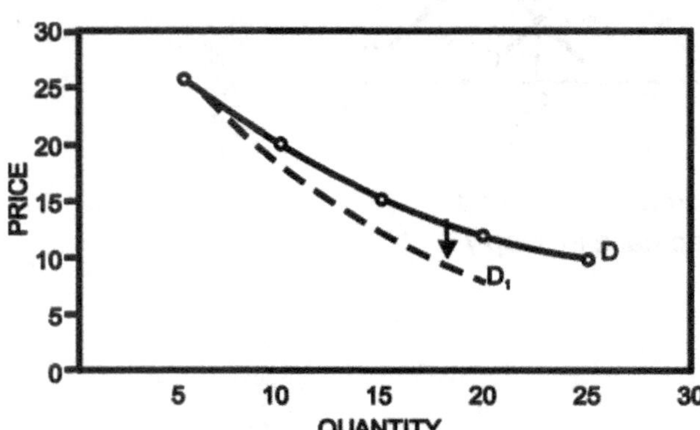

Revised Total Market Demand

2
4
9
13
18

d. See graph
   demand has decreased

"International Economics"

Self-test Questions

1. A; 2. D; 3. B; 4. D; 5. C; 6. D; 7. B; 8. B; 9. B; 10. C

Problem 1 (Table 1)

a. In case A the U.S. - corn; Switzerland - watches;
In case B the U.S. has an absolute advantage so Switzerland has an absolute disadvantage.
In case C the U.S. - corn but neither an absolute advantage or disadvantage in watches.
In case D - the U.S. has an absolute advantage in both commodities.

b. In case A, the U.S. - corn; Switzerland - watches;
In case B, the U.S. - corn; Switzerland - watches;
In case C, the U.S. - corn; Switzerland - watches;
In case D, the U.S. and Switzerland have comparable advantages in neither commodities.

c. In case A, trade is possible (absolute advantage).
In case B, trade is possible (comparative advantage).
In case C, trade is possible (comparative advantage).
In case D no trade is possible (advantage is the same in both commodities).

d. 1. The U.S. gains 1 watch
2. Switzerland gains 4 watches
3. The U.S. gains 3 watches while Switzerland gains 2 watches.

"Economic Growth"

Self-test Questions

1. B; 2. C; 3. B; 4. D; 5. D; 6. A; 7. C; 8. A; 9. D; 10. B

"Measuring Domestic Output and National Income"

Self-test Questions

1. A; 2. C; 3. B; 4. C; 5. A; 6. B; 7. C; 8. $392.86; 9. $480; 10. $559.26; 11. Deflation; 12. C; 13. B; 14. B; 15. B; 16. A

Problem 1

COUNTRIES

	1	2	3	4	5	6
GDP	210	305	400	307	623	394
NDP	200	280	390	255	580	380
NI	180	250	350	233	530	365
PI	165	244	340	228	477	326
DI	150	220	320	190	462	288

Problem 2

Year	Real GDP (billions)
1980	$6,450.4
1990	8,955.0
2000	12,559.7
2005	14,234.2
2010	14,783.8
2014	16,085.6

Problems 3

a. Complete the table below (hypothetical data) – Year 2 as the base year:

Year	Qty.	Price	Price Index	Current $	Real Constant $
1	3	$2	.5 or 50%	$6	$12
2	5	4	1.0 or 100%	20	20
3	6	5	1.25 or 125%	30	24
4	8	6	1.5 or 150%	48	32
5	9	8	2.0 or 200%	72	36

b.

Year	Qty.	Price	Price Index	Current $	Real Constant $
1	3	$2	.4	$6	$15
2	5	4	.8	20	25
3	6	5	1.0	30	30
4	8	6	1.2	48	40
5	9	8	1.4	72	45

c. This economy has been characterized by Inflation.

“Business Cycles, Unemployment and Inflation”

Self-test Questions

1. C; 2. C; 3. B; 4. B; 5. C; 6. D; 7. B; 8. D; 9. A; 10. D

<u>Problems</u> (selected):

2. Indicators such as the inflation rate, unemployment rate, GDP, housing starts, and the Government’s Index of Leading Economic indicators help to “read” the economy. The three types of indications are leading, lagging, and coincident.

3. Occupations on the upswing (to 2020) in New Jersey and in the United States are careers in healthcare and technology.

6. The auto industry represents a durable goods industry, whereas the farm industry is characterized by nondurable goods. Durable goods experience wide swings in output, employment, and income—price remains relatively stable. Nondurable goods have very small (stable) swings in output, employment and income. However, there is usually much competition and therefore, large changes in prices.

8. The economic cost of unemployment are the lost “potential” goods and services (as measured by Okun’s Law). The social cost of unemployment is measured by the social trauma it causes.

10. Briefly, the benefits of inflation are that if you have borrowed money you are paying back with cheaper dollars and property, for example, escalates tremendously. The costs of inflation are that inflation redistributes income and wealth arbitrarily, hurts those of fixed incomes, and inflation effects every consumer.

“The Phillips Curve”

Self-test Questions

1. C; 2. D; 3. A; 4. D; 5. B

“Basic Macroeconomic Relationships”

Self-test Questions

1. B; 2. B; 3. C; 4. D; 5. B; 6. B; 7. A; 8. B; 9. D; 10. C; 11. D; 12. D; 13. C; 14. B; 15. D;
16. D; 17. A; 18. C; 19. B; 20. D; 21. B; 22. A; 23. B; 24. B; 25. D; 26. A; 27. D

Problem 1

Savings	APC	APS	MPC	MPS
$-400	1.13	-.13		
			.8	.2
-200	1.05	-.05		
			.8	.2
0	1.00	0		
			.8	.2
200	.97	.03		
			.8	.2
400	.94	.06		
			.8	.2
600	.92	.08		

f. $5,000

g. Slope of consumption function = .8

h. Slope of the savings function = .2

Problem 1: cont'd

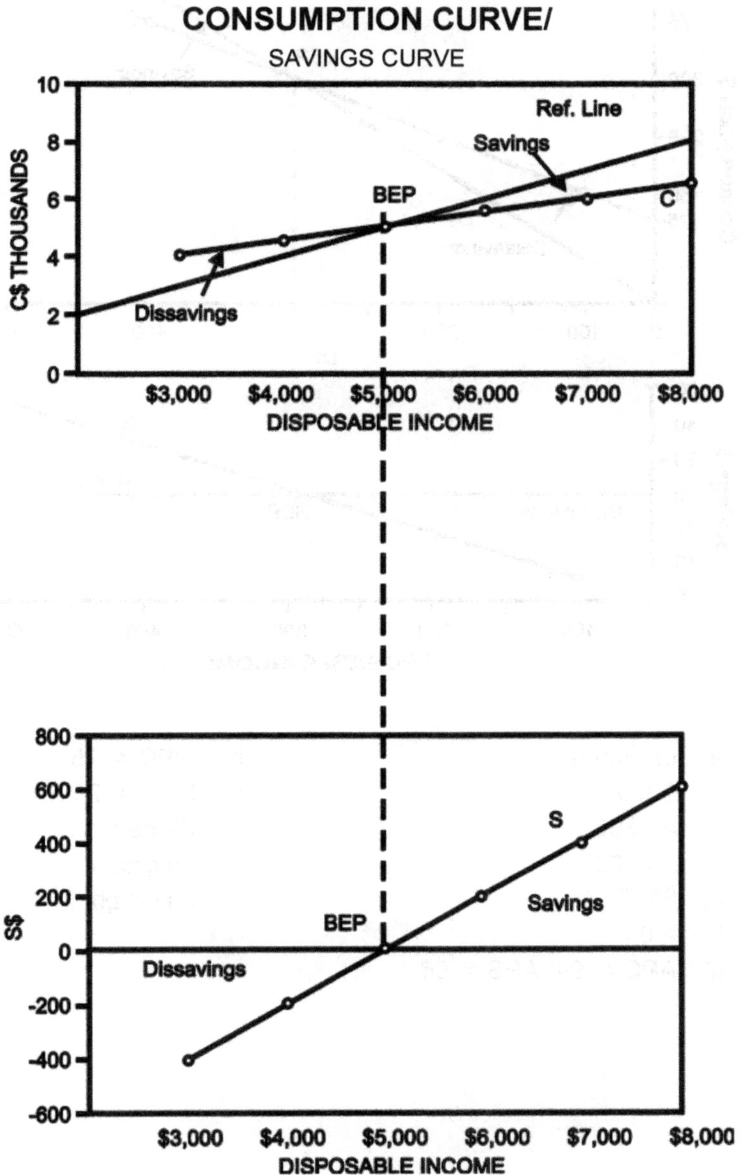

Problem 2

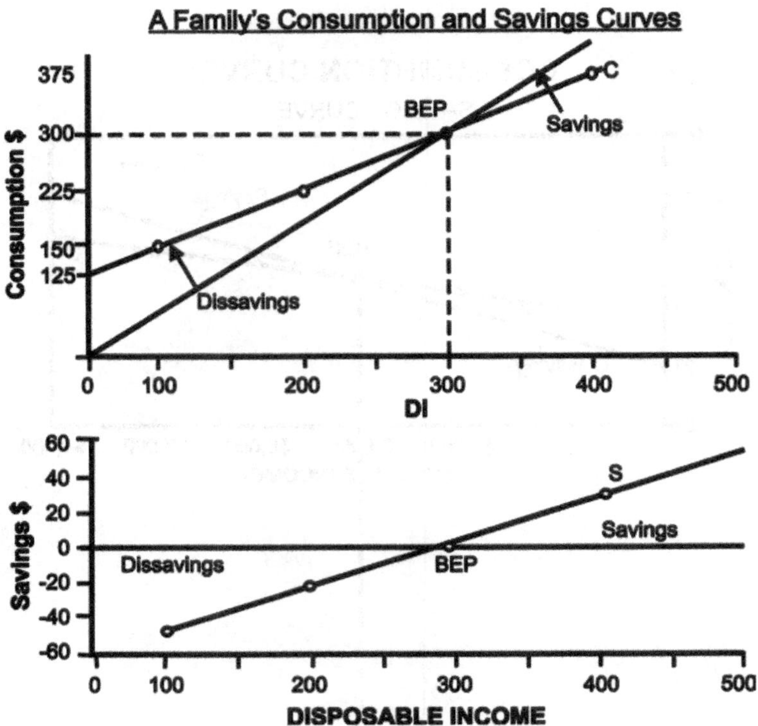

a. on graph
b. $300
c. > $300
d. < $300
e. $125
f. > 0
g. APC = .94; APS = .06
h. MPC = .75
i. MPS = .25
j. Slope = .75
k. on graph
l. on graph

Problem 3

MPC	M	Mt	BBM	MPS	M	Mt	BBM
.9	10	9	1	.2	5	4	1
.8	5	4	1	.5	2	1	1
.75	4	3	1	.4	2.5	1.5	1
.5	2	1	1	.1	10	9	1
.6	2.5	1.5	1	.05	20	19	1
.95	20	19	1				

"The Aggregate Expenditures Model"

Self-test Questions

1. B; 2. D 3. D; 4. D; 5. B; 6. A; 7. B; 8. B; 9. C; 10. D

Problem 2

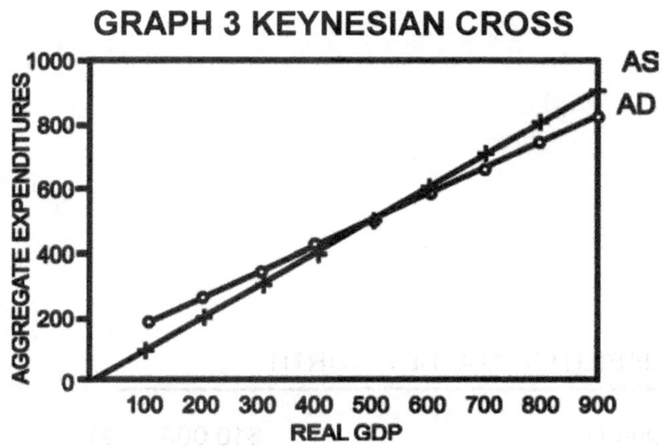

AS	AD
100	180
200	260
300	340
400	420
500 ----	500
600	580
700	660
800	740
900	820

DI	T. Leakages	Pl. Injection
100	-35	45
200	-15	45
300	5	45
400	25	45
500 ----	45 ------	45
600	65	45
700	85	45
800	105	45
900	125	45

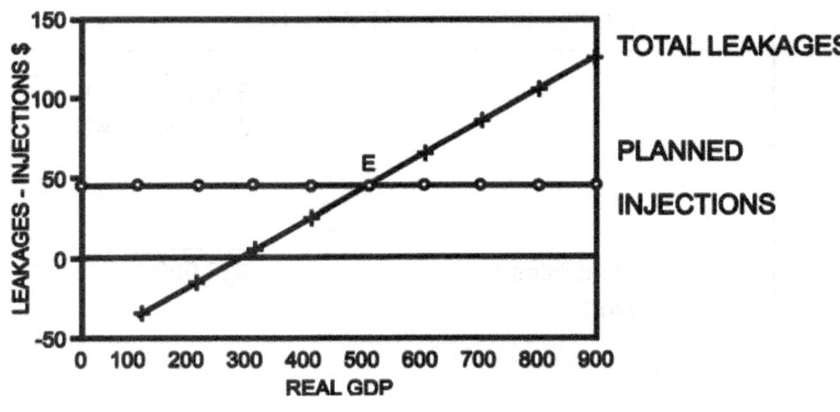

c. The equilibrium GDP level = 500
d. Either technique yields the same equilibrium level (see above)

"Classical, Keynesian and Supply-side Economics"

Self-test Questions

1. B; 2. D; 3. D; 4. C; 5. A

"Fiscal Policy, Deficits and Debt"

Self-test Questions

1. B; 2. C; 3. B; 4. C; 5. D; 6. C; 7. D; 8. D; 9. D
; 10. C

"Money, Banking and the Financial Institutions"

Self-test Questions

1. A; 2. B; 3. B; 4. D; 5. B; 6. A; 7. B; 8. A; 9. B; 10. D

"Money Creation"

Self-test Questions

1. B; 2. C; 3. A; 4. A; 5. D; 6. C; 7. C; 8. B; 9. B; 10. D

Problem 5: Simplified Bank Balance Sheet

a.

ASSETS		LIABILITIES AND NET WORTH		
Total Reserves:	2,000	Demand Deposits:	$10,000	#1
Required 2,000				
Excess 0				
Loans	8,000	Total Liabilities & Net Worth	$10,000	
Total Assets	10,000			

b. R = 20%

c. Required Reserves would become $5,000

d.

ASSETS		LIABILITIES AND NET WORTH		
Total Reserves:	17,000	Demand Deposits	$10,000	#1
			$15,000	#2
Required 5,000				
Excess 12,000				
Loans	8,000	Total Liabilities & Net Worth	$25,000	
Total Assets	25,000			

e. $M_\$ = \frac{1}{R}$

$= \frac{1}{.2} = 5$

$R = \frac{\text{Required Reserves}}{\text{Demand Deposits}}$

f. $60,000 = $12,000 x 5 (additional expansion)

Maximum Demand Deposit Expansions (in banking system) = Excess Reserves x Money Multiplier

"Interest Rates and Monetary Policy"
Self-test Questions

1. A; 2. B; 3. A; 4. A; 5. B; 6. B; 7. D; 8. B; 9. C; 10. B

Problem 1:

	Tool	"Easy $"	"Tight $"
1.	FOMC	Buy	Sell
2.	Reserve Ratio	Lower	Raise
3.	Discount Rate	Lower	Raise
4.	Interest on Reserves	Lower	Raise
5.	Margin Requirement	Lower	Raise
6.	Consumer Credit	Lower	Raise
7.	Moral Suasion ("jawboning")	Positive Comments	Negative Comments

Problem 2

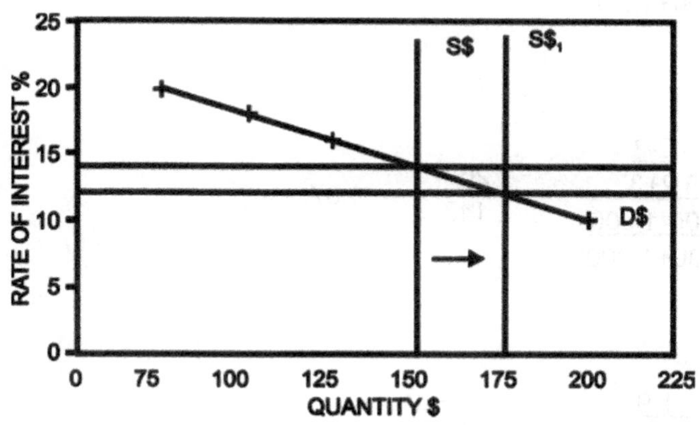

Total Demand for Money
$75
$100
$125
$150
$175
$200

Problem 3

a. Appreciated
b. Year 1: $111.11; Year 2: $83.33, U.S. Imports: Increase, Japanese Exports: Increase
c. Year 1: $6,750; Year 2: $9,000, U.S. Exports: Decrease, Japanese Imports: Decrease
d. Appreciates, increase, decrease
e. Positive: U.S. can import Japanese goods at a low cost
Negative: U.S. exports to Japan will go down (more expensive)

"Elasticity"

Self-test Questions

1. B; 2. A; 3. A; 4. B; 5. A; 6. B; 7. A; 8. C; 9. B; 10. A

Problem 3:

Price	Total Revenue	E_d
Increases	Decreases	>1
Decreases	Decreases	<1
Decreases	No Change	=1
Increases	Increases	<1
Increases	Decreases	>1
Increases	No Change	=1

Problem 4:

Chicken

E_y = .45

Normal

$$E_y = \frac{\frac{11.4-10}{11.4+10}}{\frac{1,600-1,200}{1,600+1200}} = \frac{.065}{.143} = .45$$

Peanut Butter

E_y = -.37

Inferior

$$E_y = \frac{\frac{4.5-5}{4.5+5}}{\frac{1,600-1,200}{1,600+1,200}} = \frac{-.053}{.143} = -.37$$

Steak

E_y = 1.87

Superior

$$E_y = \frac{\frac{5.2-3}{5.2+3}}{\frac{1,600-1,200}{1,600+1,200}} = \frac{.268}{.143} = 1.87$$

Hamburger

E_y = .7

Normal

$$E_y = \frac{\frac{11-9}{11+9}}{\frac{1,600-1,200}{1,600+1200}} = \frac{.1}{.143} = .70$$

Bread

E_y = 0

Normal

$$E_y = \frac{\frac{5-5}{5+5}}{\frac{1,600-1,200}{1,600+1200}} = \frac{0}{.143} = 0$$

Problem 5:

Chicken

E_{xy} = 1.08

Substitute

$$E_y = \frac{\frac{12-11.4}{12+11.4}}{\frac{2.10-2.00}{2.10+2.00}} = \frac{.026}{.024} = 1.08$$

Fish

E_{xy} = .92

Substitute

$$E_y = \frac{\frac{4.7-4.5}{4.7+4.5}}{\frac{2.10-2.00}{2.10+2.00}} = \frac{.022}{.024} = .92$$

Ketchup

E_{xy} = -3.7

Complement

$$E_y = \frac{\frac{2.5-3}{2.5+3}}{\frac{2.10-2.00}{2.10+200}} = \frac{-.091}{.024} = -3.79$$

Tofu

E_{xy} = 2.0

Substitute

$$E_y = \frac{\frac{5.5-5}{5.5+5}}{\frac{2.10-2.00}{2.10+2.00}} = \frac{.048}{.024} = 2.0$$

Hamburger Buns

E_{xy} = -2.79

Complement

$$E_y = \frac{\frac{3.5-4}{3.5+4}}{\frac{2.10-2.00}{2.10+2.00}} = \frac{-.067}{.024} = -2.79$$

Problem 6

Es	TR	TR Test		Ed
4.09	960	Elastic	>	1.37
3.48	990	Elastic	>	1.10
6.28	1,000	Inelastic	>	.91
7.27	990	Inelastic	>	.73

$TR = P \times Q_D$

↑P	↓TR	or	↓P	↑TR	Elastic
↑P	↓P	=	same TR		Unit Elastic
↑P	↑TR	or	↓P	↓TR	Inelastic

Problem 6 (cont'd)

$$E_d = \frac{\frac{90-80}{90+80}}{\frac{11-12}{11+12}} = \frac{.059}{-.043} = -1.37 = 1.37 \quad \text{Elastic}$$

$$E_d = \frac{\frac{100-90}{100+90}}{\frac{10-11}{10+11}} = \frac{.053}{-.043} = -1.10 = 1.10 \quad \text{Elastic}$$

$$E_d = \frac{\frac{110-100}{110+100}}{\frac{9-10}{9+10}} = \frac{.048}{-.053} = -.91 = .91 \quad \text{Inelastic}$$

$$E_d = \frac{\frac{120-110}{120+110}}{\frac{8-9}{8+9}} = \frac{.043}{.-059} = -.73 = .73 \quad \text{Inelastic}$$

$$E_s = \frac{\frac{70-100}{70+100}}{\frac{11-12}{11+12}} = \frac{.176}{-.043} = 4.09 \quad \text{Elastic}$$

$$E_s = \frac{\frac{50-70}{50+70}}{\frac{10-11}{10+11}} = \frac{.167}{-.048} = 3.48 \quad \text{Elastic}$$

$$E_s = \frac{\frac{25-50}{25+50}}{\frac{9-10}{9+10}} = \frac{-.333}{-.053} = 6.28 \quad \text{Elastic}$$

$$E_s = \frac{\frac{10-25}{10+25}}{\frac{8-9}{8+9}} = \frac{-.333}{.059} = 7.27 \quad \text{Elastic}$$

"Consumer Behavior and Utility Maximization"

Self-test Questions

1. B; 2. C; 3. A; 4. D; 5. (4 of A and 4 of B); 6. B; 7. C; 8. C; 9. D; 10. C

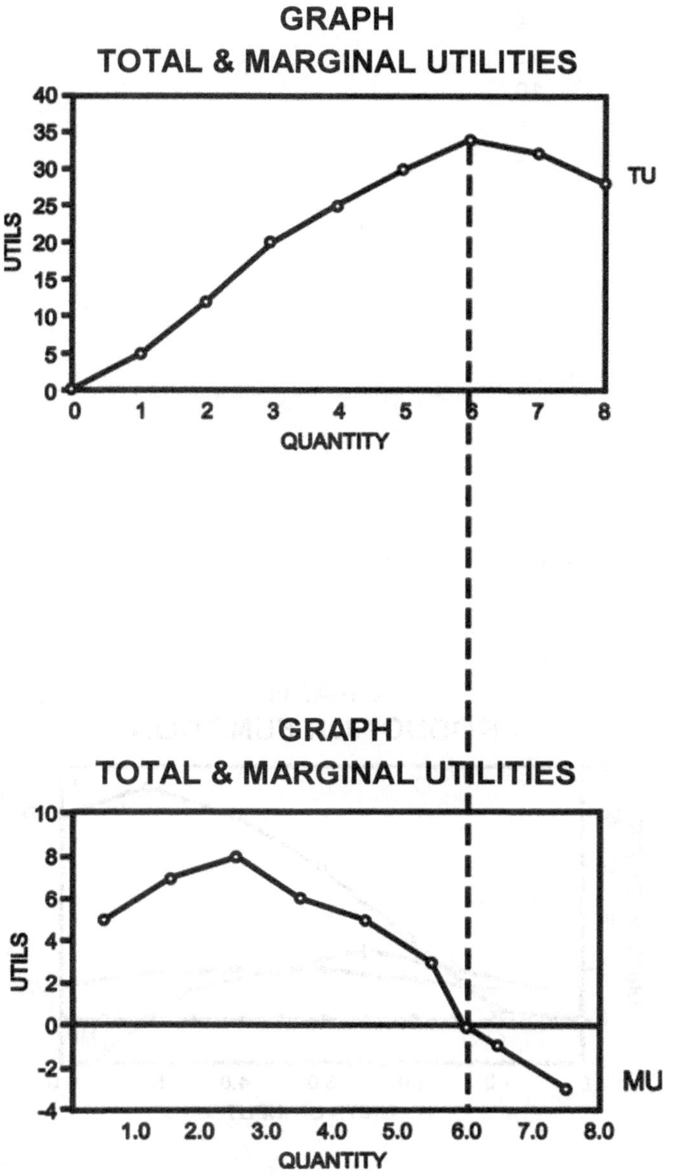

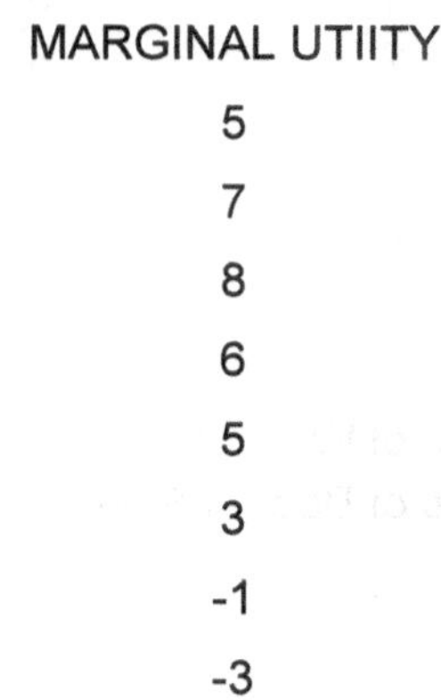

d. zero

e. slope

Problem 3

Unit	MU Wine / P Wine	MU Beer / P Beer	MU Soda / P Soda	MU$
1	10	20	1	14
2	8	16	.5	12
3	5	12	0	10
4	3	8	-.5	8
5	1	4	-1	6

2 units of Wine at $2/ea.	=	$4	
4 units of Beer at $.50 ea.	=	2	
		$6	Spent
		$4	Saved
		$10	Income

"Businesses and the Costs of Production"

Self-test Questions

1. C; 2. B; 3. C; 4. C; 5. D; 6. C; 7. A; 8. B; 9. D; 10 D; 11. C; 12. B; 13. D; 14. B; 15. C;

Problem 1

Units of Variable Factor	Total Product	Average Product	Marginal Product
0	0	-	
1	3	3	3
2	8	4	5
3	15	5	7
4	20	5	5
5	23	4.6	3
6	20	3.3	-3

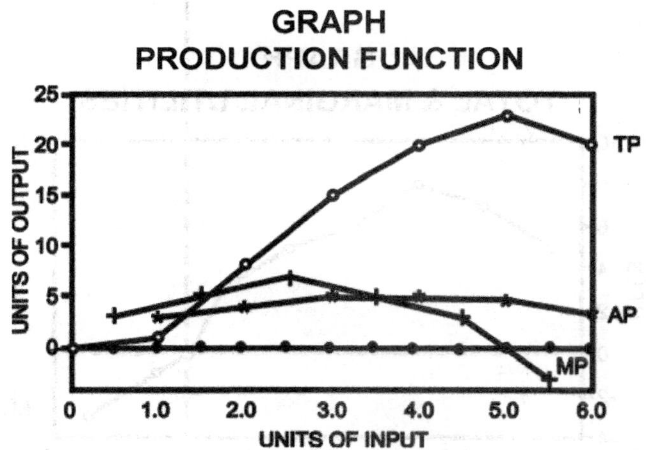

b. Answer the following questions with reference to the graphs you have drawn:
   (1) When marginal product is greater than average product, average product is (rising/constant/falling).
   (2) When marginal product is less than average product, average product is (rising/constant/falling).

Problem 2

b. Table and graph below:

Output per day	TFC	TVC	TC	ATC	AVC	MC
0	14	0	14	-	-	
1	14	2	16	16	2	2
2	14	4	18	9	2	2
3	14	6	20	6.67	2	2
4	14	10	24	6	2.5	4
5	14	16	30	6	3.2	6
6	14	24	38	6.33	4	8
7	14	34	48	6.86	4.86	10
8	14	46	60	7.5	5.76	12
9	14	60	74	8.22	6.67	14
10	14	76	90	9	7.6	16

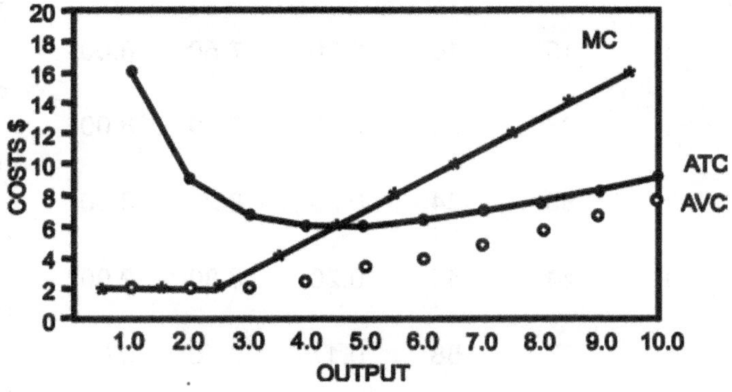

c. AFC

d. Due to efficiency and inefficiency

e. Between 4 and 5 units

"Pure Competition"

Self-test Questions

1. B; 2. D; 3. A; 4. C; 5. C; 6. B; 7. D; 8. D; 9. C; 10. B

Problem 1

Profit maximization in the short-run

Qty.	Price	TR	TVC	FC	TC	MR	MC	NR
A. Case 1								
0	$5.99	0	$0	$5	$5			$-5.00*
1	$5.99	5.99	6	$5	11	$5.99	$6	-5.01
2	$5.99	11.98	14	$5	19	$5.99	8	-7.02
3	$5.99	17.97	24	$5	29	$5.99	10	-11.03
4	$5.99	23.96	36	$5	41	$5.99	12	-17.04
B. Case 2								
0	$6.01	0	$0	$5	$5			$-5.00
1	$6.01	$6.01	6	$5	11	$6.01	$6	-4.99*
2	$6.01	12.02	14	$5	19	$6.01	8	-6.98
3	$6.01	18.03	24	$5	29	$6.01	10	-10.97
4	$6.01	24.04	36	$5	41	$6.01	12	-16.96
C. Case 3								
0	$10.01	0	$0	$5	$5			$-5.00
1	$10.01	$10.01	6	$5	11	$10.01	$6	-.99*
2	$10.01	20.02	14	$5	19	$10.01	8	1.02
3	$10.01	30.03	24	$5	29	$10.01	10	1.03*
4	$10.01	40.04	36	$5	41	$10.01	12	-.96

Problem 2

Qty.	Price	TR	TFC	TVC	TC	AFC	AVC	ATC	MC	MR	NR
0	$9.00	0	1	0	1						-1.00
									8	9	
1	$9.00	9	1	8	9	1.00	8.00	9.00			0.00 BEP
									7	9	
2	$9.00	18	1	15	16	0.50	7.50	8.00			2.00
									8	9	
3	$9.00	27	1	23	24	0.33	7.70	8.00			3.00
									10	9	
4	$9.00	36	1	33	34	0.25	8.25	8.50			2.00
									11	9	
5	$9.00	45	1	44	45	0.20	8.80	9.00			0.00 BEP
									13	9	
6	$9.00	54	1	57	58	0.17	9.50	9.67			-4.00
									17	9	
7	$9.00	63	1	74	75	0.14	10.60	10.71			-12.00

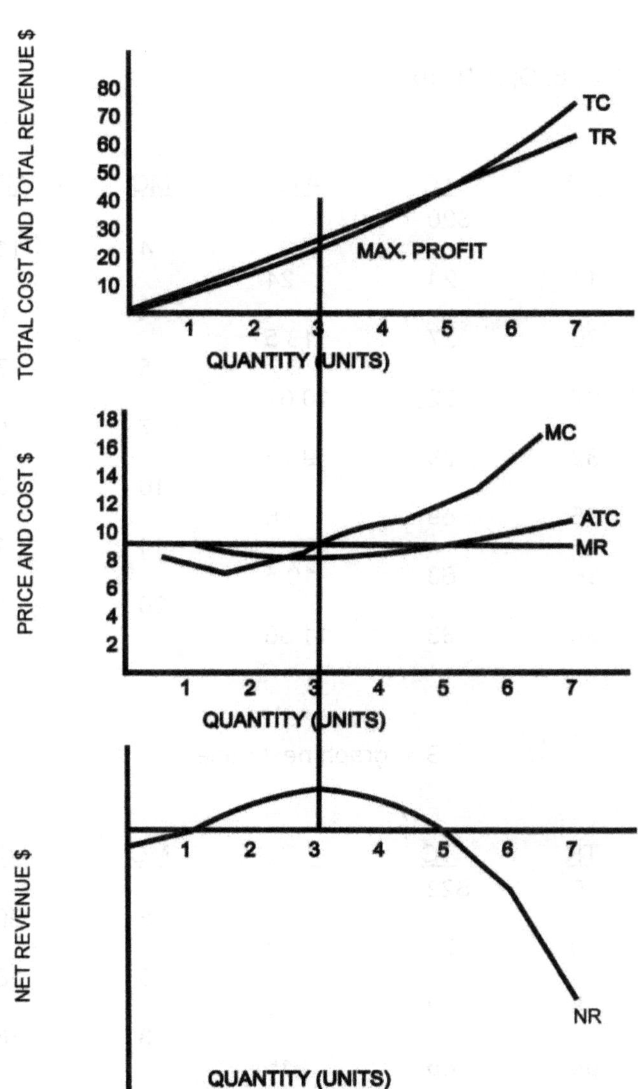

C. Profit met quantity: 3

D. TFC = 1

"Pure Monopoly"

Self-test Questions

1. B; 2. C; 3. A; 4. A; 5. B; 6. C; 7. D; 8. D; 9. B; 10. B

Problem 1

Quantity per day	AR	TR	TC	ATC	MC	MR	NR
0	$12	0	$20	-			$-20
					4	11	
1	11	11	24	24			-13
					3	9	
2	10	20	27	13.5			-7
					5	7	
3	9	27	32	10.67			-5
					7	5	
4	8	32	39	9.75			-7
					10	3	
5	7	35	49	9.8			-14
					14	1	
6	6	36	63	10.5			-27
					20	-1	
7	5	35	83	11.86			-48

C. Loss minimum qty.: 3

D. TFC: $20

See graph next page

Problem 2

Quantity per day	AR	TR	TC	ATC	MC	MR	NR
0	$21	0	$22	-			-$22
					15	20	
1	20	20	37	37			-17
					5	18	
2	19	38	42	21			-4
					3	16	
3	18	54	45	15			9
					2	14	
4	17	68	47	11.75			21
					3	12	
5	16	80	50	10			30
					4	10	
6	15	90	54	9			36
					5	8	
7	14	98	59	8.43			39
					6	6	
8	13	104	65	8.13			39
					7	4	
9	12	108	72	8			36
					8	2	
10	11	110	80	8			30
					9	0	
11	10	110	89	8.09			21
					10	-2	
12	9	108	99	8.25			9

C. Profit max qty. 7-8 units

D. TFC: $22

See graph next page

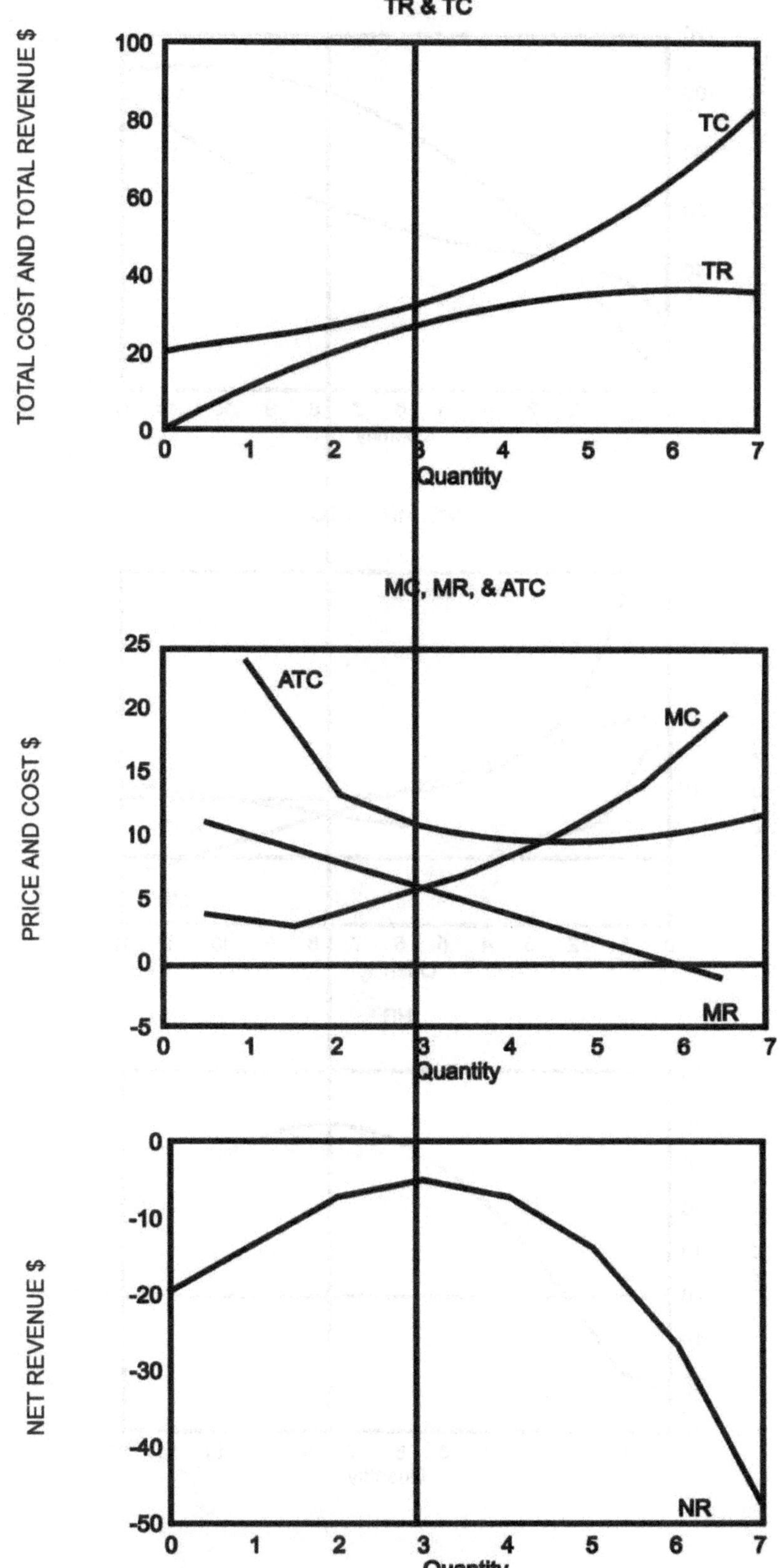

TR & TC
TOTAL COST AND TOTAL REVENUE $
100
80
60
40
20
0
TC
TR
0 1 2 3 4 5 6 7
Quantity
MC, MR, & ATC
PRICE AND COST $
25
20
15
10
5
0
-5
ATC
MC
MR
0 1 2 3 4 5 6 7
Quantity
NET REVENUE $
0
-10
-20
-30
-40
-50
NR
0 1 2 3 4 5 6 7
Quantity

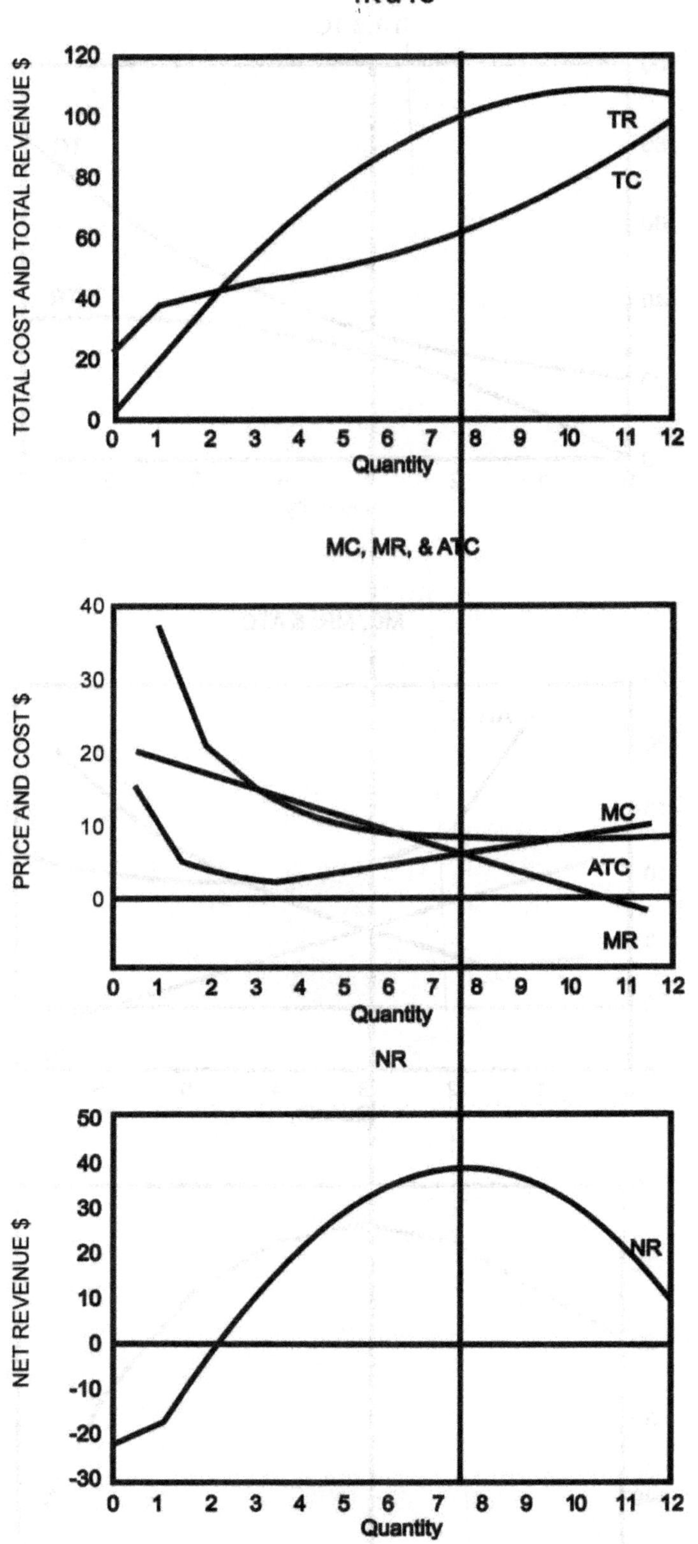
TR & TC
TOTAL COST AND TOTAL REVENUE $
120
100
80
60
40
20
0
TR
TC
0 1 2 3 4 5 6 7 8 9 10 11 12
Quantity
MC, MR, & ATC
PRICE AND COST $
40
30
20
10
0
MC
ATC
MR
0 1 2 3 4 5 6 7 8 9 10 11 12
Quantity
NR
NET REVENUE $
50
40
30
20
10
0
-10
-20
-30
NR
0 1 2 3 4 5 6 7 8 9 10 11 12
Quantity

"Monopolistic Competition and Oligopoly"

Self-test Questions

1. D; 2. D; 3. B; 4. C; 5. A; 6. B; 7. B; 8. A; 9. B; 10. B;
11. C; 12. A; 13. C; 14. C; 15. D; 16. D; 17. D; 18. D; 19. D; 20. D

Problem 1 - Monopolistic Competition

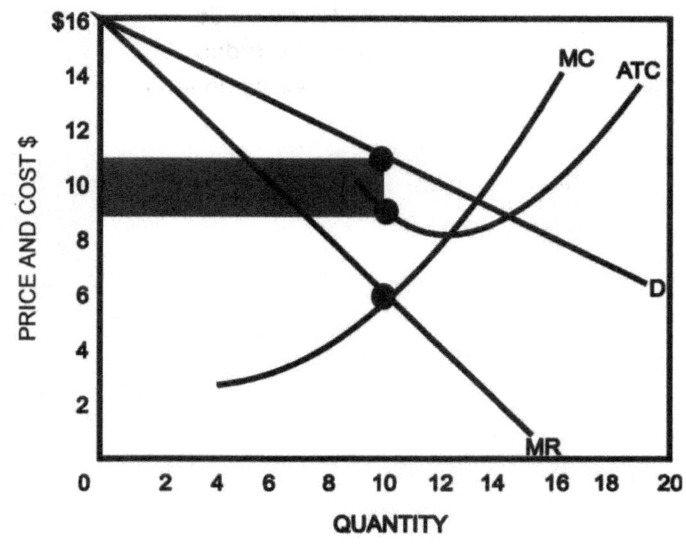

1a. 10; $11
b. $20; Eco. Profit
c. will tend to
d. will

Problem 2

*"PROFIT/LOSS POSITIONS FOR A FIRM UNDER MONOPOLISTIC COMPETITION"

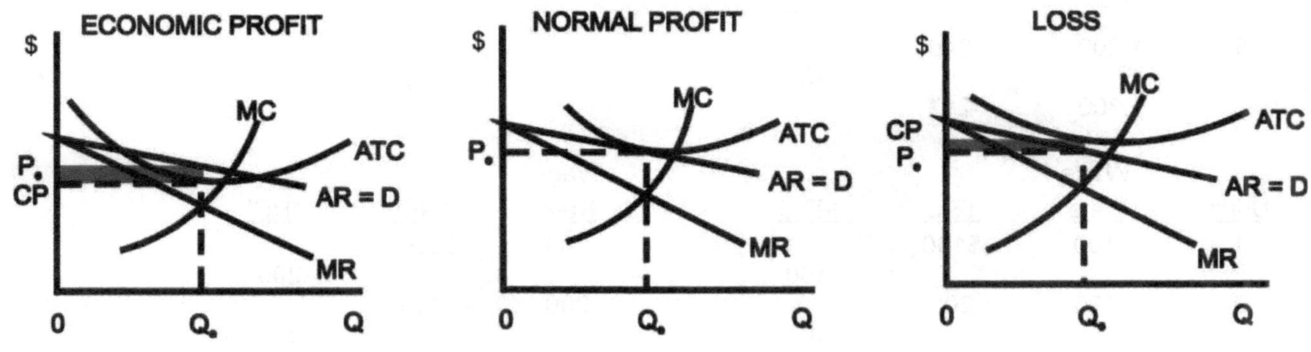

Problem 3

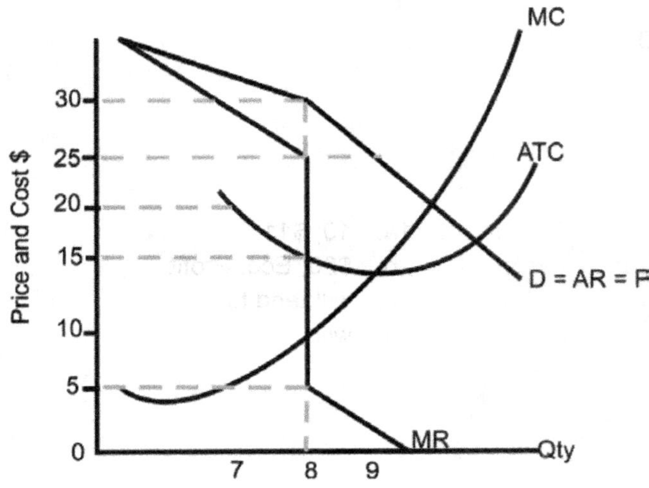

a. 8 UNITS @ $30
Net Revenue per unit = $15
Total Profit = $120

b. No greater than $25
reduce, increase
No less than $5
increase, reduce
Oligopolists do tend

"The Demand for Resources"
Self-test Questions

1. A; 2. B; 3. C; 4. C; 5. C; 6. D; 7. D; 8. D; 9. B; 10. B

Problem 1:

a.

MP	TR	ARP	MRP
14	340	340	
			280
12	620	310	
			240
10	860	287	
			200
7	1,060	265	
			140
5	1,200	240	
			100
	1,300	217	

b.

Units	Wage Rate	TRC	MRC
1	100	$100	
			100
2	100	200	
			100
3	100	300	
			100
4	100	400	
			100
5	100	500	
			100
6	100	600	

c.

Wage Rate	TRC'	MRC'
200	$200	
		200
200	400	
		200
200	600	
		200
200	800	
		200
200	1,000	
		200
200	1,200	

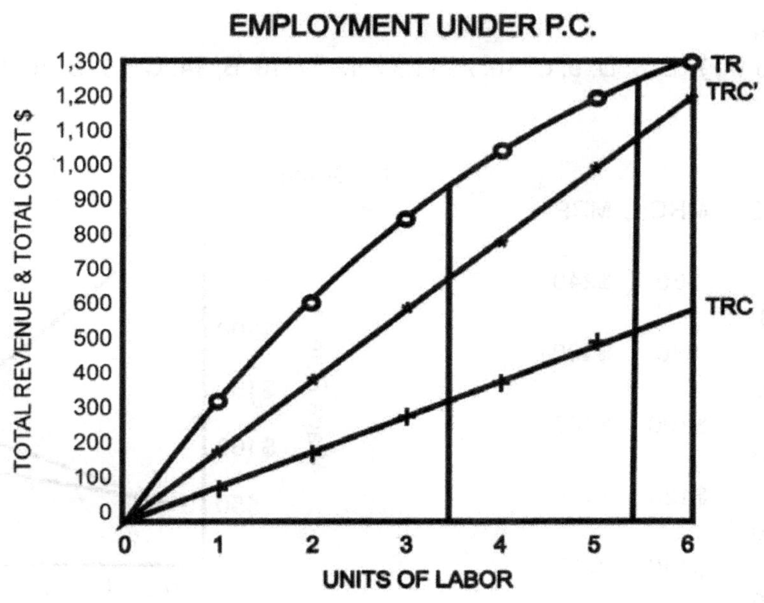

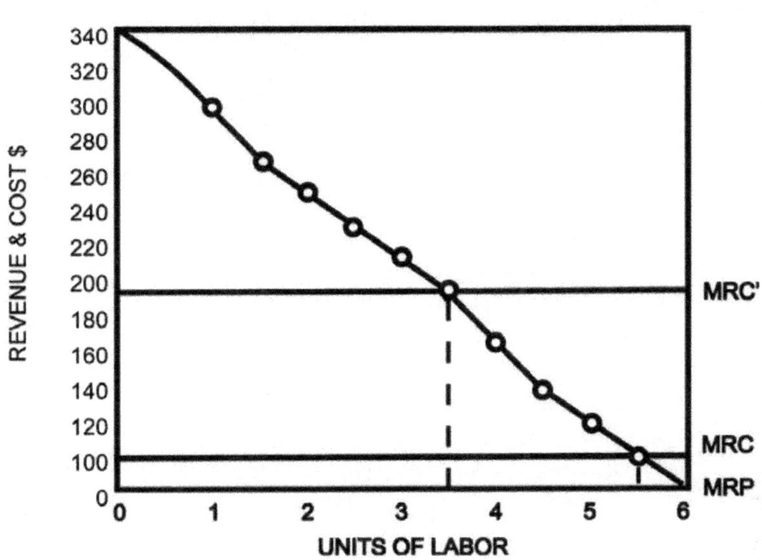

e. At $100, hire 5.5; at $200, hire 3.5

"Wage Determination"

Self-test questions

1. C; 2. C; 3. A; 4. D; 5. A; 6. A; 7. B; 8. D; 9. C; 10. A; 11. C; 12. D; 13. B; 14. C; 15. B; 16. D

Problem 1:

a.

Units of Labor	Wage Rate	TRC	MRC	MRP
0	$50	0		
			$60	$240
1	$60	60		
			$80	$200
2	$70	140		
			$100	$160
3	$80	240		
			$120	$120
4	$90	360		
			$140	$80
5	$100	500		
			$160	$40
6	$110	660		

b. Graph

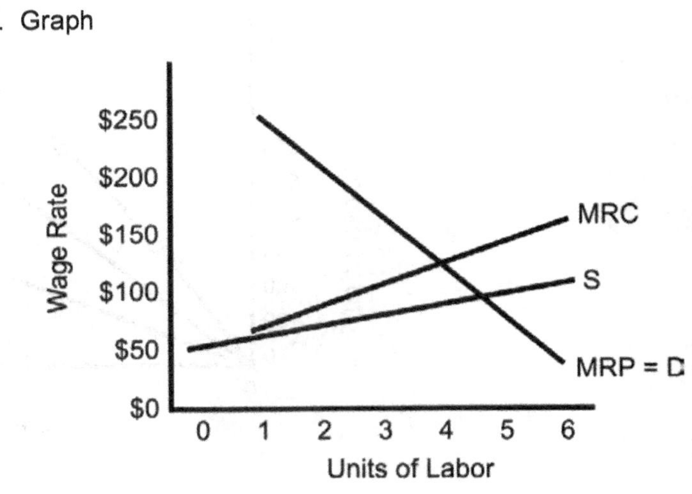

c. Wage rate: $85
Qty of Labor: Between 3 and 4

Problem 2:

1. C 4. D
2. D 5. C
3. B 6. D

Problem 3:

1. 70; $35
2. 60; $30
3. $30 and $45 (range)
4. $15

"Rent, Interest, and Profit"

Self-test Questions

1. C; 2. B; 3. C; 4. D; 5. D; 6. D; 7. C; 8. C; 9. A; 10. A

Problem 4:

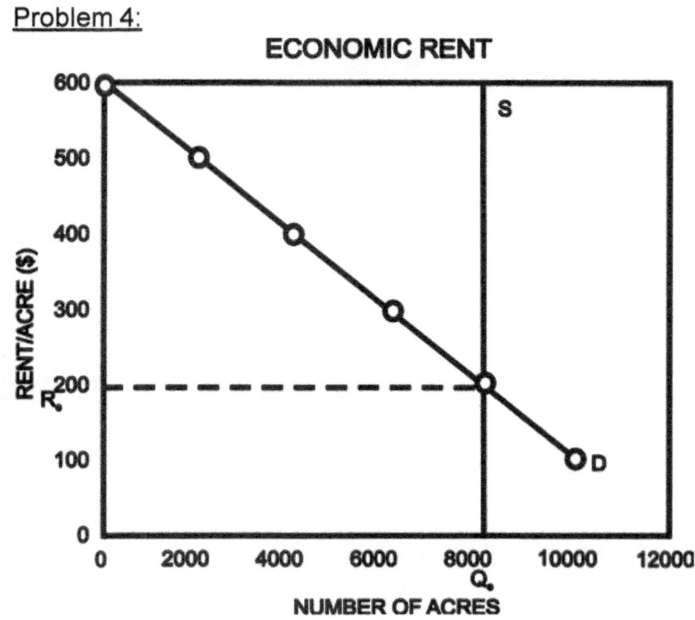

a. Rent will be $200 per acre
$200 x 8,000 acres = $1,600,000

b. 8,000 acres are demanded at $200/acre

c. graph see below

d. Still 8,000 acres (tax did not affect demand or supply)

"Labor Market Issues: Unionism, Discrimination, and Immigration"

Self-test Questions

1. D; 2. C; 3. B; 4. B; 5. B; 6. B; 7. D; 8. A; 9. C; 10. A

See answers in the "Chapter Highlights" of this workbook

MACROECONOMICS
UNIT I
WORKSHEETS

Prof. Debbie A. Meyer

Chapter 1: "Terms, the Production Possibilities Curve and Graphing"

I. The Economic Perspective

A. Scarcity and choice

B. Purposeful behavior

C. Marginal Analysis: benefits and costs

II. Theories, Principles and Models

A. The Scientific Method (positive economics)

1. Gathering of relevant facts
2. Deriving principles from facts
3. Test (inductive vs. deductive methods)

III. Macroeconomics and Microeconomics

A. Definition of Economics

B. Definition of Macroeconomics

C. Definition of Microeconomics

D. Positive versus Normative Economics

IV. Society's Economizing Problem

A. Fundamental Facts

B. Definition of the Law of Scarcity

C. Factors of Production and their Money Payments

V. Other Economic Terms

A. Efficiency

B. Fallacies:

1. Composition

2. Division

3. False Cause

C. Adam Smith, Father of Economics

1. Wealth of Nations (1776)
2. Self-interest
3. Invisible Hand

D. Opportunity Cost

E. Law of Diminishing Returns

F. Law of Comparative Advantage

Chapter 1: "Terms, the Production Possibilities Curve and Graphing"

VI. The Production Possibilities Model

A. Assumpitions

1. There are only two types of goods (ex. capital goods and agricultural goods).
2. Resources and technology are fixed.
3. Resources and technology may be shifted* from one good to the other good. (ex. land)
   *However, you may incur the "Law of Increasing Costs" – as you tradeoff resources, the sacrifice becomes greater and greater (as the resources are not perfectly shifted)
4. You are operating efficiently.

B. Production Possibilities Curve Scenarios

1. Resources are perfectly shifted (Linear PPC)

2. Resources are not perfectly shifted ("Bowed or Concave" PPC; "Law of Increasing Costs")

3. Point "G" for Growth
   Point "U" for Unemployment

4. Economic Growth (of both);
   Economic Contraction (of both)

5. ↑ In Capital Goods only
   ↓ In Capital Goods only

6. ↑ In Agricultural Goods only
↓ In Agricultural Goods only

"The society that devotes resources to capital goods will have more of both in the future"

7. Given "PPC ABC" below:

Q. At which point should an economy choose for the greatest growth in the future?

VII. Unemployment, Growth and the Future

VIII. Appendix Graphs and their Meaning

A. Plotting Points and Calculating Slope

Chapter 2 "The Market System and the Circular Flow"

I. Five Fundamental Questions:

1. What?
2. How?
3. For Whom?
4. Adapt to change?
5. Promote Progress?

II. Decided by the Economic System

A. Definitions

B. Types

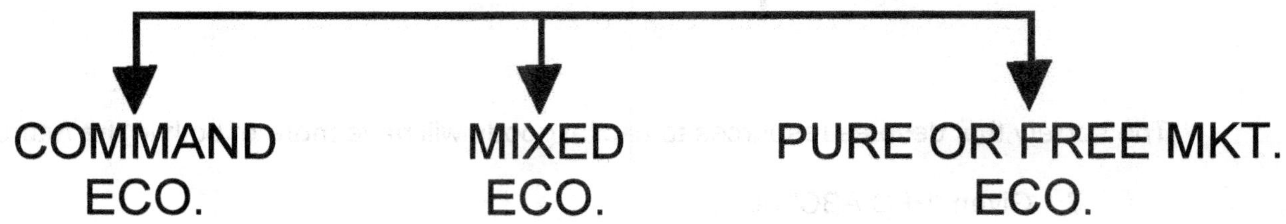

III. The Simple Circular Flow Model Of Economic Activity

A. Two Sectors: Households (HH) and Business (BUS)

B. Two Markets: Resource and Product

C. Two Flows: Goods and Services; Money

D. How the market deals with risk

Chapter 3 "Supply and Demand and Market Equilibrium"

I. Market

A. Definition

II. Demand

A. Definition

B. Law of Demand

C. Demand Schedule

D. Demand Curve

E. "Change in Quantity Demanded"

F. "Change in Demand"

P	Q_D

P

0 Q

Chapter 3 "Supply and Demand and Market Equilibrium"

III. Supply

A. Definition

P	Q_s

B. Law of Supply

C. Supply Schedule

D. Supply Curve

E. "Change in Quantity Supplied"

F. "Change in Supply"

IV. Supply & Demand

A. Equilibrium

B. Price Ceiling & Floor

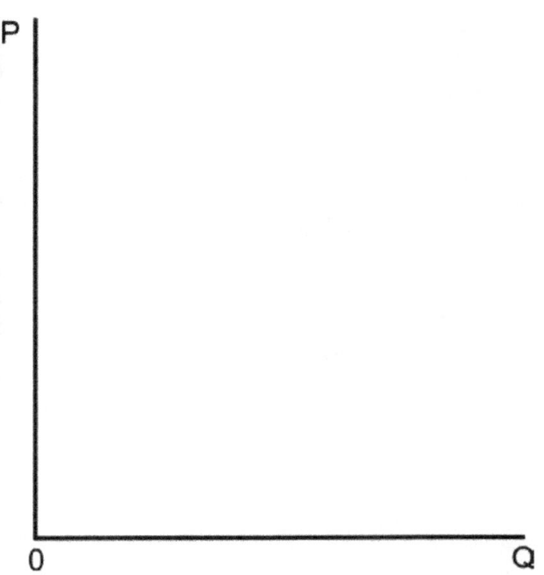

Chapter 38: "International Economics"

I. Some Key Trade Facts

A. The following are several important facts relating to international trade:

II. The Economic Basis for Trade

A. World trade is based on three considerations:

1.

2.

3.

B. Comparative Advantage

1. Definition of Comparative Advantage

2. Definition of Absolute Advantage

C. Terms of Trade

1. How trade is determined

D. Gains for Specialization and Trade

1. Improves global resource allocation

Chapter 38: "International Economics"

III. Supply and Demand Analysis of Exports and Imports

A. Determining how equilibrium prices and quantities of exports and imports are determined.

IV. Trade Barriers and Export Subsidies

A. Definition of a "trade barrier" and "export subsidies"

B. List of trade barriers: Nontariff barrier (NTB) – includes licensing requirements, unreasonable standards pertaining to product quality, or "red tape" in customs procedures.

C. Direct effects include:

D. Indirect effects include:

V. The Case for Protection: A Critical Review

A. Arguments:

Chapter 38: "International Economics"

VI. Multilateral Trade Agreements and Free-Trade Zones

A. General Agreement on Tariffs and Trade (GATT)

B. World-Trade Organization (WTO)

C. The European Union (EU)

D. North American Free Trade Agreement (NAFTA)

E. Recognizing Those Hurt by Free Trade

1. Some industries can be hurt by free trade.

F. Trade Adjustment Assistance

1. The Trade Adjustment Assistance Act of 2002

2. Critics feel it is unfair

G. Offshoring of Jobs

1. Definition of "offshoring"

2. Pros and cons

VII. Foreign Exchange Market

A. Definition

B. Changing Rates: Depreciation and Appreciation

Chapter 26 "Economic Growth"

I. Economic Growth

A. Definition

B. Growth as a goal

C. Arithmetic of Growth

1. Rule of 70

D. Growth in the U.S.

II. Modern Economic Growth

A. Impact on society

III. Institutional Structures That Promote Growth

IV. Determinants of Growth

A. Supply factors

B. Demand factors

C. Efficiency factor

V. Production Possibilities Analysis

A. Growth and PPC

B. Growth AD-AS Model

Chapter 26 "Economic Growth"

VI. Accounting for Growth

A. Contributing factors and detriments

VII. Productivity acceleration

A. Reasons for Production Acceleration

B. Macro implications for Economic Growth

VIII. Is Growth Desirable and Sustainable?

COMPARATIVE ADVANTAGE PROBLEM

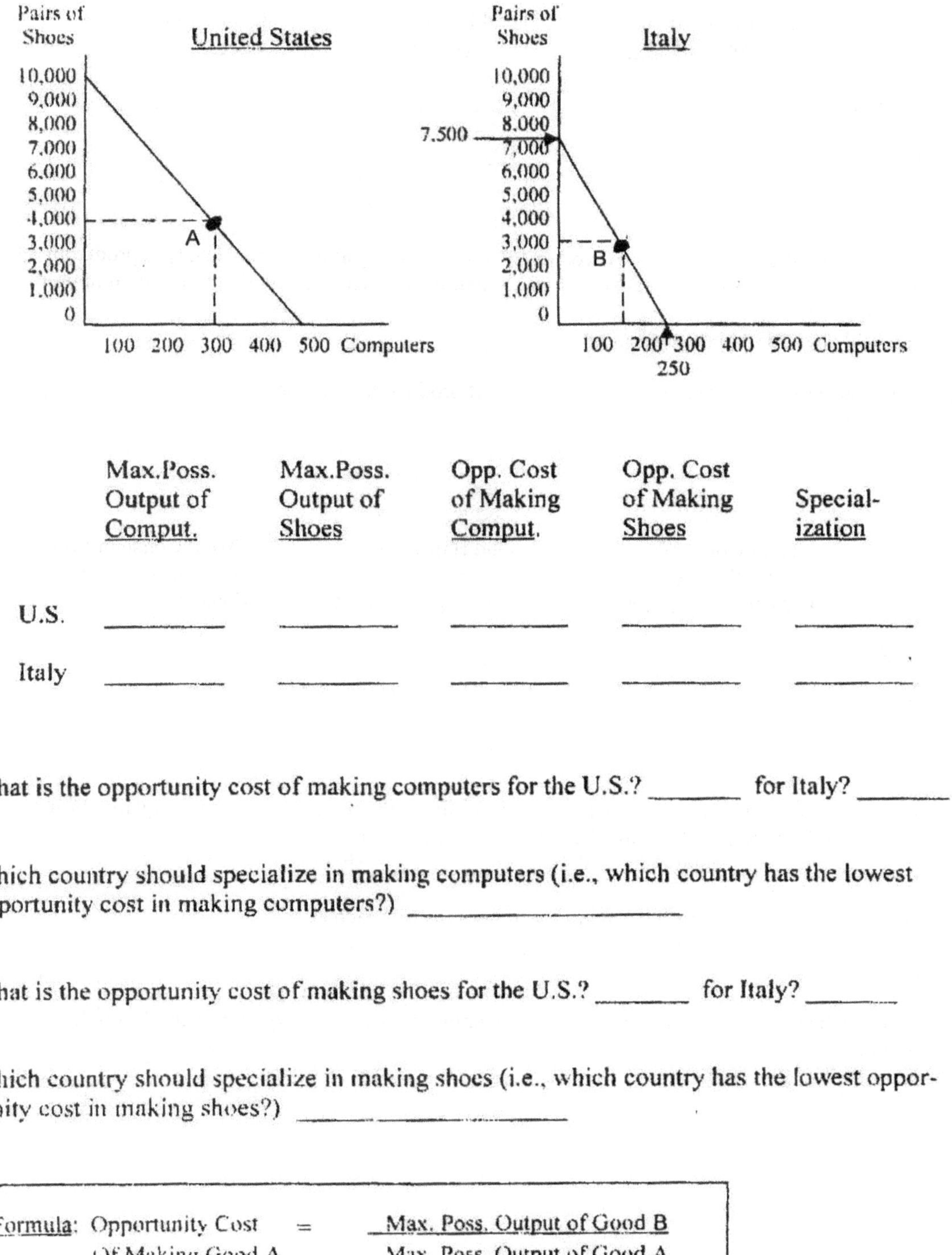

	Max.Poss. Output of Comput.	Max.Poss. Output of Shoes	Opp. Cost of Making Comput.	Opp. Cost of Making Shoes	Special-ization
U.S.	________	________	________	________	________
Italy	________	________	________	________	________

. What is the opportunity cost of making computers for the U.S.? _______ for Italy? _______

. Which country should specialize in making computers (i.e., which country has the lowest opportunity cost in making computers?) ____________________

. What is the opportunity cost of making shoes for the U.S.? _______ for Italy? _______

. Which country should specialize in making shoes (i.e., which country has the lowest opportunity cost in making shoes?) ____________________

Formula: Opportunity Cost Of Making Good A	=	Max. Poss. Output of Good B / Max. Poss. Output of Good A

	Total Product Before Specialization	Total Product After Specialization	Gains from Specialization
Computers	________	________	________
Shoes	________	________	________

5. Before specialization, the U.S. is producing and consuming at point A and Italy is producing and consuming at point B. Between the U.S. and Italy, what is the total amount of computer production? ________________
   the total amount of shoe production? ________________

6. After specialization, what is the total amount of production of computers? ____________
   of shoes? ____________

	Total Consumption Before Specialization		One/Half of Gains from Specialization		Total Consumption After Specialization	
	Computers	Shoes	Computers	Shoes	Computers	Shoes
U.S.	______	______	______	______	______	______
Italy	______	______	______	______	______	______

7. If through their terms of trade the two countries divide the gains in production equally, how much will the U.S. now have available to consume of each good?
   ____________ computers and ____________ shoes

   How much will Italy now have available to consumer of each good?
   ____________ computers and ____________ shoes

8. Indicate the consumption point, after specialization, for each country on the graphs on the previous page.

Problem 2. Comparative Advantage

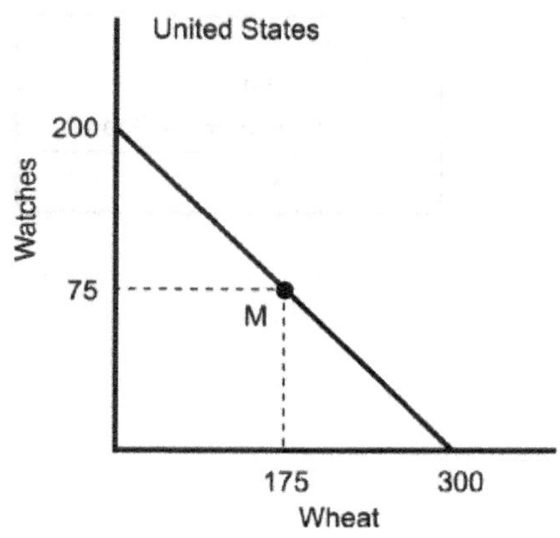

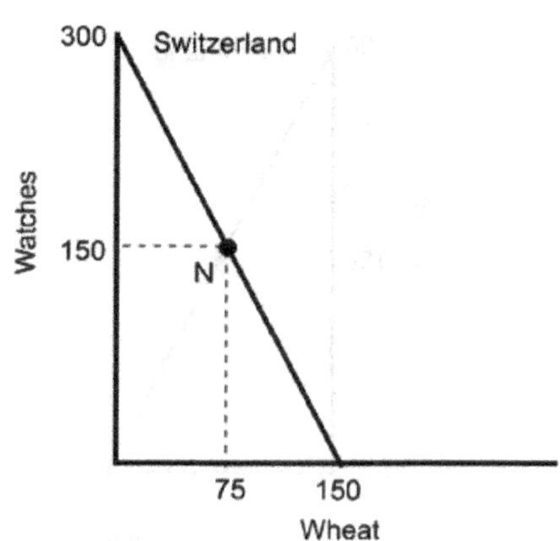

Opp. Cost of Making Good A = $\frac{\text{Max. prod. of Good B}}{\text{Max. prod. of Good A}}$

1. What is the United States' opportunity cost of making watches? ____________
2. What is Switzerland's opportunity cost of making watches? ____________
3. Which country should specialize in making watches? ____________
4. What is the United States' opportunity cost of making wheat? ____________
5. What is Switzerland's opportunity of making wheat? ____________
6. Which country should specialize in making wheat? ____________
7. Before specialization, assume that the United States is producing and consuming at point M and that Switzerland is producing and consuming at point N.

   Total wheat production for both economies combined is ____________.

   Total watch production for both economies combined is ____________.

8. After specialization,

   the United States produces ____ ____________.
   (no.) (watches or wheat)

   and Switzerland produces ____ ____________.
   (no.) (watches or wheat)

9. The gains from specialization are ________ wheat and ________ watches.
10. Assuming the two countries trade in a way so that they can consume the same amount that they did before specialization and they split the gains from specialization equally, how much of each good will they have in the end?

	Total Consumption After Specialization	
	Wheat	Watches
Unites States	________	________
Switzerland	________	________

Plot these points on the graph above.
(Label these points M1 & N1)

Answer Key - Problem 2. Comparative Advantage

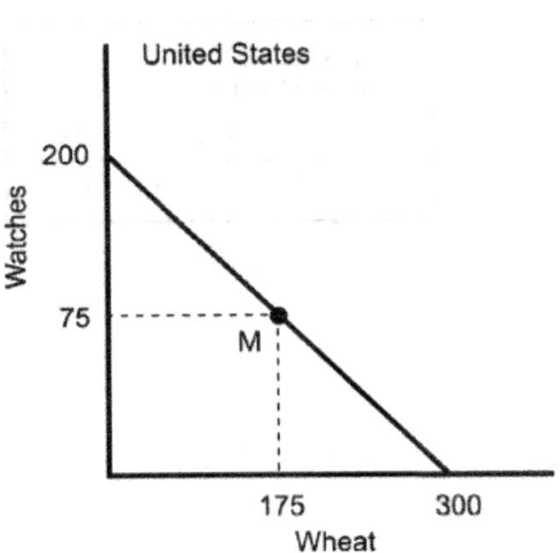

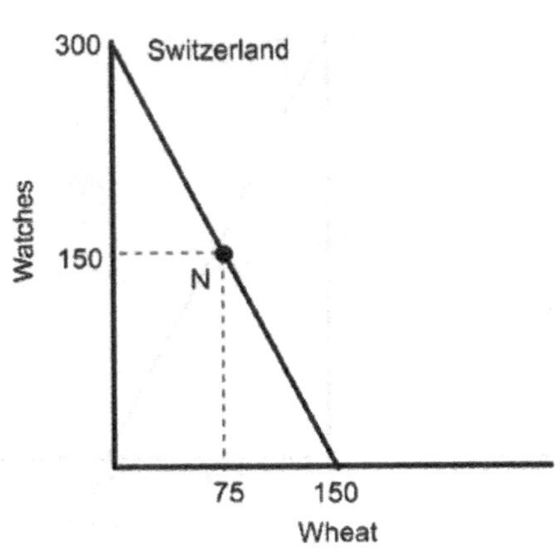

Opp. Cost of Making Good A = $\frac{\text{Max. prod. of Good B}}{\text{Max. prod. of Good A}}$

1. What is the United States' opportunity cost of making watches? $\frac{300}{200}$ = 1.5
2. What is Switzerland's opportunity cost of making watches? $\frac{150}{300}$ = 0.5
3. Which country should specialize in making watches? Switzerland
4. What is the United States' opportunity cost of making wheat? $\frac{200}{300}$ = $0.6\overline{6}$
5. What is Switzerland's opportunity of making wheat? $\frac{300}{150}$ = 2.0
6. Which country should specialize in making wheat? U.S.
7. <u>Before specialization,</u> assume that the United States is producing and consuming at point M and that Switzerland is producing and consuming at point N.

   Total wheat production for both economies combined is 250.

   Total watch production for both economies combined is 225.

8. <u>After specialization,</u>

   the United States produces 300 (no.) wheat (watches or wheat).

   and Switzerland produces 300 (no.) watches (watches or wheat).

9. The gains from specialization are 50 wheat and 75 watches.
10. Assuming the two countries trade in a way so that they can consume the same amount that they did before specialization and they split the gains from specialization equally, how much of each good will they have in the end?

Total Consumption After Specialization

	Wheat	Watches
Unites States	200	112.5
Switzerland	100	187.5

50 / 2 = 25

75 / 2 = 37.5

Plot these points on the graph above.
(Label these points M1 & N1)

MACROECONOMICS
UNIT II
WORKSHEETS

Prof. Debbie Meyer

Chapter 25: "Measuring Domestic Output and National Income"

(MEASURING OUR NATION'S ECONOMIC HEALTH)

I. Why Study NIA?

A. Mode of comparison

B. Measures economic health

C. Explains size and reasons for change

D. Helps set economic policy

II. Gross Domestic Product (GDP)

A. Def. of GDP and GNP

B. Calculation of NIA accounts—using the NIA sheet (next page)

1. Expenditures Approach

2. Income Approach

C. Included and Excluded (GDP)

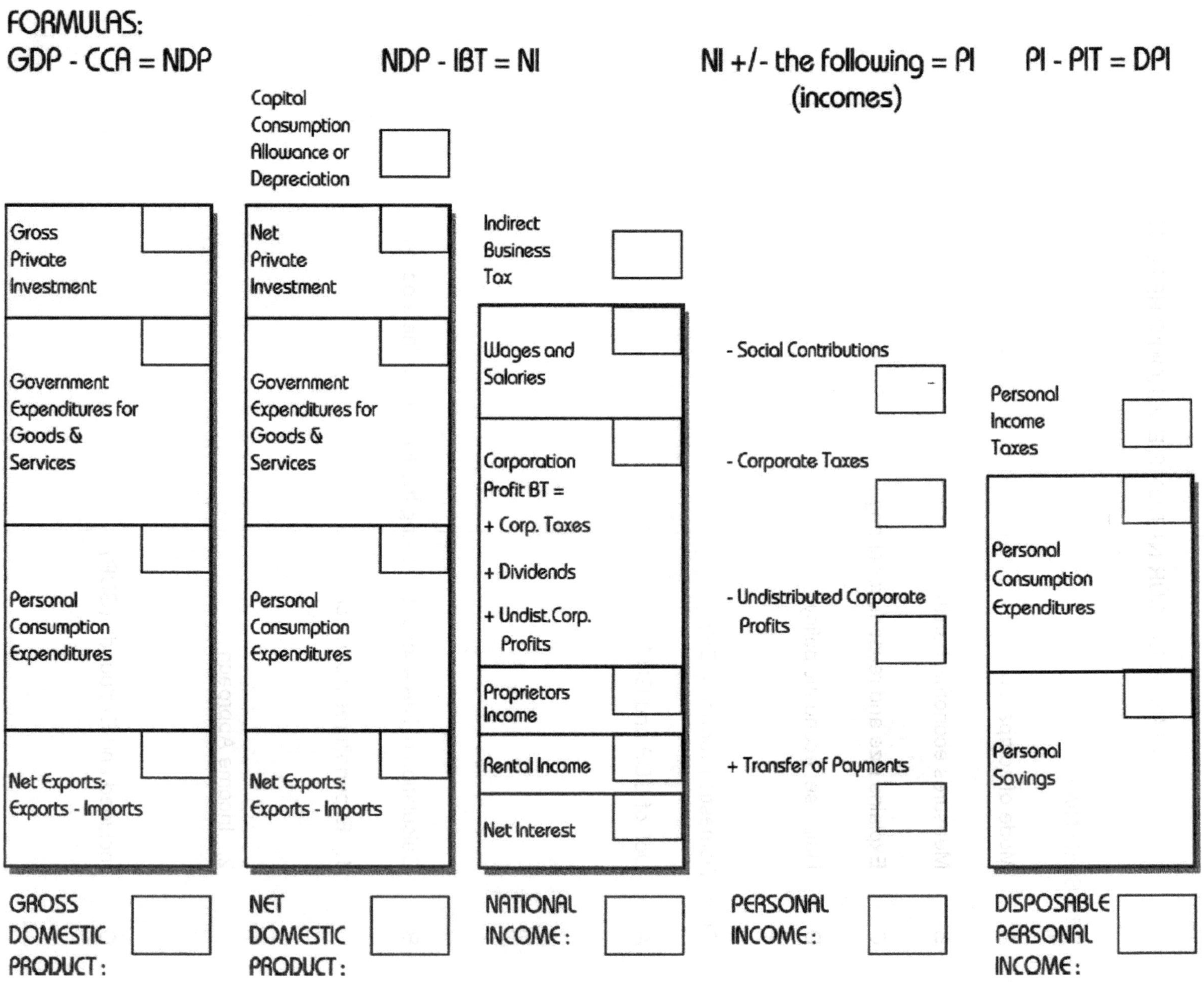

FORMULAS:

GDP - CCA = NDP | **NDP - IBT = NI** | **NI +/- the following = PI (incomes)** | **PI - PIT = DPI**

Capital Consumption Allowance or Depreciation

Gross Domestic Product	Net Domestic Product	National Income	Personal Income	Disposable Personal Income
		Indirect Business Tax		Personal Income Taxes
Gross Private Investment	Net Private Investment	Wages and Salaries	- Social Contributions	Personal Consumption Expenditures
Government Expenditures for Goods & Services	Government Expenditures for Goods & Services	Corporation Profit BT = + Corp. Taxes + Dividends + Undist.Corp. Profits	- Corporate Taxes	Personal Savings
Personal Consumption Expenditures	Personal Consumption Expenditures	Proprietors Income	- Undistributed Corporate Profits	
Net Exports: Exports - Imports	Net Exports: Exports - Imports	Rental Income	+ Transfer of Payments	
		Net Interest		

GROSS DOMESTIC PRODUCT:

NET DOMESTIC PRODUCT:

NATIONAL INCOME:

PERSONAL INCOME:

DISPOSABLE PERSONAL INCOME:

Chapter 25: “Measuring Domestic Output and National Income”

D. Def. of “REAL GDP” versus “NOMINAL GDP”

1. Example:

$$\text{REAL GDP}^* = \frac{\text{NOMINAL GDP}}{\text{GDP DEFLATOR}} \times 100$$

*chain weighted price index (reported by U.S. Dept. of Commerce)

In December 1995, when one or more goods or services is produced, the government accountants must assign weights to various categories (based upon total output — chain-weighted Real GDP).

2. Problems: WB pg. 55

3. Adjusting prices using a “price index”

$$\text{PRICE INDEX} = \frac{\text{EACH YEAR'S PRICE}}{\text{BASE YEAR'S PRICE}}$$

$$\text{CURRENT \$} = \text{PRICE X QUANTITY}$$

$$\text{REAL \$} = \frac{\text{CURRENT \$}}{\text{PRICE INDEX}}$$

D. Def. of “Per Capita GDP”

$$\text{PER CAPITA GDP} = \frac{\text{REAL GDP}}{\text{POPULATION}}$$

E. "Value-added approach"— to avoid double counting.

1. Def. of value-added

2. Example

F. Is GDP a good measure of social welfare?

1. Reasons

Chapter 9: "Business Cycles, Unemployment and Inflation"

I. Economic Growth

A. Defined and measured

B. Main sources of growth

C. Growth in U.S.

II. Business Cycle

A. Def.

B. Phases (4):

ECO.
ACTIVITY

TIME

Chapter 9: "Business Cycles, Unemployment and Inflation"

C. Cyclical Impact:

1. Durable vs. Nondurable goods

a. Definitions

b. Recession

c. Recovery

D. NBER (National Bureau of Economic Research) Indicators (3)

1. Leading
2. Lagging
3. Coincident

Chapter 9: "Business Cycles, Unemployment and Inflation"

III. Unemployment

A. Def. and rate in U.S.

B. Def. of "labor force"

C. Formula and Calculation

$$\text{Unemp. Rate } (\%) = \frac{\text{\# of Unemployed}}{\text{Labor Force}} \times 100$$

D. Understated vs. Overstated

E. Def. of the "Full-employment Unemployment Rate or Natural Rate" of Unemployment.

Chapter 9: "Business Cycles, Unemployment and Inflation"

F. Types of Unemployment (4):

1. Frictional (transitional)

2. Cyclical (BC)

3. Seasonal

4. Structural

G. Costs of Unemployment (2)

1. Social

2. Economic (Okun's Law)

3. International Comparisons

Chapter 9: "Business Cycles, Unemployment and Inflation"

IV. Inflation

A. Definition

1. Formula:

$$\text{Rate of Inflation } \% = \frac{P2 - P1}{P1} \times 100$$

2. Rule of 70

B. Measuring Inflation (indexes):

1. CPI (Consumer Price Index)

2. PPI (Producer Price Index)

3. GDP Deflator (covered in Text Chapter 25)

Chapter 9: "Business Cycles, Unemployment and Inflation"

C. Types of Inflation (2):

1. Demand-Pull

a. Definition

b. Graph (below)

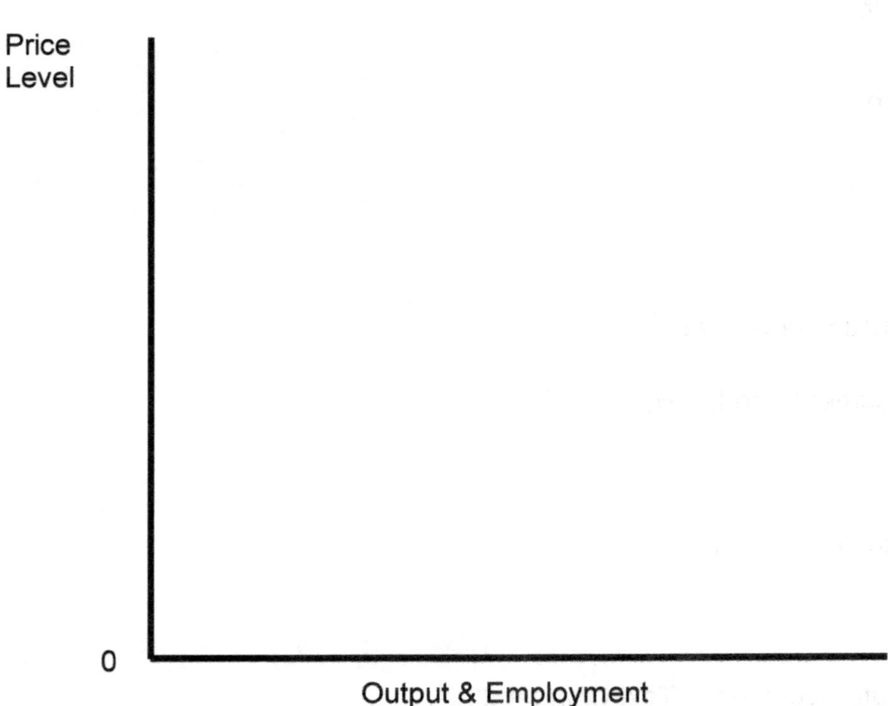

Range I: Constant prices

Range II: Creeping inflation

Range III: Hyperinflation

2. Cost-Push

   a. Definition

D. Redistributive Effects of Inflation

1. PROS vs. CONS

2. Does inflation affect output?

Chapter 36: "Extending the Analysis of Aggregate Supply" – "The Phillips Curve" - Only

I. Background

A. Historical

B. The Phillips Curve

1. A. W. Phillips studied inflation and unemployment data from the 1950s and 1960s

2. Found an inverse relationship and called it the "Phillips Curve".

II. Role of Government

A. Set Economic Policy (decide which point to strive for—"A" or "B")

B. John Maynard Keynes agreed!

Chapter 36: "Extending the Analysis of Aggregate Supply" – "The Phillips Curve" - Only

III. Movement along the Curve:

A. Due to changes in Fiscal (G or T) and/or Monetary ($) policies

Demand Management

Examples:

Expand the Economy: "A"

Contract the Economy: "B"

B. Impact of the mid-70s

1. Definition of "stagflation"

2. Impact on the Phillips Curve

Chapter 36: "Extending the Analysis of Aggregate Supply" – "The Phillips Curve" - Only

IV. Supply-Side Economics

A. Definition

B. "Supply-shocks" on the economy

1. Definition

C. Impact on the Phillips Curve

D. Impact of the mid-80s

V. The Long-Run Phillips Curve

Chapter 28: "Basic Macroeconomic Relationships"

I. The Income – Consumption and Income-Savings Relationships

$$AE = AD = C + I + G + Xn = GDP$$

A. Consumption "C" is the largest component

(2/3) of AE (=AD)

B. Avg. Propensity to Consume (APC)

$$APC = \frac{C}{DI}$$

C. Avg. Propensity to Save (APS)

$$APS = \frac{S}{DI}$$

$$APC + APS = 1.0 = 100\%$$

D. Marginal Propensity to Consume

$$MPC = \frac{\Delta C}{\Delta DI}$$

DI	C	S	MPC	MPS
100	80			
200	150			

E. Marginal Propensity to Save

$$MPS = \frac{\Delta S}{\Delta DI}$$

MPC + MPS = 1.0 = 100%

Chapter 28: "Basic Macroeconomic Relationships"

II. PROBLEM:

A. Fill in the table (below) and graph "C" and "S" separately (on two graphs)

"A Family's Consumption and Saving in Relation to Their Di"

DI	C	S	APC	APS	MPC	MPS
100	140					
200	210					
300	300					
400	340					
500	400					

III. Finding "APC", "APS", "MPC", "MPS" & Slopes, from a Graph

A. Example on board

B. Types of Consumption (2):

1. Autonomous and Induced

C. Shifting of "C" and "S" Curves versus movement along the curve (nonincome determinants):

D. The Paradox of Thrift

1. Definition

Chapter 28: "Basic Macroeconomic Relationships"

IV. Adding Investment "I" to the model

A. Definition of Investment

B. The Investment-Demand Curve

1. Definition

2. Movement along the curve

3. Reasons for a shifting of the curve"

V. The Multiplier Effect:

A. Definition

B. Simple

C. Tax

D. Balanced-Budget Multiplier (BBM)

VI. Review of the Multipliers

Type	Formula	When to Use
SIMPLE (M) =		
TAX (Mt) =		
BBM = 1		

Chapter 28: “Basic Macroeconomic Relationships”

VII. Word Problems—WB. Pgs. 79 - 81

Δ TOOL X MULTIPLIER = EFFECT ON ECO.

VIII. Contractionary Vs. Expansionary

Fiscal Policy

Chapter 29: "The Aggregate Expenditure Model"

I. Introduction

A. Adding the Public (G) & International Sectors (Xn) to the Model

II. Table (Schedule) and Graphs

A. Aggregate Expenditure – Aggregate Supply Model

B. Leakages – Injections Approach

III. Finding Equilibrium GDP

IV. Equilibrium versus Full- Employment GDP -- GDP Gaps

A. Definition

B. Types: Recessionary and Inflationary

1. Definition of Recessionary Gap

2 Definition of Inflationary Gap

C. Graphs WB pg. 91

D. Application: Great Recession of 2007-2009

V. Limitations of the Model

PROBLEMS -- COMPARING GDP OF VARIOUS COUNTRIES. GDP for each country is reported in U.S. dollars on a purchasing power parity basis. If $8100 is reported in per capita income for Mexico, that $8100 would buy the same amount of goods in the U.S. as it does in Mexico. For the following countries, find the data from the CIA World Fact Book at the following website: www.cia.gov and click "World Factbook".

	GDP U.S. $ purchasing power parity	Population	Per Capita GDP U.S. $ purchasing power parity
Brazil			
Canada			
China			
Cuba			
France			
Germany			
Hong Kong			
India			
Italy			
Japan			
Mexico			
North Korea			
Russia			
Pakistan			
South Korea			
Spain			
Sweden			
Switzerland			
U.S.			
United Kingdom			

Using the data from the previous page, list the top ten countries according to GDP, Population, and Per Capita GDP. Put the largest country at the top of the list. How do the largest countries compare on these three measures?

Real GDP	Population	Per Capita GDP
____________	____________	____________
____________	____________	____________
____________	____________	____________
____________	____________	____________
____________	____________	____________
____________	____________	____________
____________	____________	____________
____________	____________	____________
____________	____________	____________
____________	____________	____________

Note: Answers in all three columns should be names of countries.

FORMULAS:

GDP - CCA = NDP

Gross Private Investment

Government Expenditures for Goods & Services

Personal Consumption Expenditures

Net Exports: Exports - Imports

GROSS DOMESTIC PRODUCT:

NDP - IBT = NI

Capital Consumption Allowance or Depreciation

Net Private Investment

Government Expenditures for Goods & Services

Personal Consumption Expenditures

Net Exports:

NET DOMESTIC PRODUCT:

Indirect Business Tax

Wages and Salaries

Corporation Profit BT =

+ Corp. Taxes

+ Dividends

+ Undist. Corp. Profits

Proprietors Income

Rental Income

Net Interest

NATIONAL INCOME:

NI +/- the following = PI (incomes)

- Social Contributions

- Corporate Taxes

- Undistributed Corporate Profits

+Transfer of Payments

PERSONAL INCOME:

PI - PIT = DPI

Personal Income Taxes

Personal Consumption Expenditures

Personal Savings

DISPOSABLE PERSONAL INCOME:

FORMULAS:

GDP - CCA = NDP

NDP - IBT = NI

NI +/- the following = PI (incomes)

PI - PIT = DPI

GDP	NDP	NI	PI	DPI
	Capital Consumption Allowance or Depreciation			
Gross Private Investment	Net Private Investment	Indirect Business Tax		
Government Expenditures for Goods & Services	Government Expenditures for Goods & Services	Wages and Salaries	- Social Contributions	Personal Income Taxes
Personal Consumption Expenditures	Personal Consumption Expenditures	Corporation Profit BT = + Corp. Taxes + Dividends + Undist. Corp. Profits	- Corporate Taxes	Personal Consumption Expenditures
Net Exports: Exports - Imports	Net Exports:	Proprietors Income	- Undistributed Corporate Profits	Personal Savings
		Rental Income	+Transfer of Payments	
		Net Interest		
GROSS DOMESTIC PRODUCT:	NET DOMESTIC PRODUCT:	NATIONAL INCOME:	PERSONAL INCOME:	DISPOSABLE PERSONAL INCOME:

FORMULAS:

GDP - CCA = NDP

NDP - IBT = NI

NI +/- the following = PI (incomes)

PI - PIT = DPI

Gross Private Investment

Government Expenditures for Goods & Services

Personal Consumption Expenditures

Net Exports: Exports - Imports

GROSS DOMESTIC PRODUCT:

Capital Consumption Allowance or Depreciation

Net Private Investment

Government Expenditures for Goods & Services

Personal Consumption Expenditures

Net Exports:

NET DOMESTIC PRODUCT:

Indirect Business Tax

Wages and Salaries

Corporation Profit BT =

+ Corp. Taxes

+ Dividends

+ Undist. Corp. Profits

Proprietors Income

Rental Income

Net Interest

NATIONAL INCOME:

- Social Contributions

- Corporate Taxes

- Undistributed Corporate Profits

+Transfer of Payments

PERSONAL INCOME:

Personal Income Taxes

Personal Consumption Expenditures

Personal Savings

DISPOSABLE PERSONAL INCOME:

FORMULAS:

GDP - CCA = NDP

NDP - IBT = NI

NI +/- the following = PI (incomes)

PI - PIT = DPI

GDP	NDP	NI	PI	DPI
	Capital Consumption Allowance or Depreciation			
Gross Private Investment	Net Private Investment	Indirect Business Tax		
Government Expenditures for Goods & Services	Government Expenditures for Goods & Services	Wages and Salaries	- Social Contributions	Personal Income Taxes
Personal Consumption Expenditures	Personal Consumption Expenditures	Corporation Profit BT = + Corp. Taxes + Dividends + Undist. Corp. Profits	- Corporate Taxes	Personal Consumption Expenditures
Net Exports: Exports - Imports	Net Exports:	Proprietors Income	- Undistributed Corporate Profits	Personal Savings
		Rental Income	+Transfer of Payments	
		Net Interest		
GROSS DOMESTIC PRODUCT:	NET DOMESTIC PRODUCT:	NATIONAL INCOME:	PERSONAL INCOME:	DISPOSABLE PERSONAL INCOME:

FORMULAS:

GDP - CCA = NDP

NDP - IBT = NI

NI +/- the following = PI (incomes)

PI - PIT = DPI

Gross Private Investment

Government Expenditures for Goods & Services

Personal Consumption Expenditures

Net Exports: Exports - Imports

GROSS DOMESTIC PRODUCT:

Capital Consumption Allowance or Depreciation

Net Private Investment

Government Expenditures for Goods & Services

Personal Consumption Expenditures

Net Exports:

NET DOMESTIC PRODUCT:

Indirect Business Tax

Wages and Salaries

Corporation Profit BT =

+ Corp. Taxes

+ Dividends

+ Undist. Corp. Profits

Proprietors Income

Rental Income

Net Interest

NATIONAL INCOME:

- Social Contributions

- Corporate Taxes

- Undistributed Corporate Profits

+Transfer of Payments

PERSONAL INCOME:

Personal Income Taxes

Personal Consumption Expenditures

Personal Savings

DISPOSABLE PERSONAL INCOME:

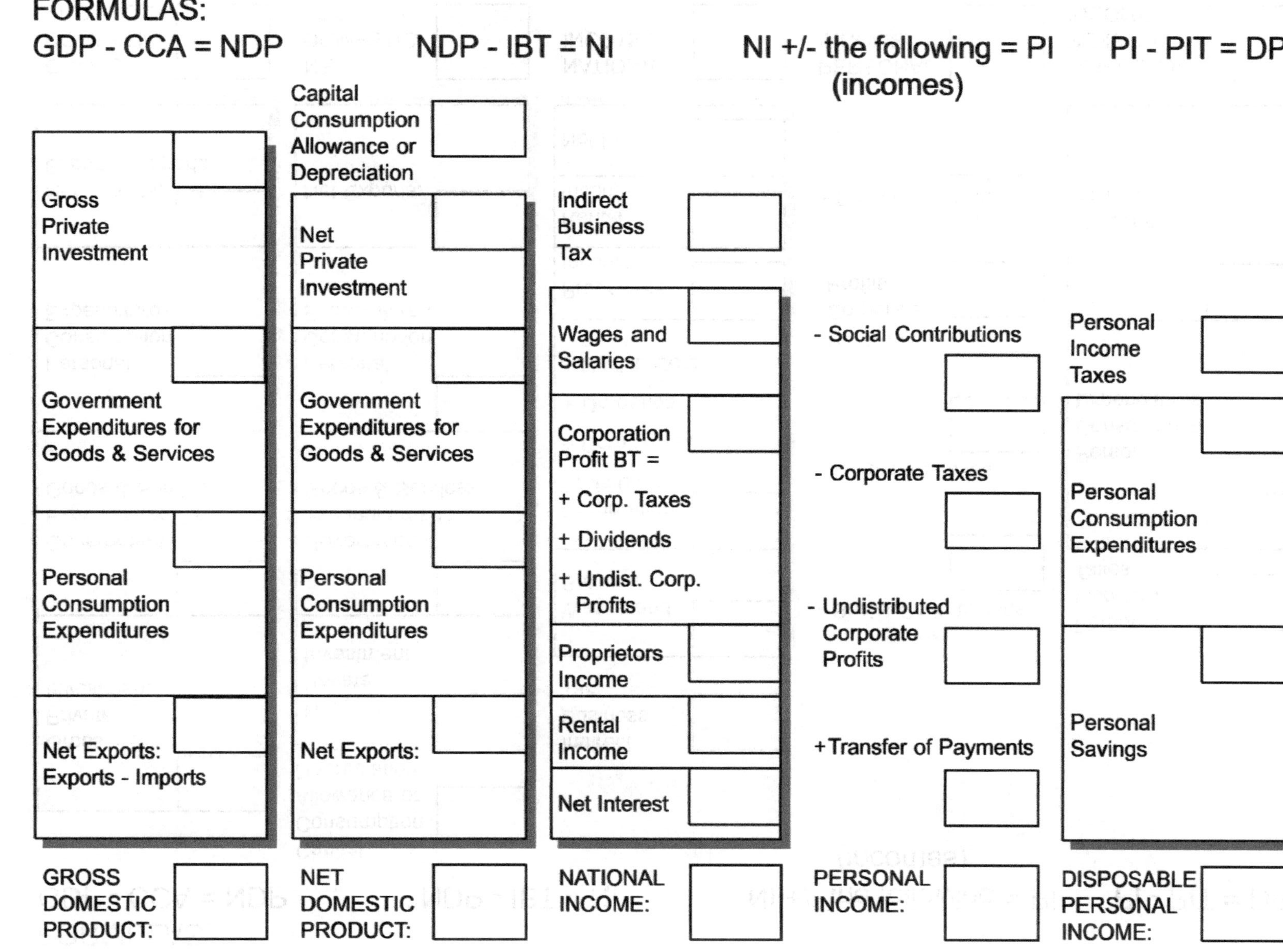

FORMULAS:
GDP - CCA = NDP
NDP - IBT = NI
NI +/- the following = PI (incomes)
PI - PIT = DPI
Gross Private Investment
Government Expenditures for Goods & Services
Personal Consumption Expenditures
Net Exports: Exports - Imports
GROSS DOMESTIC PRODUCT:
Capital Consumption Allowance or Depreciation
Net Private Investment
Government Expenditures for Goods & Services
Personal Consumption Expenditures
Net Exports:
NET DOMESTIC PRODUCT:
Indirect Business Tax
Wages and Salaries
Corporation Profit BT =
+ Corp. Taxes
+ Dividends
+ Undist. Corp. Profits
Proprietors Income
Rental Income
Net Interest
NATIONAL INCOME:
- Social Contributions
- Corporate Taxes
- Undistributed Corporate Profits
+Transfer of Payments
PERSONAL INCOME:
Personal Income Taxes
Personal Consumption Expenditures
Personal Savings
DISPOSABLE PERSONAL INCOME:

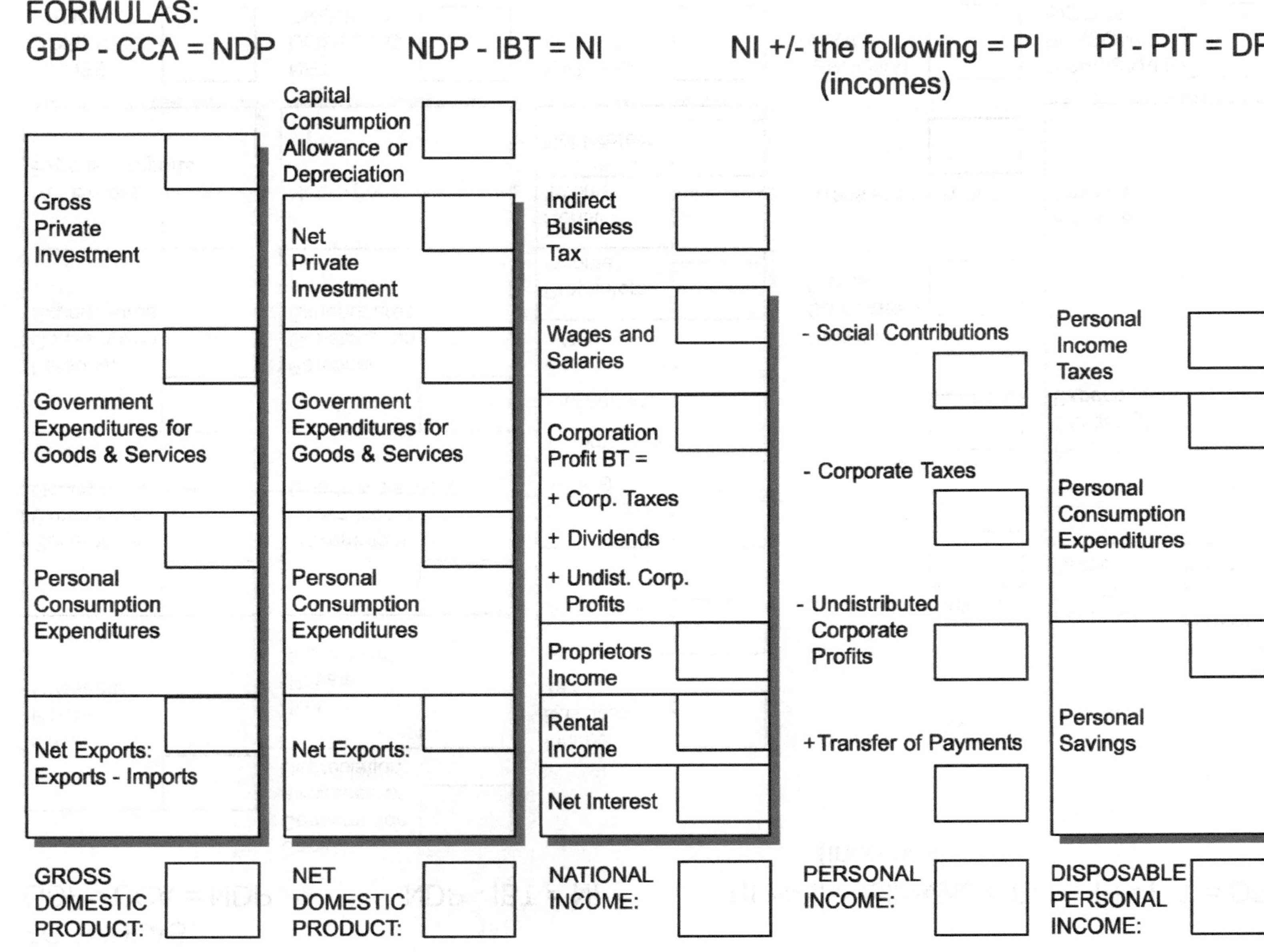

FORMULAS:
GDP - CCA = NDP
NDP - IBT = NI
NI +/- the following = PI
(incomes)
PI - PIT = DPI
Gross Private Investment
Government Expenditures for Goods & Services
Personal Consumption Expenditures
Net Exports: Exports - Imports
GROSS DOMESTIC PRODUCT:
Capital Consumption Allowance or Depreciation
Net Private Investment
Government Expenditures for Goods & Services
Personal Consumption Expenditures
Net Exports:
NET DOMESTIC PRODUCT:
Indirect Business Tax
Wages and Salaries
Corporation Profit BT =
+ Corp. Taxes
+ Dividends
+ Undist. Corp. Profits
Proprietors Income
Rental Income
Net Interest
NATIONAL INCOME:
- Social Contributions
- Corporate Taxes
- Undistributed Corporate Profits
+Transfer of Payments
PERSONAL INCOME:
Personal Income Taxes
Personal Consumption Expenditures
Personal Savings
DISPOSABLE PERSONAL INCOME:

MACROECONOMICS
UNIT III
WORKSHEETS

Prof. Debbie Meyer

THE U.S. ECONOMY

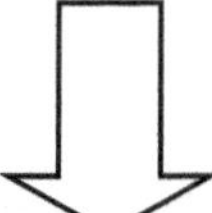

Fiscal Policy

- Congress
- President

Monetary Policy

"The Fed"
(Federal Reserve)

"Use of Discretion"

Tools

Fiscal Policy	Monetary Policy
ΔG	$\Delta i\%$
ΔI	$\Delta S\$$
ΔX	
ΔM	
ΔT	

Chapter 29: "The Aggregate Expenditures (Revisited)"

I. Economic Schools of Thought (WB pg. 103)

A. Classical School—Foundations

1. "Supply Creates Demand"
2. "Government is Laissez-Faire"
3. "Everything Has a Price (S=D)
4. "Focused on Long-Run

B. Keynesian Economics—Foundations

1. "Demand Creates Supply"
2. "Government Needed to Fine-Tune"
3. "Prices are not That Flexible"
4. "Focused on Short-Run"

C. Supply-Side—Foundations

1. "Supply Creates Demand—Outgrowth of Classical School"
2. "Government Needed to Set Stage"
3. "Use of Incentives". . ."Trickle-Down Economics"
4. "Focused on Long-Run"
5. Employment Act of 1946 (WB pg. 104)

Chapter 36: "Extending the Analysis of Aggregate Supply" ("Supply-Side Economics" – only)

I. From Short-Run to Long-Run Aggregate Supply

A. Definition

B. Short-Run

C Long-Run

II. Long-Run Equilibrium in the AD-AS Model

A. Demand – Pull

B Cost Push

C. Recession

III. Historical Backdrop

A. Foundations of Classical and Keynesian Economics

B. Keynesians versus Supply-Siders

C. Legislative Mandates

1. Employment Act of 1946

IV. Taxation and Aggregate Supply

A. Taxation

1. Incentives to work

2. Incentives to save and invest

Chapter 36: “Extending the Analysis of Aggregate Supply” (“Supply-Side Economics” – only)

B. Laffer Curve

1. Definition

2. Criticisms of the Laffer Curve

C. Rebuttal and Evaluation

1. Overregulation

2. Reaganomics

3. Clinton Administration

4. Bush Administration

5. Financial Crisis 2007-2009

6. Role of Supply-Side Economics

Chapter 31: "Fiscal Policy, Deficits and Debt"

I. Fiscal Policy and the AD-AS Model

A. Definition

B. Types of Fiscal Policy

1. Discretionary

2. Nondiscretionary (Built-in Stability)

II. Evaluating How Expansionary or Contractionary Fiscal Policy is Determined

A. "Cyclically Adjusted Budget" (or Full Employment Budget)

III. Recent and Projected U.S. Fiscal Policy

A. Fiscal Policy from 2000-2007

1. Tax cuts

B. Fiscal Policy from 2007-2009

1. 2008 stimulus for $152 billion

2. American Recovery and Reinvestment Act of 2009 ($787 billion)

IV. Problems, Criticism and Complications of Implementing Fiscal Policy

A. Timing Problems:

B. Political Considerations:

C. Future Policy Reversals

D. Offsetting State and Local Finance

E. Restrictive Effects ("Crowding Out"):

V. The Public Debt: Facts and Figures

A. Definitions:

1. Budget Deficit

2. Budget Surplus

3. Balanced Budget

B. Public Debt: Facts and Figures

1. Causes:

2. Numbers:

3. Ownership

Chapter 31: "Fiscal Policy, Deficits and Debt"

VI. False Concerns

A. Government Bankruptcy?

B. Burdening Future Generations?

C. Income Distribution?

VII. Substantive Issues

A. Income Distribution

B. Raising Taxes

C. External Debt

D. Increased Government Spending (crowding-out revisited)

Chapter 32: "Money, Banking and Financial Institutions"

I. Functions of Money (3)

II. Money (Stock) Supply: M1, M2 and MZM

A. Definition of liquidity

B. Money definition M1

C. Near monies: M2 and MZM

1. Definition of M2

2. Definition of MZM

III. Legal Tender: Commodity vs. Fiat Money

A. What backs money?

B. Value of money

C. Money and prices

D. Stabilization of money value

Chapter 32: "Money, Banking and Financial Institutions"

IV. The Federal Reserve System

A. Historical Background

B. Structure (WB pg. 123)

V. Financial Crisis of 2007- 2009

A. The Mortgage Crisis Default

B. Securitization

C. Failure and Near Failure

D. The Treasury Bailout: TARP

E. The Fed's Lender of Last Resort

Chapter 32: "Money, Banking and Financial Institutions"

VI. Post Crisis U.S. Financial Services Industry

A. Evolution to Larger Firms with Wider Selection of Services

B. Generated Introspection

C. Wall St. Reform and Consumer Protection Act of 2010

Chapter 33: "Money Creation"

I. The Fractional Reserve System

A Definition

B. History

C. Significant Characteristics

II. A Single Commercial Bank

A. Definition of a Balance Sheet (B/S)

B. Steps in organizing a single bank:

Step 1: Creating a bank

Step 2: Becoming a "going concern"

Step 3: Accepting deposits

Step 4: Depositing reserves in a Federal Reserve Bank

a. Required (Legal) Reserves

b. Required Reserve Ratio (R)

c. Total (Actual) Reserves

d. Excess Reserves

Step 5: A check is drawn against the bank

III. Money-Creating Transactions of a Commercial Bank

Step 6: Granting a loan

Step 7: Buying government securities

Chapter 33: "Money Creation"

IV. Banking System: Multiple Deposit Expansion

A. The Monetary (Money) Multiplier $M\$ = \frac{1}{R}$

1. Definition

2. Assumptions

B. Formula:

$$M\$ = \frac{1}{R}$$

C. Reversibility – works in both directions

D. B/S Problem w/M$

C. B/S Problem w/M$:

SIMPLIFIED BANK BALANCE SHEET

ASSETS			LIABILITIES & NET WORTH	
Total Reserves:		______	Demand Deposits:	______
Required	______			
Excess	______			
Loans		______		
Total Assets		______	Total Liabilities & Net Worth	______

Chapter 34: "Interest Rates and Monetary Policy"

I. Interest Rates

A. Definition

B. Demand for Money - see WB pg. 135 (graph)

C. Supply of Money - see WB pg. 135 (graph)

II. Consolidated Balance Sheet of 12 Federal Reserve Banks

A. Assets

B. Liabilities

III. TOOLS OF MONETARY POLICY

A. Major Tools:

1. Open-market operations
2. Reserve Ratio (R)
3. Discount Rate
4. Interest on Reserves

B. Minor Tools:

1. Margin Requirement
2. Consumer Credit
3. Moral Suasion or "Jawboning"

Chapter 34: “Interest Rates and Monetary Policy”

C. “EASY $” (Recession) and “TIGHT $” (Inflation)

TOOL	EASY $	TIGHT $
1.		
2.		
3.		
4.		
5.		
6.		
7.		

IV. Targeting the Federal Funds Rate

A. Definition

B. Targeted by the Federal Reserve to announce changes in Monetary Policy

C. The Taylor Rule

1. Definition

2. Parts (3):

Chapter 34: "Interest Rates and Monetary Policy"

V. Monetary Policy, Real GDP and the Price Level

A. Cause-Effect Chain

B. Board of Governors Directs Banks

C. Investment Effect

D. Equilibrium GDP

E. Effects of Expansionary "Easy $" or Restrictive Monetary Policy "Tight $"

VI. Monetary Policy: Evaluation and Issues

A. Strengths of Monetary Policy over Fiscal Policy

B. Recent U.S. Monetary Policy

1. The 2001 Recession

2. The 2007-2009 Recession (or "Great Recession")

3. After the Great Recession

a. Zero Interest Rate Policy (ZIRP)

b. Zero Lower Bound Problem

c. Quantitative Easing (QE1&2)

d. Forward Commitment

e. Operation Twist

f. QE3

C. Problems and Complications

D. Monetary Policy and the International Economy
(WB pg 139, Table 4) - Monetary Policy and the Net Export Effect

VII. The Big Picture

A. Fiscal Policy

B. Fiscal and Monetary Policy

ORGANIZATION OF THE FEDERAL RESERVE SYSTEM

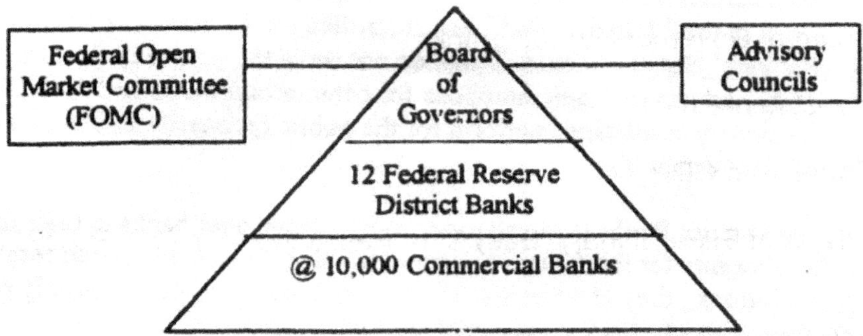

Congress created the **Federal Reserve System** in 1913 with the **Federal Reserve Act.** The "Fed" is an independent agency and serves as our nation's central bank.

Board of Governors: The head and basic policy-making body of the U.S. banking system. The Board is comprised of 7 members who are appointed by the President of the U.S. and confirmed by the Senate for 14-year terms. Appointments are staggered with replacements every two years (members cannot be reappointed). The purpose of the staggered replacements is to keep the "Fed" independent of the Administration. The Board's Chairperson and Vice Chairperson are appointed by the President for 4-year terms. (They can be reappointed within their 14-year term as a Board member.)

Functions of the Board:

1. Formulate and influence and cost and supply of money and credit in the economy. (Monetary Policy)
2. Supervise the entire Federal Reserve banking system.

Federal Open Market Committee (FOMC): Assists the Board of Governors in regulating the money supply through the purchase and sale of government (Treasury) securities in the open market (Open Market Operations). It consists of 12 members (the 7 Board of Governors plus 5 of the Federal Reserve District Banks' presidents — one of which is always the president of the Federal Reserve Bank of New York, the remaining 4 rotate amongst the other 11 District Bank presidents and serve one year terms.

Advisory Councils: There are three councils that provide input to the Board of Governors on the monetary/financial status and needs of their represented sectors of the economy. Each holds only an advisory status, no policy-making powers.

1. Federal Advisory Council: Comprised of 12 members (one from each Federal Reserve District). Members usually prominent commercial bankers and serve one year terms.
2. Thrift Institutions Advisory Council: Comprised of representatives from "thrift institutions" --- savings and loan associations (S&L's), savings banks, and credit unions.
3. Consumer Advisory Council: Consists of 30 representatives from academia, consumers of financial services, and legal specialists.

Federal Reserve District Banks: The 12 District Banks serve as the central bank in their district and are the operating arms of the Federal Reserve Board and the FOMC.

1. Quasi-Public Banks: The District Banks are "owned" by the private commercial banks in their district who are required to purchase shares of stock in their District "Fed", but controlled by the Board of Governors.
2. Bankers' Banks: District Banks do not serve the general public directly. They perform the same functions for commercial banks and thrifts that these depository institutions perform for the public (primarily making loans and holding deposits).

Functions: The District Banks exercise supervisory power over banks in their district; they act as fiscal agents for the federal government; they hold the required reserves of depository institutions; they clear checks of the banks in their district; supply paper currency for their district; lend money to depository institutions.

Commercial Banks:

- State Banks: Private banks with a charter to operate within that state. Approximately 2/3 of commercial banks are State Banks.
- National Banks: Private banks with a charter issued by the federal government's Comptroller of the Currency to operate nationally. Approximately 1/3 of commercial banks are National Banks.

Thrift Institutions: Thrift Institutions include savings and loan associations, savings banks and credit unions. They are regulated by federal agencies other than the Federal Reserve System, they are subject to the monetary controls and policies of the Board of Governors and their District Bank.

VALUE OF THE DOLLAR
EFFECT OF FLOATING EXCHANGE RATES ON FREE TRADE

Appreciation – When one currency's value rises in relation to another. If the dollar appreciates, it will buy more of the other currency. When the dollar appreciates, the other currency depreciates.

Depreciation – When one currency's value falls in relation to another. If the dollar depreciates, it will buy less of the other currency. When the dollar depreciates, the other currency appreciates.

Effect on Product Prices – If the exchange rate changes, then the price one must pay for imported goods will change. If the dollar depreciates, it will buy less of another country's currency, therefore the goods of that country become more expensive in the U.S.

$$\text{Price of a Good in Dollars} = \frac{\text{Price of Good in Foreign Currency}}{\text{Foreign Currency Equivalent of \$1}}$$

Effect on Imports – If the value of the dollar falls, and as a result the prices of foreign goods rise, then imports will decrease. If the value of the dollar rises, and as a result the prices of foreign goods fall, then imports will increase.

Effect on Exports – If the value of a nation's currency falls, and as a result its goods become more attractive to foreign buyers, exports will rise. If the value of a nation's currency rises, and as a result its goods become less attractive to foreign buyers, exports will fall.

Exchange Rate Problem #1: Yen/Dollar

Given the following currency exchange rates:

Year 1: $1 = 200 Japanese yen   Year 2: $1 = 100 Japanese yen

a. Has the U.S. dollar appreciated or depreciated relative to the Japanese yen between year 1 and year 2? Has the Japanese yen appreciated or depreciated relative to the U.S. dollar between year 1 and year 2?

b. Importing Japanese Cars to the U.S.

	Price of Car in Japanese Yen	Price of Car in U.S. Dollars	U.S. Imports	Japanese Exports
Year 1:	2,000,000	$ ________		
Year 2:	2,000,000	$ ________	________	________
			(increase or decrease)	

c. Using the same exchange rate shown above, complete the table below.

Exporting U.S. Computers to Japan

	Price of Computer in Japan.Yen	Price of Computer in U.S. Dollars	U.S. Exports	Japanese Imports
Year 1:	________	$ 20,000		
Year 2:	________	$ 20,000	________	________
			(increase or decrease)	

d. Describe what happened above by completing the following statement:

"If the value of the dollar ____________________ (appreciates or depreciates), U.S. imports will ________________ (increase or decrease) and U.S. exports will ________________ (increase or decrease).

e. Describe what happened above by completing the following statement:

"If the value of the dollar ____________________ (appreciates or depreciates), the foreign country's imports will ________________ (increase or decrease) and the foreign country's exports will ________________ (increase or decrease).

Exchange Rate Problem #2: Euro/Dollar

Given the following currency exchange rates:

Year 1: $1 = .85 Euro (€) Year 2: $1 = 1.05 Euros (€)

a. **Has the U.S. dollar appreciated or depreciated relative to the Euro between year 1 and year 2? Has the Euro appreciated or depreciated relative to the U.S. dollar between year 1 and year 2?**

b.

Importing European Pottery to the U.S.:

	Price of Pottery in Euros	Price of Pottery in U.S. Dollars	U.S. Imports	European Exports
Year 1:	60 €	$ ________		
Year 2:	60 €	$ ________	________	________
			(increase or decrease)	

c. Using the same exchange rate shown above, complete the table below.

Exporting U.S. Wheat to Europe:

	Price of Bu. Wheat in Euros	Price of Bu. Wheat in U.S. Dollars	U.S. Exports	European Imports
Year 1:	________	$ 4.00		
Year 2:	________	$ 4.00	________	________
			(increase or decrease)	

d. Describe what happened above by completing the following statement:

"If the value of the dollar ________________, U.S. imports will
(appreciates or depreciates)
________________ and U.S. exports will ________________.
(increase or decrease) (increase or decrease)

e. Describe what happened above by completing the following statement:

"If the value of the dollar ________________, the foreign country's
(appreciates or depreciates)
imports will ________________ and the foreign country's exports will
(increase or decrease)

________________.
(increase or decrease)

SIMPLIFIED BANK BALANCE SHEET

ASSETS			LIABILITIES & NET WORTH	
Total Reserves:		______	Demand Deposits:	______
Required	______			
Excess	______			
Loans		______		
		______		______
Total Assets			Total Liabilities & Net Worth	

SIMPLIFIED BANK BALANCE SHEET

ASSETS			LIABILITIES & NET WORTH	
Total Reserves:		______	Demand Deposits:	______
Required	______			
Excess	______			
Loans		______		
		______		______
Total Assets			Total Liabilities & Net Worth	

SIMPLIFIED BANK BALANCE SHEET

ASSETS			LIABILITIES & NET WORTH	
Total Reserves:		______	Demand Deposits:	______
Required	______			
Excess	______			
Loans		______		
		______		______
Total Assets			Total Liabilities & Net Worth	

SIMPLIFIED BANK BALANCE SHEET

ASSETS			LIABILITIES & NET WORTH	
Total Reserves:		______	Demand Deposits:	______
Required	______			
Excess	______			
Loans		______		
		______		______
Total Assets			Total Liabilities & Net Worth	

SIMPLIFIED BANK BALANCE SHEET

ASSETS			LIABILITIES & NET WORTH	
Total Reserves:		______	Demand Deposits:	______
Required	______			
Excess	______			
Loans		______		
Total Assets		______	Total Liabilities & Net Worth	______

SIMPLIFIED BANK BALANCE SHEET

ASSETS			LIABILITIES & NET WORTH	
Total Reserves:		______	Demand Deposits:	______
Required	______			
Excess	______			
Loans		______		
Total Assets		______	Total Liabilities & Net Worth	______

SIMPLIFIED BANK BALANCE SHEET

ASSETS			LIABILITIES & NET WORTH	
Total Reserves:		________	Demand Deposits:	________
Required	______			
Excess	______			
Loans		________		
		________		________
Total Assets			Total Liabilities & Net Worth	

SIMPLIFIED BANK BALANCE SHEET

ASSETS			LIABILITIES & NET WORTH	
Total Reserves:		________	Demand Deposits:	________
Required	______			
Excess	______			
Loans		________		
		________		________
Total Assets			Total Liabilities & Net Worth	

MICROECONOMICS

UNIT I

WORKSHEETS

Prof. Debbie A. Meyer

Chapter 1: "Limits, Alternatives and Choices"

Chapter 1: Terms

1. Economics - Production of goods + services with limitted resources for cosumption now + in the future
2. Factors of Production
   land - payments/rent   Capital goods - interest
   LABor - wages   entrepreneurship - profit
3. Law of Scarcity
   • unlimited wants
   ↳ limited resources (make a choice)
4. Macro vs. Micro
   Big picture / global perspective / inflation/interest/GDP | small picture / Paticular company
5. Adam Smith: Self Interest & The Invisible Hand
   Founder of econ.; gov gets in way; Both sides need profit → self interest; invisible Hand → market guided By profit
   (1776) *Wealth of Nations*
6. Efficiency
   - no waste
   - getting the most output w/ the least input
7. Fallacies:
   Composition - whole ~~well~~ we all like I to many)
   Division - Part (many to one) we like → I like
   False Cause - two events occur and you assume one ~~controled~~ caused the other
8. Opportunity Cost
   • value of Best alternative
   • what DiD you sacrifice
9. Law of Diminishing Returns
   • fixed factor
   • continually add variables (ex employees) inefficiency → reduces rate of return
10. Comparative Advantage
   • States should DO (specialize) in what they Do Best
     • ~~to~~ then trade
     • everyone would Be Better off
     • "rely" → proBlems all eggs in one Basket

Chapter 1: "Limits, Alternatives and Choices"

Chapter 1: Graphing Review

Plotting Points & Calculating the Slope

Chapter 2: "The Market System and the Circular Flow" (Five Questions Only)

I. Five Fundamental Questions

A. What?

B. How?

C. For Whom?

D. Adapt to Change?

E. Promote Progress?

II. Questions Decided by the Economic System

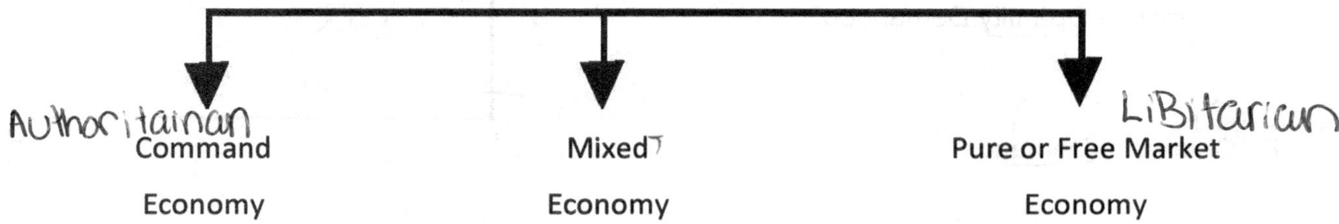

Chapter 3 "Supply and Demand and Market Equilibrium"

(x, y)

C. Demand Sch.

Y P	Q_D X	Q_R	Q
$10	2	4	1
9	4	7	3
			5
8	7	10	7
7	10	13	

I. Market

A. Definition Buyer + seller

II. Demand

A. Definition -various amounts of a commodity that consumers are willing + able to purchase at all prices During a certain time period; ceteris paribus

B. Law of Demand

↓P ↑Q_D

↑P ↓Q_D

C. Demand Schedule

D. Demand Curve

inverse Relationship- Downhill

E. "Change in Quantity Demanded"

one line (price Δ)

↑or↓ in Quantity Demanded is a movement along the Demand curve due to a change in price

F. "Change in Demand"

2 lines or more (not price)

↑or↓ in Demand in a shifting of the Demand Curve (right is ↑; Left is↓) due to non price Determinants

- income changes (normal/superior + inferior goods)
- related goods (substitute + complement)
- taste, fad.
- expectation

P_y: 10, 9, 8, 7; ↑ in Demand; ↓ in Demand; D_2, D, D′; 0, 2, 4, 6, 8, 10, 13; Q_x

Inverse

Chapter 3 "Supply and Demand and Market Equilibrium"

III. Supply

P	Q_s	Q	Q
$2	2	4	1
4	4	6	3
6	7	9	5
8	11	13	7

A. Definition

various amounts of commodity that the seller are willing to make avilible for a sale at alt. prices. During a certain time period

B. Law of Supply

↑P ↑Q

↓P ↓Q

C. Supply Schedule

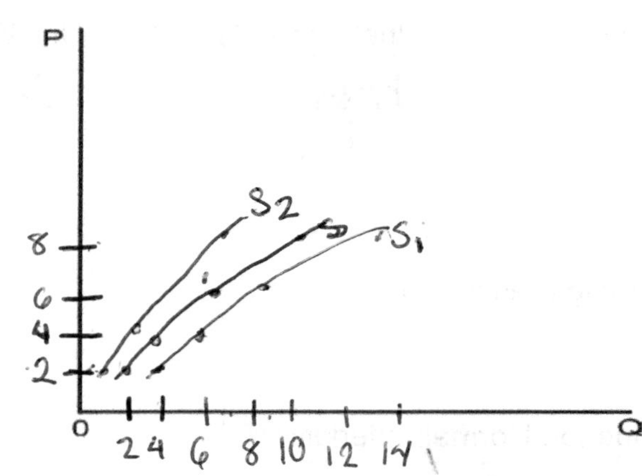

D. Supply Curve

E. "Change in Quantity Supplied"

F. "Change in Supply"

↑ or ↓ in supply is shifting of the supply curve (right is ↑; left is ↓) Due to non price determinants (resource pricing, tech change, gov change, expectation, Demand)

IV. Supply & Demand

A. Equilibrium (S = D)

supply = Demand at a particular price and Quantity (Pe, Qe)

B. Price Ceiling & Floor

(reverse)

Ceiling – protects consumer keeping price low

Floor – protect seller keeping price high

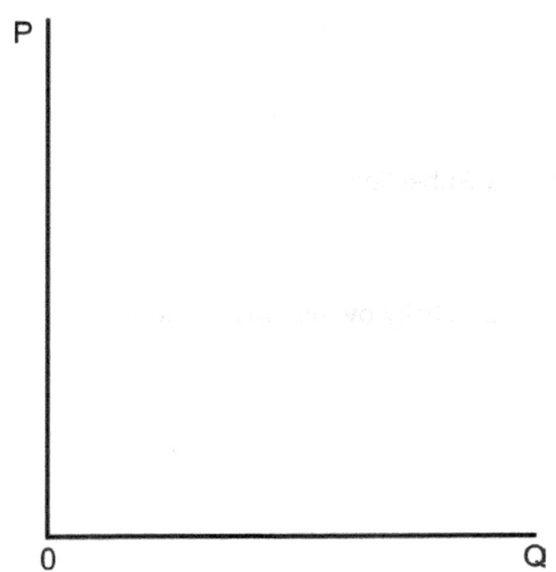

Chapter 6: "Elasticity"

I. Introduction

II. Price Elasticity of Demand (Ed) & Supply (Es)

↑P ↑TR or ↓P ↓TR

↑P ↓TR or ↓P ↑TR Elastic (>1) Inelastic (<1) Unit Elastic (=1) ↑P ↓P same TR

III. Income Elasticity (Ey)

Superior; Normal; Inferior

Ey>1 Ey=0-1 Ey<0

IV. Cross Elasticity (Exy)

Substitute; Complement; Independent

V. Taxes & Subsidies

Use of Elasticity by the Government

Chapter 6: "Elasticity"

Price Elasticity of Demand (Ed)

A. Definition - the percentage change in quantity Demand resulting from a one percent change in price
measures consumer sensitivity to change in price

B. Ways to Measure

1. Formula $E_d = \frac{\% \Delta Q_D}{\% \Delta P}$

Elastic = cares about price $E_d > 1$

Inelastic = $E_d < 1$

Unit elastic = $E_d = 1$

* Take absoluted value of final answer

2. Total Revenue Test ("TR Test")

$$E_d = \frac{\frac{Q_2 - Q_1}{Q_2 + Q_1}}{\frac{P_2 - P_1}{P_2 + P_1}}$$

Price Elasticity of Supply (Es)

A. Definition

B. Formula

C. Factors that Influence

Consumers Ed	&	Sellers Es
# of substitutes		time
% of income		
time		
lux v. nessessity		

Chapter 6: "Elasticity"

Income Elasticity of Demand (Ey)

A. Definition

B. Formula

Cross Elasticity of Demand (Exy)

A. Definition

B. Formula

Chapter 6: "Elasticity"

Taxes & Subsidies

A. Definition a specific tax is an amount of money placed on a particular good (inelastic) paid to the govt ex: cigarettes

B. Graphs

WHO PAYS THE TAX??

1. In which graph does the consumer (D) bear the greatest portion of tax? 3
2. In which graph does the seller (S) bear the greatest portion of tax? 1

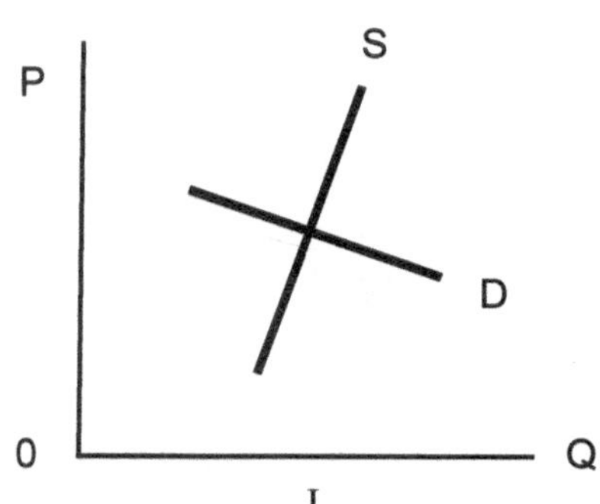

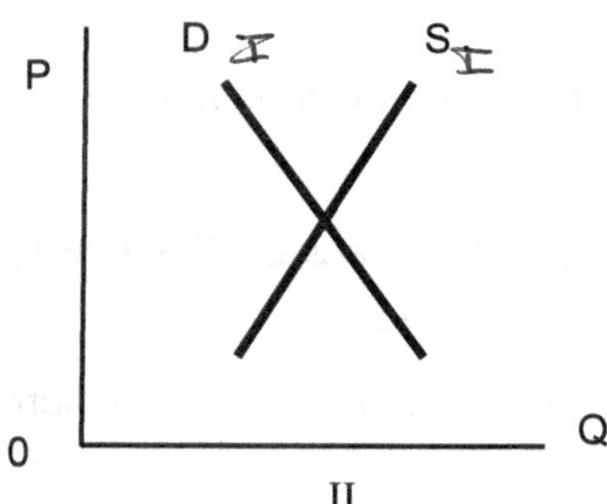

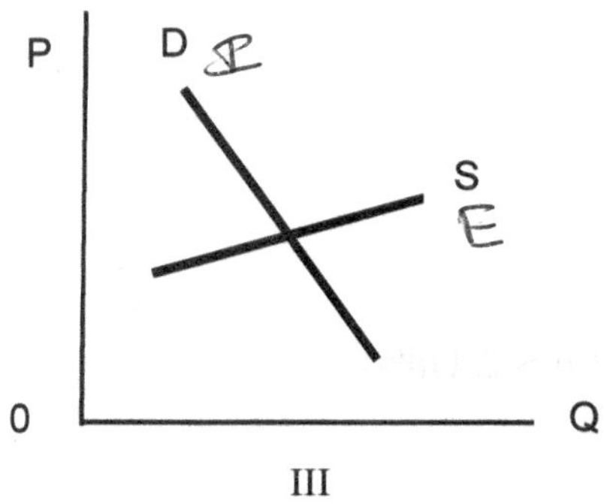

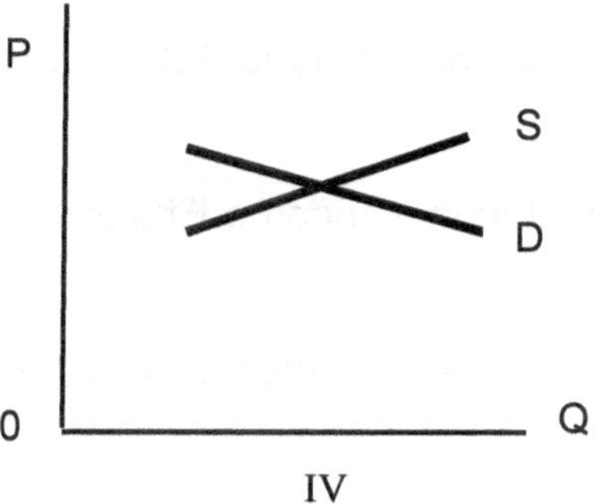

Flatter curve
more elastic
(price sensitive)

Chapter 7: "Utility Maximization"

I. Law of Diminishing Marginal Utility (DMU)

II. Terminology

III. Total Utility (TU) & Marginal Utility (MU)

A. Definitions & Formulas

B. Relationship of TU & MU

C. Relationship to Demand & Elasticity

IV. Theory of Consumer Behavior

A. Consumer Choice & Budget Constraint

B. Utility Maximizing Rule (or Consumer Equilibrium)

V. Utility Maximization & the Demand Curve

A. Deriving the Demand Schedule & Curve

B. Substitution & Income Effects

VI. Calculation of Consumer Expenditure & Consumer Surplus (In $ & Utils)

A. Graphs

VIII. Applications & Extensions

Chapter 7: "Utility Maximization"

Law of Diminishing Marginal Utility (DMU)

A. Definition ability or power of a good to satisfy a want

"~~units of satis~~faction"

Terminology

A. Definition of Utility

1. Does not mean usefulness

2. Subjective

3. Difficult to quantify

$$MU = \frac{\Delta TU}{\Delta Q}$$

Total Utility (TU) & Marginal Utility (MU)

A. Definitions & Formulas

1. Definition of Total Utility (TU)

2. Definition of Marginal (extra) Utility (MU)

certain time period as you consume successive units eventually the extra satisfaction decreases

B. Relationship of TU & MU

C. Relationship to Demand & Elasticity

Utility Table Showing TU & MU

Quantity	Total Utility (TU)	Marginal Utility (MU)
0	0	
		2
1	2	
		4
2	6	
		6 ← Dim MU
3	12	
		4
4	16	
		-1
5	15	

Chapter 7: "Utility Maximization"

Theory of Consumer Behavior

A. Consumer Choice & Budget Constraint

1. Rational behavior

2. Preferences

3. Budget constraint

4. Prices

B. Utility Maximizing Rule (or Consumer Equilibrium)

1. Definition

2. Marginal Utility per Dollar

a. Rule I: To maximize your satisfaction, allocate your income such that MU per dollar spent on two items is equal:

$$\frac{MUa}{Pa} = \frac{MUb}{Pb} = \frac{MU\$ \text{ Saved}}{P\$ = \$1}$$

$$\frac{MUa}{Pa} > \frac{MUb}{Pb} \quad \text{Choose More of "A"}$$

b. Rule II: Spend and/or save all of your income (given)

3. Decision-making Process

4. Word Problems & Table Format (WB Pages: 164)

Chapter 7: "Utility Maximization"

Utility Maximization & The Demand Curve

A. Deriving The Demand Schedule & Curve

B. Substitution & Income Effects

1. Income effect

2. Substitution effect

Calculation of Consumer Expenditure & Consumer Surplus (In $ & UTILS)

A. Graphs (WB Pages: 166)

Applications & Extensions

MICROECONOMICS

UNIT II

WORKSHEETS

Prof. Debbie A. Meyer

Chapter 9: "Businesses & The Costs of Production"

I. Economic Costs

A. Definition of Opportunity Cost

B. Definition of Economic Cost

1. Explicit Cost - expenses

2. Implicit Cost - normal profit

C. Definition of Economic (Pure) Profit

II. Short-run Production Relationships

A. Definition of Law of Diminishing Returns

B. The Production Function or Input/Output Model: TP, AP, MP, & QTY

III. Costs in the Short-run

A. Total Cost Curves: TFC, TVC, & TC

B. Average Cost Curves: AFC, AVC, & ATC

C. Marginal Cost Curve: MC - cost of 1 more

D. Most Efficient Level of Production: MC = ATC

IV. Costs in the Long-run

A. Definition of Planning Curve (LRATC)

B. Economies & Diseconomies of Scale

C. MES & Industry Structure

Chapter 9: "Businesses & The Costs of Production"

Economic Costs

A. Definition of Opportunity Cost
Value of Best Alternative (sacrifice)

B. Definition of Economic Cost
cost is a sacrifice it may tangable or intangable

1. Explicit Cost - tangable (receipts)

2. Implicit Cost - intangable expenses; including a normal profit

Economic Cost = Explicit + Implicit

C. Definition of Economic (Pure) Profit
- surplus or excess profit   when it = 0 a normal profit or "Break even" occurred

Total Revenue – Explicit Cost = Accounting Profit – Implicit Cost = Economic Profit

~ or ~

Total Revenue – Economic Costs = Economic Profit

Which is usually larger, Accounting Profit or Economic Profit?

Short-run Production Relationships

A. Definition of Law of Diminishing Returns

fixed factor - and you continually add varibles eventually become inefficient (↓)

Chapter 9: "Businesses & The Costs of Production"

B. The Production Function or Input/Output Model: TP, AP, MP, & QTY

0 ÷ 0 = undefined
0 ÷ # = 0

TP = Given $\qquad AP = \frac{TP}{Q} \qquad MP * = \frac{\Delta TP}{\Delta Q}$

*Graph at the Midpoints

MP > AP ; AP↑
MP < AP ; AP↓

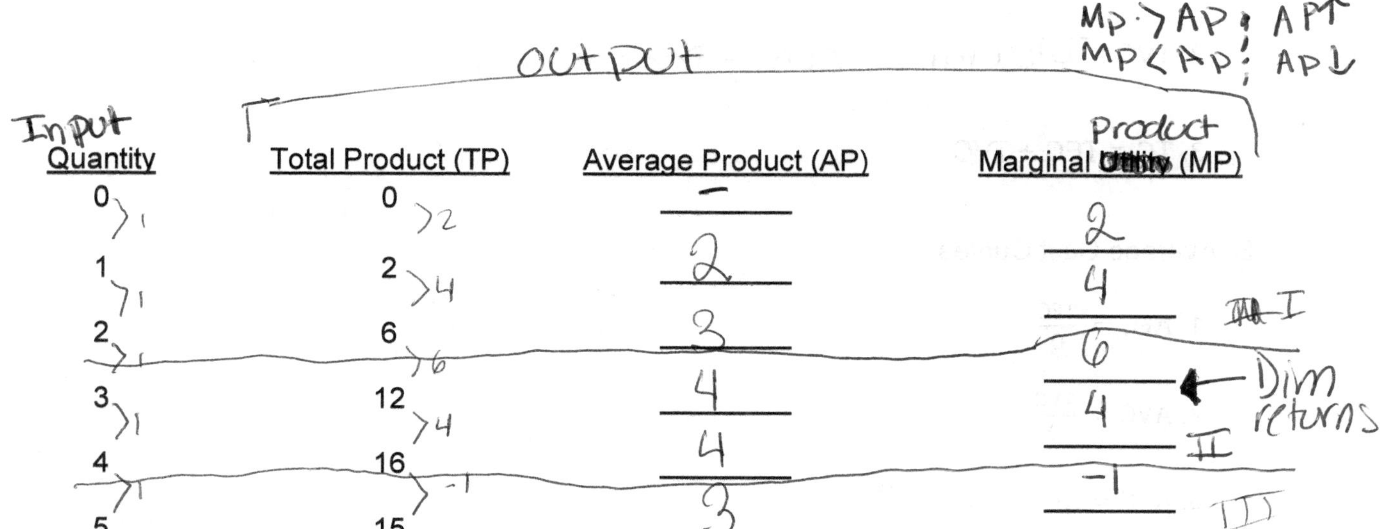

OUTPUT

Input Quantity	Total Product (TP)	Average Product (AP)	Marginal ~~Utility~~ Product (MP)
0	0	–	2
1	2	2	4
2	6	3	6
3	12	4	4 ← Dim returns
4	16	4	-1
5	15	3	

I, II, III

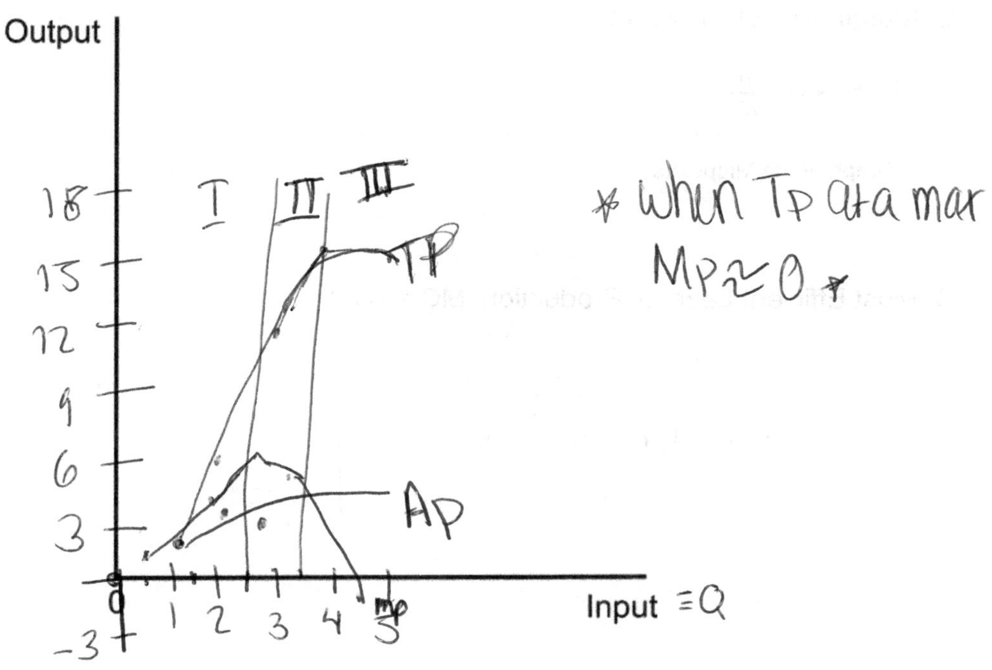

* When TP at a max MP ≈ 0 *

Chapter 9: "Businesses & The Costs of Production"

Costs in the Short-run -you have one fixed cost
in the long run all costs are variable or changeable

A. Total Cost Curves

1. TFC -total Fixed cost - Does not change w/ output

TFC

2. TVC -Total varible cost - Does change w/ output
(corporating cost or cost of materials)

3. TC = TFC + TVC

TC TVC
FC -paraleli

B. Average Cost Curves "per unit"

1. $\text{AFC} = \frac{\text{TFC}}{\text{Q}}$

2. $\text{AVC} = \frac{\text{TVC}}{\text{Q}}$

3. $\text{ATC} = \text{AFC} + \text{AVC} = \frac{\text{TC}}{\text{Q}}$

C. Marginal Cost Curve: MC

1. $\text{MC} * = \frac{\Delta\text{TC}}{\Delta\text{Q}}$

*Graph at the Midpoints

D. Most Efficient Level of Production: MC = ATC

most efficient level of production is where
the cost per unit is the lowest or cheapest (MC=ATC)

Chapter 9: "Businesses & The Costs of Production"

Costs in the Long-run

A. Definition of Planning Curve (LRATC)
The long run refers to a period of time which the firm can vary all inputs

B. Economies & Diseconomies of Scale

1. Definition of Economies of Scale - as output ↑ the cost per unit ↓

2. Definition of Diseconomies of Scale as output ↑ cost per unit ↑

C. MES & Industry Structure

1. Definition of MES

2. Definition of Natural Monopoly

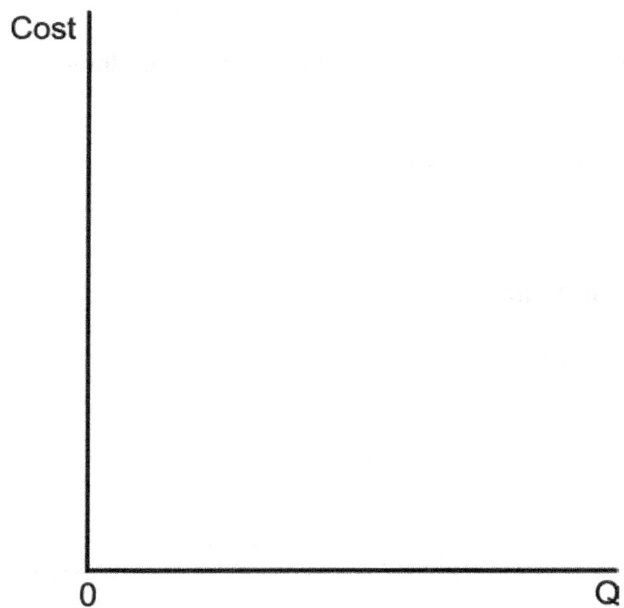

Chapters 10/11: "Price & Output Determination: Pure Competition"

I. Overview of Four Market Models (Text Page 221, Table 10-1)

II. Pure Competition: Characteristics & Occurrence

A. Characteristics

B. Demand Curves (in Short-run) for the Industry & Firm

C. Revenue Terms: TR, AR, MR

III. Profit Maximization (or Loss Minimization) in the Short-run

A. Difference between the "Most Efficient" Level (MC = ATC) & the "Most Profitable Level" of Output

B. Three Techniques to Maximize Profit (or Minimize Loss) in the Short-run

1. MC = MR Rule

2. TR-TC Rule

3. NR at a Maximum

Net Revenue = TR − TC "Total profit"

C. Derivation of the Short-run Supply Curve under Pure Competition

IV. Long-Run Costs under Pure Competition

A. Long-run Assumption

B. Profit and Long-run Equilibrium

C. The Long-run Supply Curve

D. Profit/Loss Possibilities

V. Pure Competition & Efficiency

Characteristics of the Four Basic Market Models

Overview of Four Market Models (Text Page 221, Table 10-1)

Pure Competition: Characteristics & Occurrence

A. Characteristics (4)

B. Demand Curves (in Short-run) for the Industry & Firm

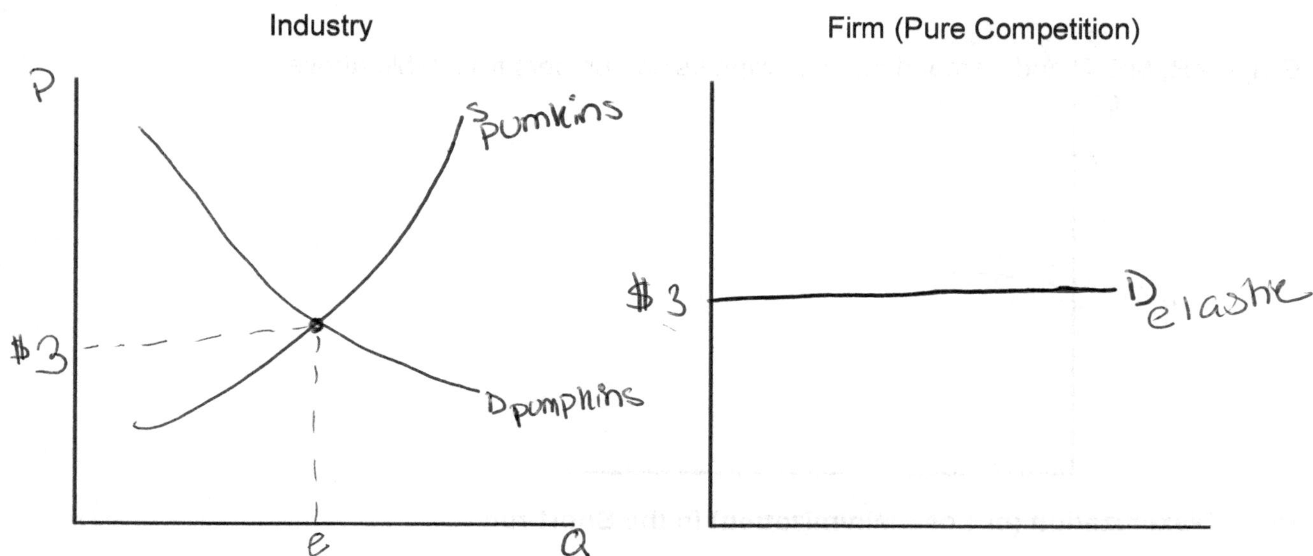

The *Industry* faces a downward sloping demand curve, while the individual *Firm* faces a perfectly elastic demand curve.

C. Revenue Terms

Total Revenue (TR) = P X Q sales

Average Revenue (AR) = $\frac{TR}{Q}$ per unit

Marginal Revenue (MR)* = $\frac{\Delta TR}{\Delta Q}$ sell one more

*Graphed at the midpoints.

Characteristics of the Four Basic Market Models

Perfectly Competitive Firm

Quantity	Price	TR	AR	MR
1	$6	6	6	6
2	↓	12	6	6
3	↓	18	6	6
4	↓	24	6	6
5	↓	30	6	

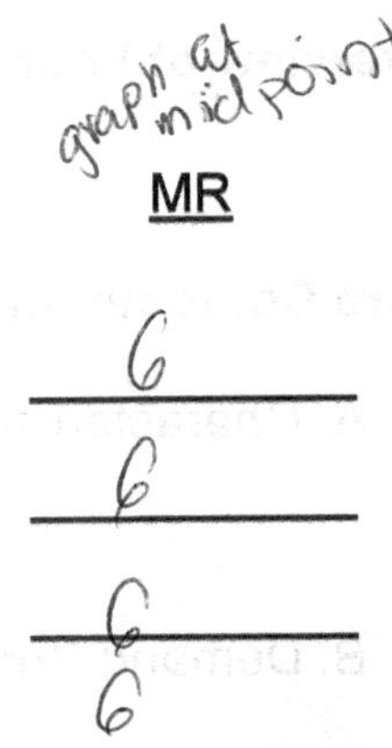

Graph AR, MR, P and Demand on one graph using numbers from table above.

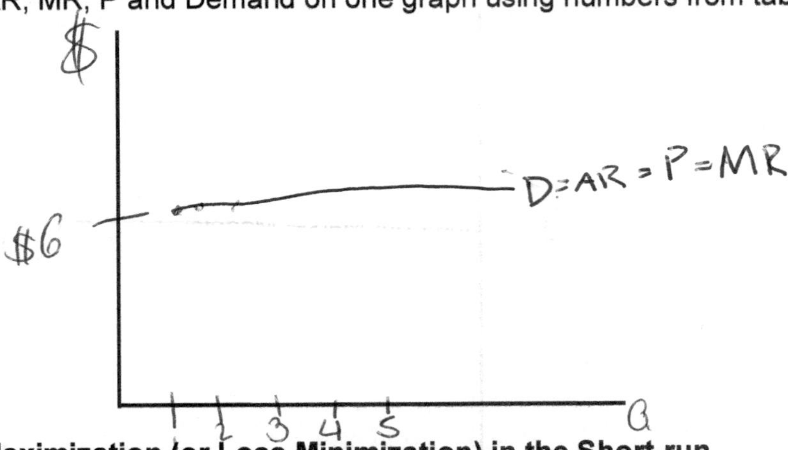

Profit Maximization (or Loss Minimization) in the Short-run

A. Difference between the "Most Efficient" Level (MC = ATC) & the "Most Profitable Level" of Output

B. Three Techniques to Maximize Profit (or Minimize Loss) in the Short-run

1. MC = MR Rule
2. TR-TC Rule
3. NR at a Maximum

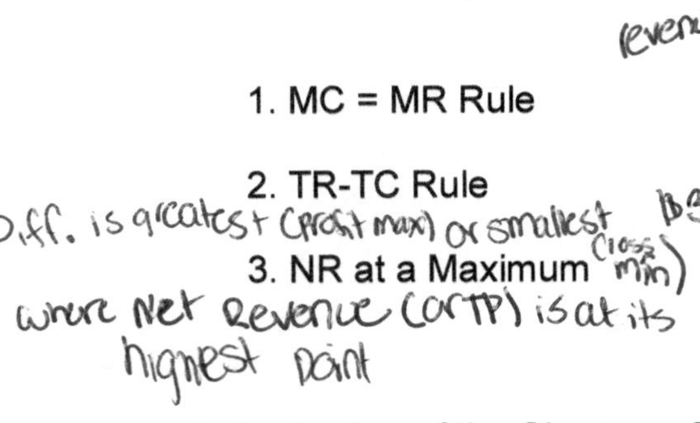

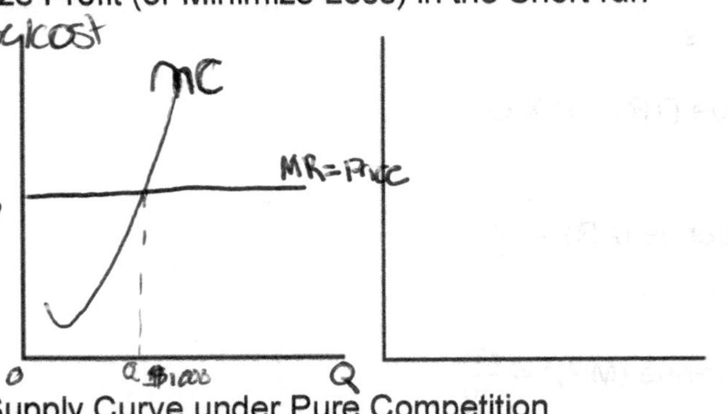

C. Derivation of the Short-run Supply Curve under Pure Competition

1. Definition
2. Graph (Workbook Page 191)

Characteristics of the Four Basic Market Models

Long-Run Costs under Pure Competition

A. Long-run Assumption – they can expand or not increase or decrease

B. Profit and Long-run Equilibrium

C. The Long-run Supply Curve (Workbook Page 192)

1. Constant Cost
2. Increasing Cost
3. Decreasing Cost

D. Can a PC Firm earn an economic profit in the long-run? What are the profit/loss possibilities in the long-run and short-run?

Profit/Loss Possibilities under the Four Market Models		
Market Model	Short-run	Long-run
Pure Competition	eco Profit	
	Normal	normal
	LOSS	LOSS

Pure Competition & Efficiency

A. Productive Efficiency

B. Allocative Efficiency

C. Dynamic Adjustments

D. "Invisible Hand" Revisited

E. Technological Advanced Competition

Chapter 12: "Price & Output Determination: Pure Monopoly"

I. Overview of Four Market Models (Text Page 221, Table 10-1)

II. Pure Monopoly: Barriers to Entry

   A. Characteristics

   B. Demand Curve for the Industry & Firm

   C. Revenue Terms: TR, AR, MR

III. Determining Price & Output for a Pure Monopolist

   A. Three Techniques to Maximize Profit (or Minimize Loss) in the Short-run

IV. Economic Effects of Monopolies

   A. Economic Effect of the Economy as a Whole

V. Price Discrimination

   A. Definition

   B. Conditions Required

VI. Pricing Policies for a Monopolist

   A. Three Pricing Policies (Regulated vs. Unregulated)

VII. Dilemma of Regulation

VIII. Long-run under Pure Monopoly

   A. Profit/Loss Possibilities

Chapter 12: "Price & Output Determination: Pure Monopoly"

Overview of Four Market Models (Text Page 221, Table 10-1)

Pure Monopoly (PM): Barriers to Entry

A. Characteristics (Table 10-1)

1. Definition

2. Characteristics

B. Monopoly Demand

1. Industry (Market) vs. The Firm

C. Revenue Terms

Total Revenue (TR) = P X Q

Average Revenue (AR) = $\frac{\text{TR}}{\text{Q}}$

Marginal Revenue (MR)* = $\frac{\Delta\text{TR}}{\Delta\text{Q}}$

*Graphed at the midpoints.

Monopolist

Quantity	Price	TR	AR	MR
1	$9	9	9	
2	$8	16	8	7
3	$7	21	7	5
4	$6	24	6	3

Graph AR, MR, P and Demand on one graph using numbers from table above.

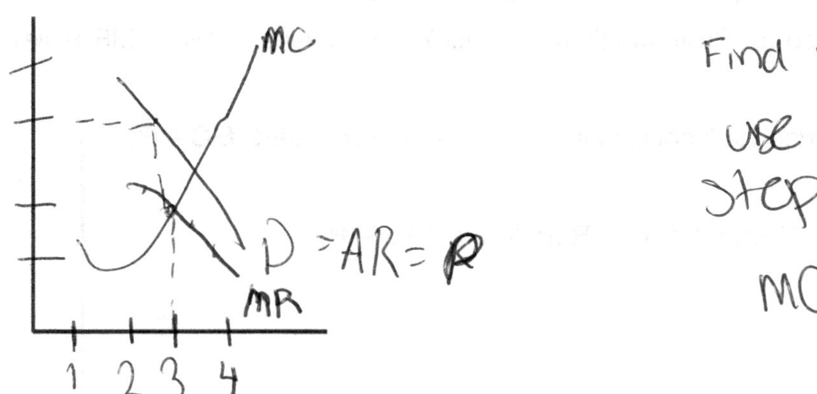

Find Pe Qe

use

step 1

MC = MR rule

Chapter 12: "Price & Output Determination: Pure Monopoly"

Determining Price & Output for a Pure Monopolist

A. Three Techniques to Maximize Profit (or Minimize Loss) in the Short-run

1. MC = MR Rule

2. TR-TC Rule

3. NR at a Maximum

Economic Effects of Monopolies

A. Economic Effect of the Economy as a Whole

1. High price and low quantity

2. Justification for a monopoly

3. Assessment of policy options

Price Discrimination

A. Definition

B. Conditions Required

C. Consequences

Is price discrimination legal? Profitable?

D. Examples

Pricing Policies for a Monopolist

A. Three Pricing Policies (Regulated vs. Unregulated)

1. Monopolist's Price (or Profit Maximizing Price) – Unregulated (MC = MR Rule)

2. Marginal Cost Price (or Socially Optimal Price) – Regulated (MC = P)

3. Full Cost (or Fair Return Price) – Regulated (ATC = P)

Chapter 12: "Price & Output Determination: Pure Monopoly"

Dilemma of Regulation

A. Tradeoffs of Pricing Policies

Long-run under Pure Monopoly

A. Economic Profits Depend on (3):

1.

2.

3.

Can a PM Firm earn an economic profit in the long-run?_________________

What are the profit/loss possibilities in the long-run and short-run?

Profit/Loss Possibilities under the Four Market Models		
Market Model	Short-run	Long-run

Chapter 13: "Price & Output Determination: Monopolistic Competition & Oligopoly"

I. Overview of Four Market Models (Text Page 221, Table 10-1)

II. Monopolistic Competition

A. Characteristics

B. Demand Curve - Elasticity Comparison w/Pure Competition & Pure Monopoly

C. Revenue Terms: TR, AR, MR

III. Determining Price & Output in Monopolistic Competition

A. Three Techniques to Maximize Profit (or Minimize Loss) in the Short-run

IV. Monopolistic Competition & Efficiency

A. Definition

B. Excess Plant Capacity

C. Defense Of (or Offsets)

V. Product Variety

A. Benefit

B. Advertising Pros/Cons

C. Offset "Wastes" of Monopolistic Competition

VI. Long-run Costs under Monopolistic Competition

A. Profit/Loss Possibilities

Chapter 13: "Price & Output Determination: Monopolistic Competition & Oligopoly"

Overview of Four Market Models (Text Page 221, Table 10-1)

Monopolistic Competition

A. Characteristics (Table 10-1)

1. Definition

2. Characteristics

B. Demand Curve – More Elastic than Pure Monopoly; Less Elastic than Pure Competition

C. Revenue Terms

Total Revenue (TR) = P X Q

Average Revenue (AR) = $\frac{\text{TR}}{\text{Q}}$

Marginal Revenue (MR)* = $\frac{\Delta\text{TR}}{\Delta\text{Q}}$

*Graphed at the midpoints.

elastic Comparison of Monopolistic Competition & Pure Monopoly not elastic

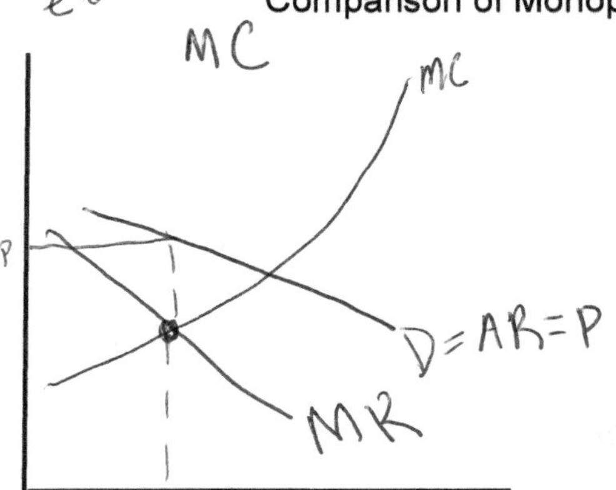

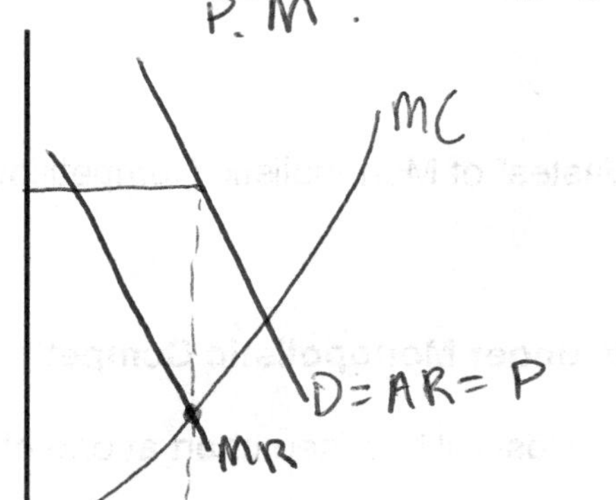

Determining Price & Output in Monopolistic Competition

A. Three Techniques to Maximize Profit (or Minimize Loss) in the Short-run

1. MC = MR Rule

2. TR-TC Rule

3. NR at a maximum

Chapter 13: "Price & Output Determination: Monopolistic Competition & Oligopoly"

Monopolistic Competition & Efficiency

A. Definition

B. Excess Plant Capacity - too many

C. Defense of (or Offsets)

Product Variety

A. Benefit

B. Advertising Pros/Cons

C. Offset "Wastes" of Monopolistic Competition

Long-run Costs under Monopolistic Competition

A. Profit/Loss Possibilities (see chart at end of worksheet)

Chapter 13: "Price & Output Determination: Monopolistic Competition & Oligopoly"

I. Overview of Oligopoly (Text Page 221, Table 10-1)

II. Oligopoly

A. Characteristics

B. Demand Curve – "Bend"

C. Concentration Ratio – top 4 firms

D. Game Theory & Mutual Interdependence

C. Revenue Terms: TR, AR, MR

III. Determining Price & Output in Oligopoly

A. Three Techniques to Maximize Profit (or Minimize Loss) in the Short-run

IV. Models to Explain Oligopoly Behavior

A. Kinked Demand Curve

B. Collusion & Cartels

C. Price Leadership

V. Oligopoly & Advertising Pros/Cons

VI. Long-run Costs under an Oligopoly Model

A. Profit/Loss Possibilities

VII. Oligopoly & Efficiency

Chapter 13: "Price & Output Determination: Monopolistic Competition & Oligopoly"

Overview of Oligopoly (Text Page 221, Table 10-1)

Oligopoly

A. Characteristics (Table 10-1)

B. Demand Curve – Has a bend or "kink" in it due to changes in elasticity (shown in kinked demand curve model)

C. Concentration Ratio

1. Definition

2. Shortcomings of Concentration Ratios

D. Game Theory & Mutual Interdependence

1. Definition of Game Theory

2. Definition of Mutual Interdependence

3. Collusive Tendencies

4. Incentives to Cheat

C. Revenue Terms: TR, AR, MR

Total Revenue (TR) = P X Q

Average Revenue (AR) = $\frac{TR}{Q}$

Marginal Revenue (MR)* = $\frac{\Delta TR}{\Delta Q}$

*Graphed at the midpoints.

Chapter 13: "Price & Output Determination: Monopolistic Competition & Oligopoly"

Determining Price & Output in Oligopoly

A. Three Techniques to Maximize Profit (or Minimize Loss) in the Short-run

1. MC = MR Rule

2. TR-TC Rule

3. NR at a Maximum

Models to Explain Oligopoly Behavior

A. Kinked Demand Curve (due to changing elasticities)

1. Has a "bend" in the demand curve

2. Has a "step" in the MR curve

3. When MC falls out of the "step" of the MR curve, selling price and quantity must change

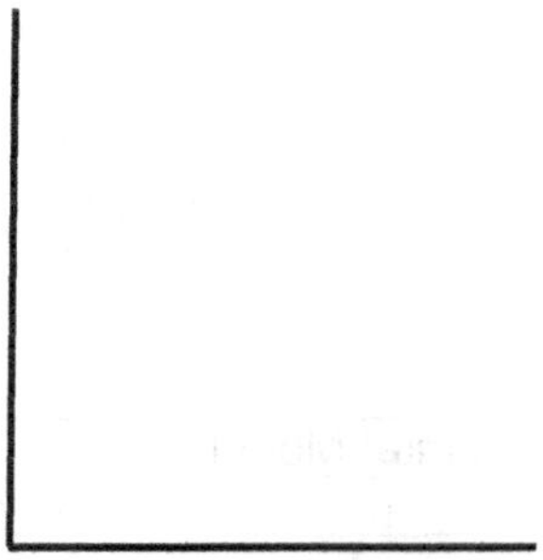

B. Collusion & Cartels

1. Definition of Collusion

2. Is it legal in U.S.?

3. Definition of Cartel ("Shared" Monopoly)

4. Obstacles to Collusion

5. Overt Collusion – Example: OPEC

6. Covert Collusion – Example: "Gentlemen's Agreement"

Chapter 13: "Price & Output Determination: Monopolistic Competition & Oligopoly"

C. Price Leadership: Model

1. Definition

2. Tactics

3. Example

Oligopoly & Advertising Pros/Cons

A. Both Monopolistic Competition & Oligopoly Rely on Advertising

B. Pros & Cons

Long-run Costs under an Oligopoly Model

A. Profit/Loss Possibilities in Long-run & Short-run

	Profit/Loss Possibilities under the Four Market Models		
	Market Model	Short-run	Long-run
1.	Pure Competition	eco. Profit Normal Profit Loss ↓	Normal P. loss
2.	Pure Monoply	"	economic P Normal P. Loss
3.	monopolistic Comp	"	Normal P. Loss
4.	Oligopoly	"	economic P. Normal P. loss

Oligopoly & Efficiency

A. Pros & Cons

Chapter 13: "Price & Output Determination: Monopolistic Competition & Oligopoly"

	Market Model			
Characteristic	**Pure Competition**	**Monopolistic Competition**	**Oligopoly**	**Pure Monopoly**
Number of firms	A very large number	Many	Few	One
Type of product	Standardized	Differentiated	Standardized or differentiated	Unique; no close substitutes
Control over price	None—PRICE TAKER	Some, but within rather narrow limits	Limited by mutual interdependence; considerable with collusion	Considerable—PRICE MAKER
Conditions of entry	Very easy, no obstacles	Relatively easy	Significant obstacles	Blocked
Non-price competition	None	Considerable emphasis on advertising, brand names, trademarks	Typically a great deal, particularly with product differentiation	Mostly public relations advertising
Examples	Agriculture	Retail trade, dresses, shoes	Steel, automobiles, farm implements, many household appliances	Local utilities

MICROECONOMICS

UNIT III

WORKSHEETS

Prof. Debbie Meyer

Chapter 14 "The Demand for Resources"

I. Introduction of the input (resource) markets

A. Background

1. Simple circular flow model (wb pg 230)

B. Def. Of marginal productivity theory

C. Reasons for studying resource pricing - money incomes Determination, resource allocation, cost minimization, Policy issues.

D. Determining worth
going market wage, worker perf. education, JOB Responsibility, gender + Race

II. Marginal productivity theory of resource demand

A. Terms in a purely competitive market a worker will be paid a wage of their worth

Production	TP (total product) MP (marginal product)
Revenue	TR (total revenue) ARP (average revenue product) MRP (marginal revenue product) - worth Labor Demand curve
Cost	TRC (total resource cost) Payroll MRC (marginal resource cost) cost of hiring one more worker

B. Formulas

production
1. TP (given)

2. MP* = $\frac{\Delta \text{ total product}}{\Delta \text{ units of resources}}$

revenue
3. TR = TP x products price

4. ARP = $\frac{\text{total revenue}}{\text{units of resource}}$

5. MRP* = MP x products price = $\frac{\Delta \text{ total revenue}}{\Delta \text{ units of resource}}$

Cost
6. TRC = # workers x wage rate

7. MRC* = $\frac{\Delta \text{ total resource cost}}{\Delta \text{ units of resource}}$

*graph at midpoint

Chapter 14 "The Demand for Resources"

III. Profit max (or loss min) in short-run

A. Techniques to find the profit max (or loss min)

worm = cost: including a normal profit

1. MRP = MRC Rule

2. TR --TRC Rule - where Dif. BTWN sales + payroll is the greatest (profit max) or smallest (loss min)

IV. Market Demand for a Resource

Business Households

A. Who demands? Who supplies?

B. The MRP curve is always the resource demand curve

V. Changes in resource demand and supply

A. A change in the quantity of resource demand

1. Movement along the resource demand curve due to changes in the price (wage) of a factor (see figure 2 below)

Figure 2
Change in Quantity Demanded

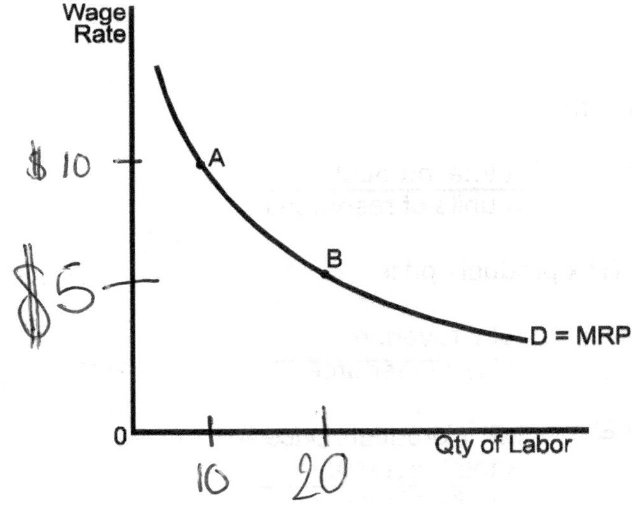

B. A change in resource demand

1. The resource demand curve will shift due to:

Figure 3: Change in Demand - 2 lines

Due to non-wage reasons

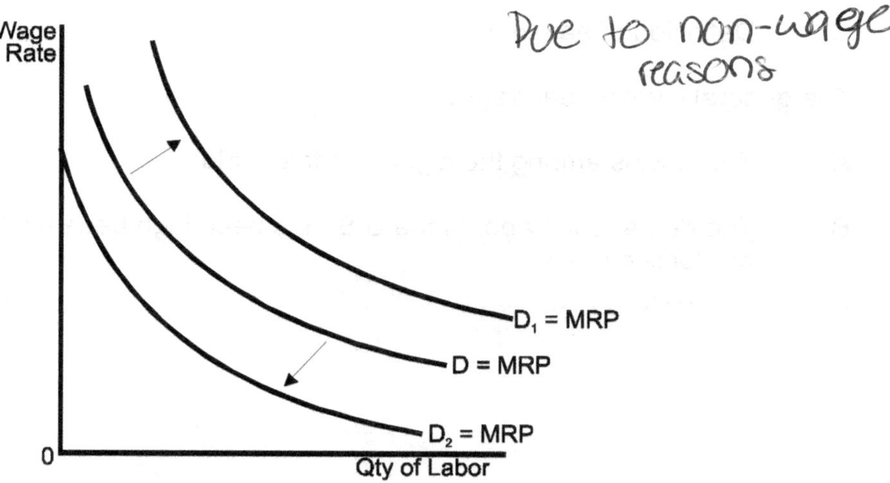

c. The Supply Curve

1. Direct relationship

2. Graph

Figure 4: Supply Curve

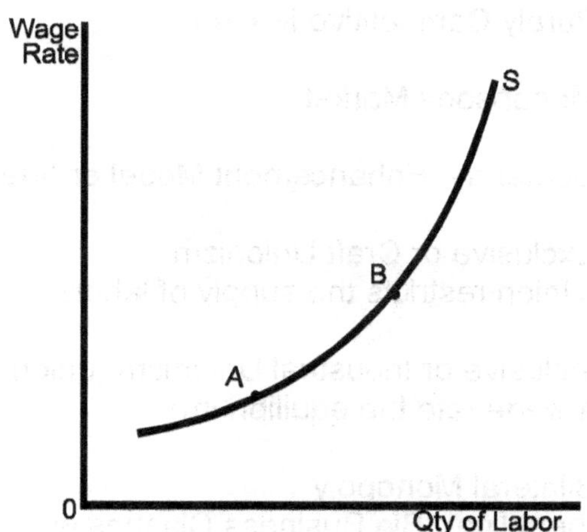

VI. Optimum Combination of Resources

A. Least Cost Rule

VII. Marginal Productivity Theory (revisited)

A. Shortcomings

<u>Chapter 15 "Wage Determination"</u>

I. Labor, Wages and Earnings

A. Definition of labor

B. Definition of wages

C. Definition of earnings

II. The general level of real wages

A. The U.S. is among the highest in the world

B. The demand for labor in the U.S. has been high because labor has been highly productive due to:

III. Real Wages and Productivity

A. Types of labor market models

1. We will be examining <u>six</u> different labor market models:

a. Purely Competitive Market

b. Monopsony Market

c. Demand – Enhancement Model or "Ideal"

d. Exclusive or Craft Unionism
(Union restricts the supply of labor)

e. Inclusive or Industrial Unionism (union threatens a strike to secure a wage rate the equilibrium)

f. Bilateral Monopoly
(headline: "Big Business Clashes with Big Union")

2. The wage rate (we) and the level of employment (Qe) depends upon the supply and the demand for labor and market competitiveness.

Chapter 15 "Wage Determination"

Economic power	Market Model
1. No one	1. Purely Competitive Model (S = D)
2. Business	2. Monopsony Model
3. Union	3. Demand – Enhancement Model or Ideal Model (↑D)
4. Union	4. Exclusive or Craft Unionism supply curve shifts left
5. Union	5. Inclusive or Industrial Unionism
6. Indeterminate	6. Bilateral Monopoly (range) Big business clashes w/ big union

B. Purely Competitive

1. The wage rate (we) and level of employment (Qe) is determined by the intersection of the labor demand and supply curves in the market.

    a. Market demand is found by summing the individual MRP curves in the market.

    b. The market supply curve is upward sloping, because the wage must rise to attract more workers.

2. Once the going-rate has been established, the individual firm faces a perfectly elastic supply curve.

3. An individual worker's supply curve is backward bending due to the tradeoffs between work and leisure hours.

    a. The substitution effect replacing leisure hours with work hours

    b. The income effect (see Figure 1 below)

Figure 1: Purely Competitive Model

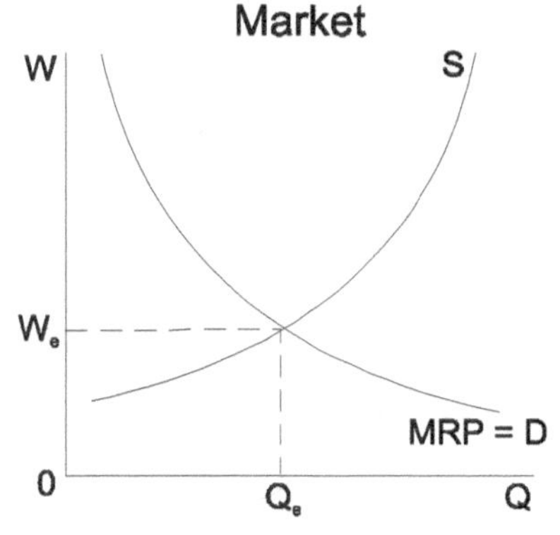

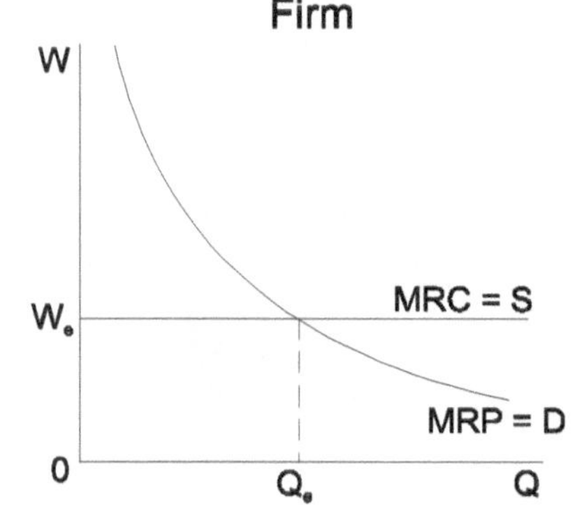

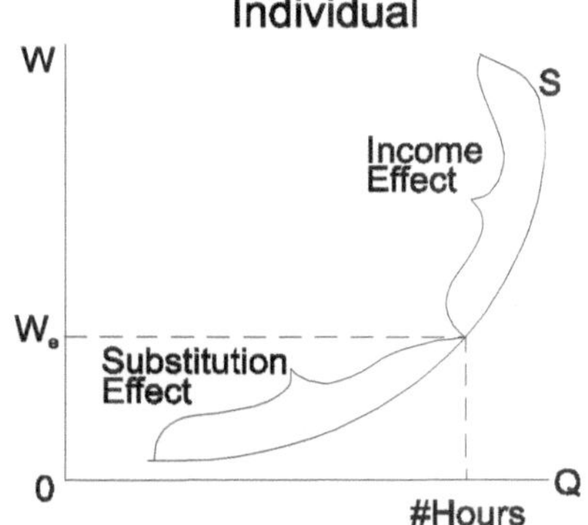

C. Monopsony (from the Greek word meaning "single buyer"

1. Definition - one buyer (employer) in a populated, nonunionized area.

2. Examples of monopsony markets: professional athletes, or a "company town", etc.

3. A monopsonist must increase wages to attract new workers and should increase the wages of the present employees (or else suffer low morale).

Therefore, the MRC is higher than the wage rate (the cost of hiring a new worker (MRC) plus the extra amount that should be paid to the present workers). See Figure 2.

Figure 2: Monopsony

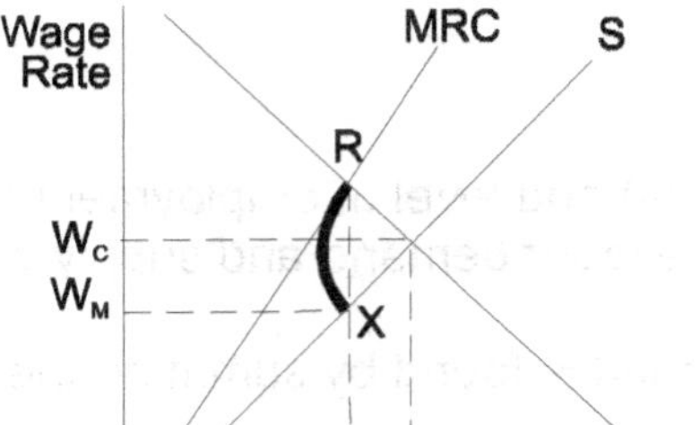

4. The relationship of a monopsonist is similar to a monopolist's demand and marginal revenue curves.

5. The monopsonist will hire until MRC = MRP.

6. Compare the monopsonist's wage rate (we) and quantity (q) with that of a purely competitive market.

7. Definition of "monopsonistic exploitation".

D. Union Models

1. Unions seek many goals, but the basic objective is to raise wage rates. Three models are illustrated.

2. Demand – Enhancement Model - unions seek to raise wage rates by increasing the demand for labor (see figure 3)

Figure 3: Demand – Enhancement Model

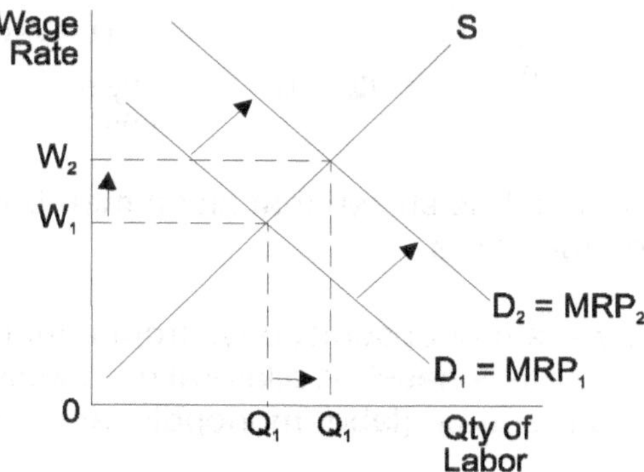

3. Exclusive or Craft Unionism – by limiting the supply of labor, unions may increase wage rates – also called "labor monopoly". (see figure 4)

Figure 4: Exclusive or Craft Unionism

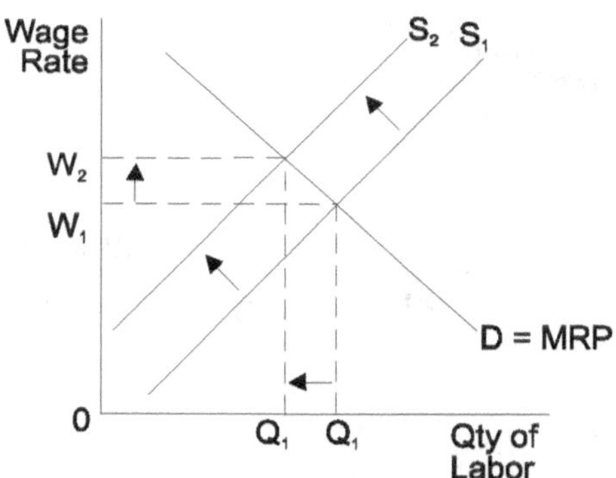

4. Inclusive or industrial unionism - most unions want to organize all potential workers (a characteristic of industrial unions such as automobile workers). A "strike threat" by all the workers will deprive the firm of its labor supply (…."In numbers there is strength!" (see figure 5)

Figure 5: Inclusive or Industrial Unionism

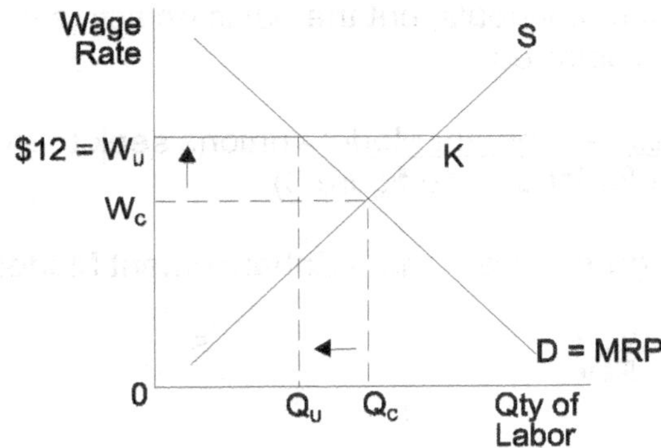

5. Empirical evidence has shown that union members receive a wage advantage over nonunion members.

E. Bilateral Monopoly - "a monopsonist buys from a monopolist". For example: "big labor clashes with big business". A bilateral monopoly is a market in which there is only one seller of a resource (labor monopoly) and only one buyer (monopsonistic) - see figure 6

Figure 6: Bilateral Monopoly

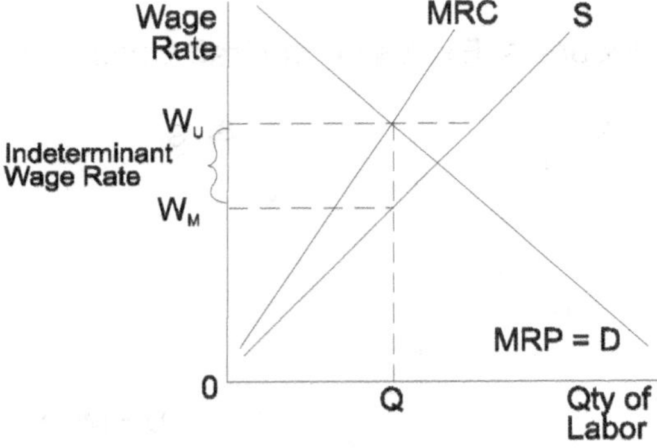

*problems in workbook page 246

IV. The Minimum Wage Controversy

A. Pros - in certain markets, wages can increase without causing unemployment; also it increases worker productivity.

B. Cons - minimum-wage causes firms higher costs which results in the hiring of fewer workers or closing down the business.

C. Empirical evidence suggests that minimum- does cause unemployment—because of higher cost; (especially among teenagers), however, those who are employed have a better standard of living with the higher rate.

Chapter 15 "Wage Determination"

V. Wage Differentials

A. Definition of wage differential:

B. Reasons for wage differentials:

1. Marginal Revenue Productivity

2. Noncompeting groups

3. Compensating differences

4. Market imperfections

VI. Investment in Human Capital

A. A human capital investment is any action that improves the productivity of workers; such as expenditures on education and improving health of workers.

VII. Pay and Performance

A. Principal Agent Problem

1. Definition

2. Ways to remedy

Chapter 16 "Rent, Interest and Profits"

I. Economic Rent

A. Definition

B. Graph of Economic Rent and Equilibrium Changes

C. Application: A single tax on land

1. Henry George (1839-1897) – wrote a book titled, Progress and Poverty (1879)

a. Caused a single-tax movement in U.S.

2. Criticisms of the single-tax movement

3. Those in favor argued:

4. Alternative use of land

Chapter 16 "Rent, Interest and Profits"

II. Interest

A. Definition of interest

B. Loanable Funds Theory of Interest (determining the equilibrium interest rate)

1. Intersection of D$ and S$

   a. Supply is upward sloping
   b. Demand is downward sloping

2. D$ > s$—>

3. Time Value of Money

C. Definition of Pure Rate of Interest:

D. Definition of Real Rate of Interest:

1. Formula

2. Application: Usury Laws

Chapter 16 "Rent, Interest and Profits"

III. Economic Profit

A. Definition of Economic Profit

B. Economic vs. Accounting Profits

C. Insurable and Uninsurable Risks

1. Definitions:

2. Four categories of uninsured risk:

D. Sources of Eco. Profits

IV. Income Shares

A. Current Shares

1. Trends

a. Percentage of distribution

I. Introduction: Unionism in America

II. Repression Phase (1790-1930)

1. Local craft unions

2. Unskilled workers

3. Obstacles to unions:

a. Yellow-dog contracts

b. Injunctions

c. Etc.

4. AFL (1886, Samuel Gompers)

III. Union Growth (1930-1947)

A. Norris-Laguardia act of 1932

B. Wagner Act of 1935

C. CIO (1936, John L. Lewis)

IV. Curbing Union Power (1947 to date)

A. Taft Hartley Act of 1947 ("Labor-Management Relations Act")

Union Security: (WB pg. 262)

1. Open shop
2. Closed shop
3. Union shop
4. Agency shop

B. Landrum-Griffin Act of 1959

C. Merger of AFL-CIO in 1955

D. Percentage of the labor force

V. Collective Bargaining

A. Definition

B. The Bargaining Process

VI. Eco. Effects of Unions

A. Wages and benefits

B. Efficiency and Productivity

1. Unions exert a negative impact by:

2. Unions exert a positive impact by:

VII. Labor Market Discrimination

A. Definition of labor market discrimination

B. Costs of Discrimination

C. Economic Analysis of Discrimination

1. Taste-for-Discrimination Model

D. Occupational Segregation: The Crowding Model

VIII. Immigration

A Number of Immigrants

B. Economics of Immigration

1. Supply and Demand

C. Complications and Modifications

1. Costs of migration

2. Remittances and backflows

3. Full employment versus unemployment

4. Fiscal Impacts:

5. Research Findings:

D. The Illegal Immigration Debate

1. Two viewpoints

2. Economists "weigh in"

3. "Braindrain"

Microeconomics
Case Study

I. Classification as One of the Four Basic Market Models

A. Select a company from a current business periodical or where you work, and state which market model is represented by this company. Explain your reasoning using a narrative format.

B. State the basic industry problem and proceed to analyze using the following methodology where appropriate. Be sure to include the ***six*** (6) graphs, as indicated.

II. Supply & Demand and the Price System Graphs

A. What is the current demand situation – is the curve changing (use graphs)?
<u>Graph #1:</u> Demand Curve and any Changes
1. Curve shift and underlying causes
2. Movement along the curve and causes

B. What is the current supply situation – is the curve changing (use graphs)?
<u>Graph #2:</u> Supply Curve and any Changes
1. Curve shift and underlying causes
2. Movement along the curve and causes

C. Market Equilibrium (use graphs)
<u>Graph #3:</u> Demand & Supply Curves with Changes
1. Surplus/shortage (where appropriate)
2. Price ceilings and price floors (where appropriate)

D. Changes in Income & Results
1. Superior/normal or inferior goods

E. Changes in Prices of Related Goods & Results
1. Substitute, complementary, independent goods

III. Costs & Profits

A. Short-run Costs (use graphs)
<u>Graph #4:</u> Short-run Profit or Loss (use MC, AR, ATC, and AR; shade where appropriate)
1. State whether firm is earning a normal or economic profit, or a loss. Illustrate on graph 4.
2. State any productivity and pertinent cost problems and the resulting effects on graphs.

B. Long-run Costs (use graphs)

<u>Graph #5:</u> Long-run Profit or Loss (use MC, AR, ATC, and AR; shade where appropriate)

1. State whether firm is earning a normal or economic profit, or a loss. Illustrate on graph 5.

<u>Graph #6:</u> The Planning Curve: LRATC & Optimal Plant Size (Economies & Diseconomies of Scale)

1. Graph the LRATC, show economies and diseconomies of scale, and mark with an "X" the company's position.

IV. Conclusion/Summary

A. Recapitulation of Findings

B. How could the economic problem be corrected?

V. Prediction for Future

A. State your personal prediction for the future. Support your answer.

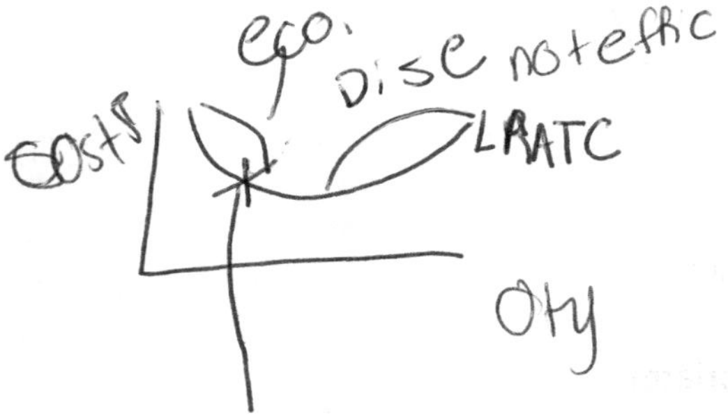

Can expand more!

On Test!!

Microeconomics
Perfectly Competitive Input Market

Units of Labor	MRP = D	Wage Rate	Market Supply	Market Demand
1	$15	$15	850	_______
2	$14	$14	800	_______
3	$13	$13	750	_______
4	$12	$12	700	_______
5	$11	$11	650	_______
6	$10	$10	600	_______
7	$9	$9	550	_______
8	$8	$8	500	_______

a. Assume that there are 100 firms with the same marginal revenue product schedules for this particular type of labor. Compute the total or market demand for this labor. (Market Demand = Units of Labor x # of Firms)

b. Using the market demand and market supply schedules, what will be the equilibrium wage rate? (where Market Demand = Market Supply → Wage Rate)

c. What will be the total (equilibrium) amount of labor hired in this market? (the level where Market Demand = Market Supply)

d. What will be the wage rate paid and the amount of labor hired by each of the 100 purely competitive firms? (where Market Demand = Market Supply → Wage Rate & the Units of Labor)

e. Graph the market demand and supply curves for labor and indicate the equilibrium wage rate and the total quantity of labor employed in the market. (refer to questions "b" and "c" above)

f. Graph the firm's demand curve for labor, the supply curve for labor, and the marginal resource (labor) cost curve which confronts the individual purely competitive firm. Indicate the quantity of labor the firm will hire and the wage rate it will pay. (refer to question "d" above)

g. The imposition of a $12 minimum wage rate would change the total amount of labor hired in this market to _______. How much unemployment would be created by the imposition of a $12 minimum wage? Illustrate the $12 minimum wage and the resulting unemployment on the graph from question "e".

Microeconomics
Perfectly Competitive Input Market

Units of Labor	MRP = D	Wage Rate	Market Supply	Market Demand
1	$15	$15	850	__100__
2	$14	$14	800	__200__
3	$13	$13	750	__300__
4	$12	$12	700	__400__
5	$11	$11	650	__500__
6	$10	$10	600	__600__
7	$9	$9	550	__700__
8	$8	$8	500	__800__

a. Assume that there are 100 firms with the same marginal revenue product schedules for this particular type of labor. Compute the total or market demand for this labor. (Market Demand = Units of Labor x # of Firms) **See Above**

b. Using the market demand and market supply schedules, what will be the equilibrium wage rate? (where Market Demand = Market Supply → Wage Rate) **$10**

c. What will be the total (equilibrium) amount of labor hired in this market? (the level where Market Demand = Market Supply) **600 units of labor**

d. What will be the wage rate paid and the amount of labor hired by each of the 100 purely competitive firms? (where Market Demand = Market Supply → Wage Rate & the Units of Labor) **$10, 6 workers**

e. Graph the market demand and supply curves for labor and indicate the equilibrium wage rate and the total quantity of labor employed in the market. (refer to questions "b" and "c" above) **See Graph**

f. Graph the firm's demand curve for labor, the supply curve for labor, and the marginal resource (labor) cost curve which confronts the individual purely competitive firm. Indicate the quantity of labor the firm will hire and the wage rate it will pay. (refer to question "d" above) **See Graph**

g. The imposition of a $12 minimum wage rate would change the total amount of labor hired in this market to **400 Q_D**. How much unemployment would be created by the imposition of a $12 minimum wage? **300** Unemployed Illustrate the $12 minimum wage and the resulting unemployment on the graph from question "e". **See Graph**

Microeconomics
Perfectly Competitive Input Market - Graphs

Total Market Demand and Supply

1e.

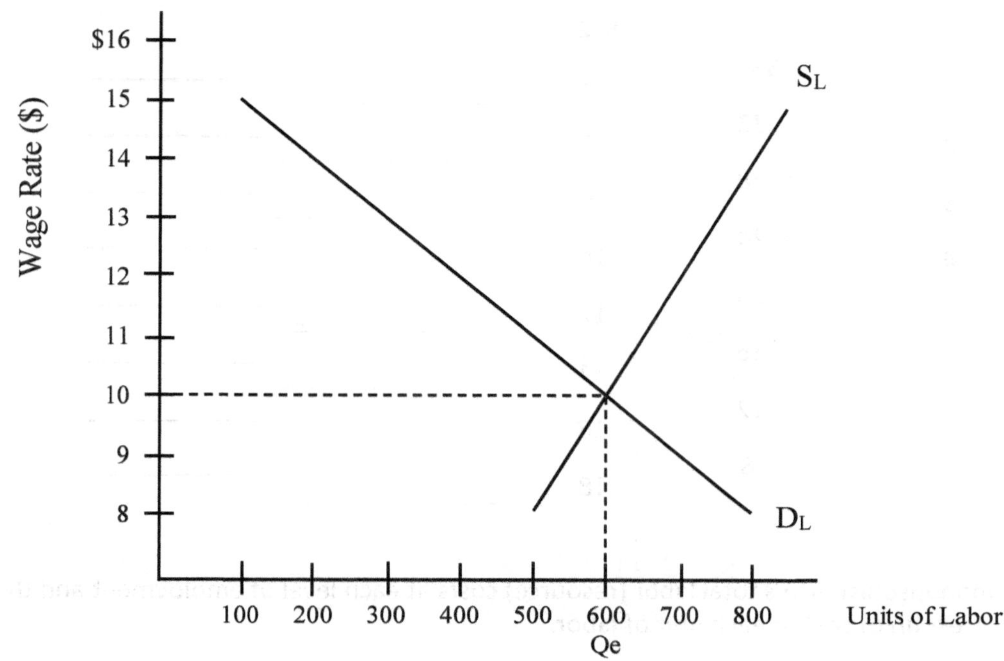

Individual Firm

f.

$15
14
13
12
11
10
9
8
Wage Rate ($)
S=MRC
D=MRP
1 2 3 4 5 6 7 8 9
Units of Labor

Effect of Minimum Wage

g.

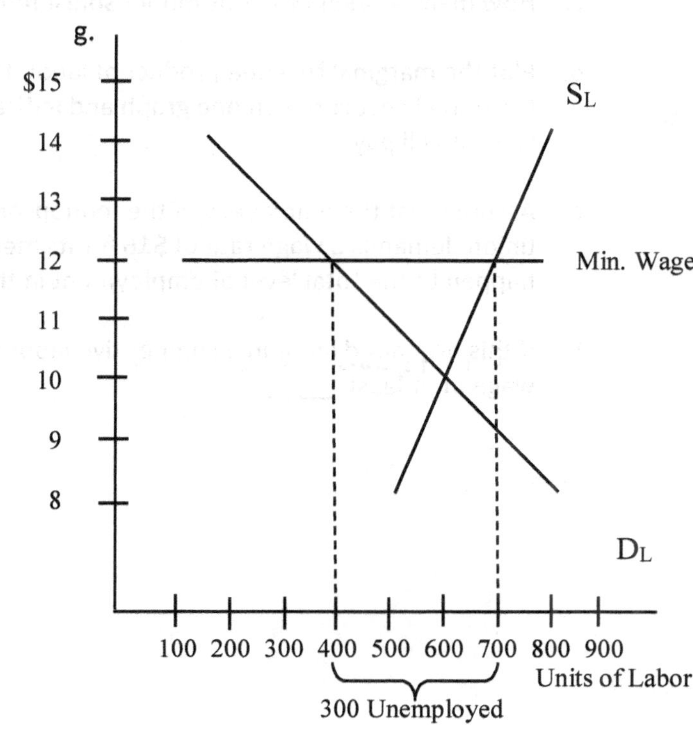

Microeconomics
Monopsony Input Market

Units of Labor	MRP = D	Wage Rate	(TRC) Total Resource Cost	(MRC) Marginal Cost
0		$ 2	______	
1	$36	4	______	______
2	32	6	______	______
3	28	8	______	______
4	24	10	______	______
5	20	12	______	______
6	16	14	______	______
7	12	16	______	______
8	8	18	______	______

a. Compute this monopsonist firm's total labor (resource) costs at each level of employment and the marginal labor (resource) cost of each unit of labor.

b. What will be the equilibrium marginal labor (resource) cost to the firm for the last unit of labor employed?

c. How many workers will this monopsonist hire and what wage rate will be paid?

d. Plot the marginal revenue product of labor, the supply of labor curve, and the marginal labor (resource) cost curve on one graph and indicate the quantity of labor the firm will employ and the wage it will pay.

e. Assume that the employees of the monopsonist organize a strong industrial (inclusive) union. The union demands a wage rate of $16 for its members. Illustrate the union wage graphically. What will happen to the total level of employment in the monopsony firm?

f. If this firm hired labor in a competitive labor market, it would hire at least _____ workers and pay a wage of at least _____ .

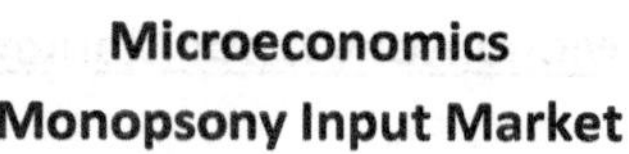

Microeconomics
Monopsony Input Market

Units of Labor	MRP = D	Wage Rate	(TRC) Total Resource Cost	(MRC) Marginal Cost
0		$ 2	0	
1	$36	4	4	**4**
2	32	6	12	**8**
3	28	8	24	**12**
4	24	10	40	**16**
5	20	12	60	**20**
6	16	14	84	**24**
7	12	16	112	**28**
8	8	18	144	**32**

a. Compute this monopsonist firm's total labor (resource) costs at each level of employment and the marginal labor (resource) cost of each unit of labor. **(see above)**

b. What will be the equilibrium marginal labor (resource) cost to the firm for the last unit of labor employed? **$20, MRP = MRC**

c. How many workers will this monopsonist hire and what wage rate will be paid? **4.5 workers; $11 wage; MRP = MRC → Supply Curve**

d. Plot the marginal revenue product of labor, the supply of labor curve, and the marginal labor (resource) cost curve on one graph and indicate the quantity of labor the firm will employ and the wage it will pay. **(see graph)**

e. Assume that the employees of the monopsonist organize a strong industrial (inclusive) union. The union demands a wage rate of $16 for its members. Illustrate the union wage graphically. What will happen to the total level of employment in the monopsony firm? **employment increases**

f. If this firm hired labor in a competitive labor market, it would hire at least **6** workers and pay a wage of at least **$14**. **(Supply = Demand)**

Monopsony Input Market

2a.

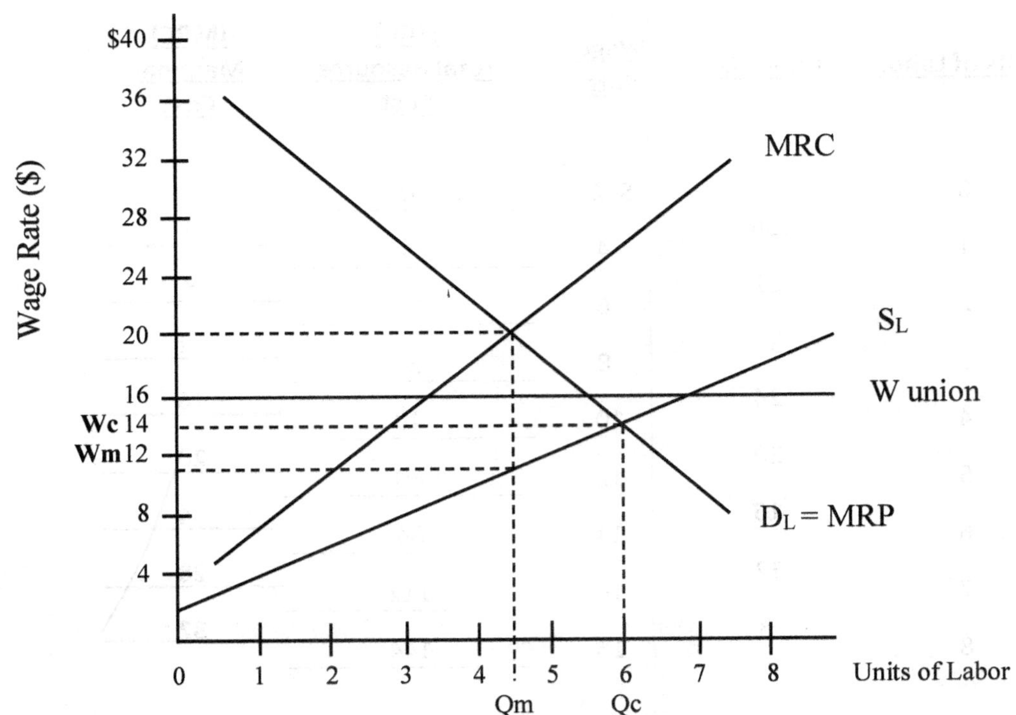

steps to calulate profit/loss

- find pofit max/loss price and qty

  MC=MR
  ATC=AFC+AVC

- Calculate the profit/loss per unit

  selling price (Pe)
  Cost price (Cp) - from ATC curve

- If lossing need to see if you should "shut Down"

the short run supply curve under pc follows the path of MC curve above the shut Down point the shut Down points Bellow-...